The General Electric Story
A Heritage of Innovation
1876 - 1999

Hall of Electrical History
Schenectady Museum
Schenectady, New York
December 1, 1999
First Printing - Third Edition

To the memory of

Dr. Arthur M. Bueche
Senior Vice President -
Corporate Technology
General Electric Company

for the vision, encouragement and support that helped make
the Hall of Electrical History a reality.

ISBN 0-9679231-0-7
Copyright © 1999
Schenectady Museum Association
Schenectady, New York

Printed February 2000
Fort Orange Press
Albany, New York
United States of America

FOREWORD

THE GENERAL ELECTRIC STORY - A HERITAGE OF INNOVATION *(1876-1999) is the third edition in a series of photo histories which chronicle milestones in the growth of the General Electric Company since its origins in the late 1870s. The original volume,* **A CENTURY OF PROGRESS** *(1876-1978) was published in 1981. It combined materials from a chronological series of four short books that we had published earlier. In 1989, that edition was updated and renamed* **THE GENERAL ELECTRIC STORY** *(1876-1986). In this revised and updated version of that book, we look back at the far-reaching changes that took place throughout the Company during the closing years of the 20th Century.*

The format for this volume is much the same as that of the earlier editions. Again, we chose to treat a broad number of topics, arranged in chronological order. These milestones are punctuated with biographies of some of the key contributors to General Electric's history as well as more extensive discussions of subjects that were pivotal to the growth of the company. The text is illustrated with a number of the best prints from a treasure of some 800,000 photographs in our archives at the Schenectady Museum, Schenectady, New York. Many of the more recent color photographs were supplied by a number of GE businesses and support organizations. On the following page, we gratefully acknowledge the contributions of these organizations and the work of their communications personnel who researched the achievements of their predecessors and their contemporaries, and organized and submitted their findings. This list of contributors presented here must of necessity be a partial one, but to any who have been omitted, our appreciation is undiminished.

THE GENERAL ELECTRIC STORY - A HERITAGE OF INNOVATION *(1876-1999) tells the story of human achievement on many frontiers and of outstanding leaders who directed and nurtured that achievement. This book is dedicated to the GE men and women who created that proud heritage and to those who will be helping to extend it into the 21st Century and beyond.*

December, 1999
Schenectady, New York

Publications Committee
Hall of Electrical History
Schenectady Museum

Editor-in-Chief and Committee Chairman
BERNARD GOROWITZ

Co-Editors
Joan A'Hearn
John Anderson
George Wise

Editors of Previous Editions
Bernard Gorowitz and George Wise

Associate Contributing Editors of Previous Editions

Edith M. Aliberti	Wayne H. Harvey	Edward L. Owen
John M. Anderson	Robert L. Hendrickson	Herbert C. Pollock
Willam R. Atherton	Fred. H. Holub	John Powell
Walter C. Bloomquist	Virginia M. Kelley	William A. Reich
Bernard M. Cain	Charles Q. Lemmond	Edwin W. Riggs
Jeffrey Daly	Horace M. Lockwood	Benjamin W. Roberts
Rudolph A. Dehn	Louis Navias	George M. Robertson
Stephen J. Fallick	Adelaide B. Oppenheim	John C. Rucigay
		Herbert M. Strong

Acknowledgments

Our special thanks to Raymond K. Andresen, former Manager of Communications Programs at GE in Fairfield, for his contributions of a wealth of information contained in a collection of Company publications, magazines and reprints of speeches, interviews, etc. We are also particularly grateful to William K. Lane, Jr., Manager - Executive Communications, for his valuable comments and advice.

Contributors to this Edition

Jack Batty	Fairfield, Connecticut	Beth Klein	Waukesha, Wisconsin
Susan Breon	Erie, Pennsylvania	Nancy Kmetz	Fairfield, Connecticut
William Bartlett	New York, New York	Paula Kollstedt	Evendale, Ohio
Bruce Bunche	Fairfield, Connecticut	Norman Kuchar	Schenectady, New York
Beth Comstock	Fairfield, Connecticut	Bo Liu	Beijing, China
Valerie Di Maria	Stamford, Connecticut	Hank Meincke	Croton-on-Hudson, New York
Christian Flathman	Fairfield, Connecticut	Cody Pearce	Waukesha, Wisconsin
Janice Fraser	Cleveland, Ohio	Philip Recchia	Fort Lee, New Jersey
Beth Gotti	Cleveland, Ohio	Joan Schoevaars	Bergen op Zoom, The Netherlands
Robert Hess	Pittsfield, Massachusetts	Ricki Shapiro	Niskayuna, New York
Joyce Hergenhan	Stamford, Connecticut	James Stump,	Evendale, Ohio
Linda Heuring	Waterford, New York	Chikage Tashiro	Tokyo, Japan
Mary Horne	Stamford, Connecticut	Marika Terao	Tokyo, Japan
William Lane, Jr.	Fairfield, Connecticut	Helen Weltin	Troy, New York
Chip Keeling	Louisville, Kentucky	Deborah Wexler	Niskayuna, New York
Carol Keirstead	Schenectady, New York	Pamela Wickham	Fairfield, Connecticut
Rick Kennedy	Evendale, Ohio	Anne Witkavitch	Plainville, Connecticut
		Alla Ziselson	Rockville, Maryland

Contributors to Previous Editions

M.W. Allee	Salem, Virginia	B.J. Leavitt	Fitchburg, Massachusetts
P.A. Loucka	Detroit, Michigan	A.E. Lindholm	Mt. Vernon, Indiana
W.G. Anderson	Louisville, Kentucky	J.S. Lindsay	Hendersonville, North Carolina
W.C. Mackey	Charlottesville, Virginia	P.A. Loucka	Detroit, Michigan
J.P. Arvanites	Wilmington, Massachusetts	W.C. Mackey	Charlottesville, Virginia
R.J. Magill	Schenectady, New York	R.J. Magill	Schenectady, New York
J.S. Barber	San Jose, California	L. Marinakos	Chicago Heights, Illinois
L. Marinakos	Chicago Heights, Illinois	E.C. Martt	Twinsburg, Ohio
J. Barry	Schenectady, New York	T.J. McLaren	Somersworth, New Hampshire
E.C. Martt	Twinshurg, Ohio	T.S. McKnight	Caracas, Venezuela
J. Batty	Pittsfield, Massachusetts	S.L. McMillan	Louisville, Kentucky
T.J. McLaren	Somersworth, New Hampshire	W. McShain	Ft. Wayne, Indiana
J.M. Baur	Cleveland, Ohio	G. Medford	Milwaukee, Wisconsin
K. Beecher	Sunnyvale, California	L.A. Miller	Louisville, Kentucky
R.L. Bowersox	Erie, Pennsylvania	W. Moffitt	Albany, New York
D.V. Brown	Waterford, New York	W.T. Neal	Hendersonville, Tennessee
A.V. Brancati	Charlottesville, Virginia	M. Ohkawa	Tokyo, Japan
W.L. Buchanan	Rome, Georgia	J.O'Neal	Fairfield, Connecticut
D. Carpenter	Fairfield, Connecticut	P.A. Perchonok	Portsmouth, Virginia
B. Cooper	De Kalb, Illinois	R. Rhodes	Tyler, Texas
R. Currie	Croton-On-Hudson, New York	A. W. Rickard	Owensboro, Kentucky
E. Danford	Pittsfield, Massachusetts	B. Rogers	Toronto, Canada
T.S. Davis	Pittsfield, Massachusett	W.A. Sager	Bridgeport, Connecticut
F.J. Dooley	Utica, New York	D.O. St. John	Cleveland, Ohio
F.R. Dulaney	Stamford, Connecticut	Marion Smith	Schenectady, New York
D.E. Edwards	Cleveland, Ohio	J.K. Snell	Waynesboro, Virginia
M. Finn	Cleveland, Ohio	C.F. Stowell	Schenectady, New York
A. Flynn	Pittsfield, Massachusetts	W.L. Teeple	Philadelphia, Pennsylvania
C.P. Gnau	Ft. Wayne, Indiana	W.G. Thiessen	Bridgeport, Connecticut
C.V. Grasso	Syracuse, New York	W.R. Travers	Evendale, Ohio
J.B. Harris	Hendersonville, North Carolina	A.D. Vaber	Schenectady, New York
W.J. Hendry	Wilmington, North Carolina	P. VanAvery	Schenectady, New York
W.G. Hoke	Worthington, Ohio	G.W. VanCitters	Philadelphia, Pennsylvania
J.W. Hunter	Cleveland, Ohio	J.E. Waller	Burlington, Vermont
B. Isard	Rockville, Maryland	J. Wilfore	Schenectady, New York
R.H. Kimball	Hudson Falls, New York	H. Winn	Burlington, Vermont
W.G. Kroll	Schenectady, New York	E.J. Yamartino	Lynn, Massachusetts
Ken Lauderdale	Pittsfield, Massachusetts	R. Zukowski	Utica, New York

Finally, we wish to pay our respects to the numerous unidentified photographers who recorded for posterity the events of their time.

The General Electric Story
A Heritage of Innovation
1876 - 1999

CONTENTS

Page

Chapter 1   Edison and the Early Years 1876 - 1892 7

Chapter 2   Steinmetz and the Dawn of Industrial Research 1893- 1923 57

Chapter 3   Turning Innovation into Industry 1924 - 1946 129

Chapter 4   Pathways of Progress 1947 - 1980 209

Chapter 5   Building a Company Without Boundaries 1981- 1999 313

Epilogue 380

CHAPTER ONE

EDISON AND THE EARLY YEARS
1876-1892

The year 1876 marked America's centennial. For most Americans it was a time for looking backward with pride. For others it was a time to look forward to the possibilities that lay ahead. The electrical exhibits at the Centennial Exposition in Philadelphia marked the beginning of an era where people sought new targets for invention. Later that year, Thomas Alva Edison would open a new and better equipped laboratory in Menlo Park, New Jersey, where he could explore the possibilities of the dynamo and other electrical devices that he had seen at the Exposition. Out of that laboratory was to come perhaps the greatest invention of all — a successful incandescent electric lamp. There was no lack of competition in a field ripe for new ideas. Elihu Thomson and Charles Francis Brush had their own ideas about dynamos and electric lighting. Frank Sprague and Charles Van Depoele wondered how horsecars might be replaced by electrically powered streetcars. And James J. Wood was thinking of ways of reducing the size and weight of arc-light generators and of transmitting and using the power of steam. Eventually their paths would cross as they became associated with the companies that were the predecessors of the General Electric Company. It took great courage for these men to abandon secure occupations for the risks of an untried field. Yet courage was a trait that they had in common – together with their ingenuity.

THE PREDECESSORS
of the
GENERAL ELECTRIC COMPANY

The chart on the following page illustrates the evolution of the company and the rapid growth of the electrical industry during the last twenty years of the nineteenth century. The various companies and their founders intended to promote the particular inventions they felt would revolutionize their fields. Edison's incandescent lighting systems; Brush's arc lamps and dynamos; Wood's "spark-free dynamos" and electric regulating systems; Thomson's and Houston's arc lamps, dynamos, motors, generators, transformers, and alternating-current power systems; and Sprague and Van Depoele's electric street railway systems were all developed by their own companies.

By 1890, Edison had organized his various businesses into the Edison General Electric Company. The Thomson-Houston Company and the various companies that had merged it were led by Charles A. Coffin, a former shoe manufacturer from Lynn, Massachusetts. These mergers with competitors and the patent rights owned by each company put them into a dominant position in the electrical industry. As businesses expanded, it had become increasingly difficult for either company to produce complete electrical installations relying solely on their own technology. In 1892, these two major companies combined to form General Electric.

EDISON COMPANIES

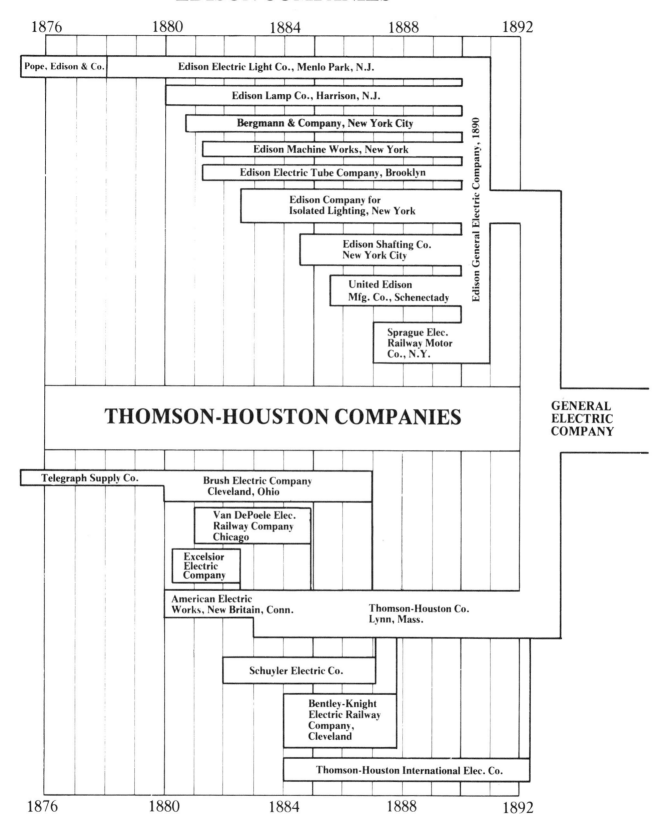

1876   1880   1884   1888   1892

Pope, Edison & Co.

Edison Electric Light Co., Menlo Park, N.J.

Edison Lamp Co., Harrison, N.J.

Bergmann & Company, New York City

Edison Machine Works, New York

Edison Electric Tube Company, Brooklyn

Edison Company for Isolated Lighting, New York

Edison Shafting Co. New York City

United Edison Mfg. Co., Schenectady

Sprague Elec. Railway Motor Co., N.Y.

Edison General Electric Company, 1890

THOMSON-HOUSTON COMPANIES

GENERAL ELECTRIC COMPANY

Telegraph Supply Co.

Brush Electric Company Cleveland, Ohio

Van DePoele Elec. Railway Company Chicago

Excelsior Electric Company

American Electric Works, New Britain, Conn.

Thomson-Houston Co. Lynn, Mass.

Schuyler Electric Co.

Bentley-Knight Electric Railway Company, Cleveland

Thomson-Houston International Elec. Co.

1876   1880   1884   1888   1892

Thomas Alva Edison
1847-1931

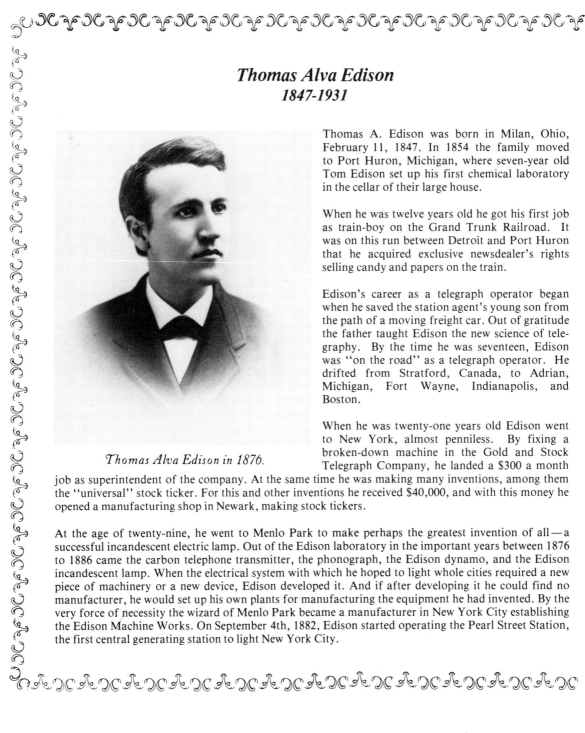

Thomas Alva Edison in 1876.

Thomas A. Edison was born in Milan, Ohio, February 11, 1847. In 1854 the family moved to Port Huron, Michigan, where seven-year old Tom Edison set up his first chemical laboratory in the cellar of their large house.

When he was twelve years old he got his first job as train-boy on the Grand Trunk Railroad. It was on this run between Detroit and Port Huron that he acquired exclusive newsdealer's rights selling candy and papers on the train.

Edison's career as a telegraph operator began when he saved the station agent's young son from the path of a moving freight car. Out of gratitude the father taught Edison the new science of telegraphy. By the time he was seventeen, Edison was "on the road" as a telegraph operator. He drifted from Stratford, Canada, to Adrian, Michigan, Fort Wayne, Indianapolis, and Boston.

When he was twenty-one years old Edison went to New York, almost penniless. By fixing a broken-down machine in the Gold and Stock Telegraph Company, he landed a $300 a month job as superintendent of the company. At the same time he was making many inventions, among them the "universal" stock ticker. For this and other inventions he received $40,000, and with this money he opened a manufacturing shop in Newark, making stock tickers.

At the age of twenty-nine, he went to Menlo Park to make perhaps the greatest invention of all — a successful incandescent electric lamp. Out of the Edison laboratory in the important years between 1876 to 1886 came the carbon telephone transmitter, the phonograph, the Edison dynamo, and the Edison incandescent lamp. When the electrical system with which he hoped to light whole cities required a new piece of machinery or a new device, Edison developed it. And if after developing it he could find no manufacturer, he would set up his own plants for manufacturing the equipment he had invented. By the very force of necessity the wizard of Menlo Park became a manufacturer in New York City establishing the Edison Machine Works. On September 4th, 1882, Edison started operating the Pearl Street Station, the first central generating station to light New York City.

The Edison interests were expanding, and in 1886 Edison sent his agents to look for suitable sites for a new factory. On the outskirts of Schenectady stood two unfinished factory buildings, which were to have been the McQueen Locomotive Works. The location of these buildings impressed Edison, and he negotiated to purchase the two plants which were soon turning out the dynamos needed by the Edison generating stations. Other buildings sprang up alongside the original shops, and in 1892 this plant became the headquarters of the newly formed General Electric Company.

It began to be apparent early in the 1890's that electrical development was being held up because no company controlled the patents on all the necessary elements for installing an efficient and serviceable system. The conviction was taking shape that the incandescent lamp and the alternating-current transformer system belonged together. The outcome in 1892 was the formation of the General Electric Company with the consolidation of the Thomson-Houston and the Edison General Electric Companies. At this period, however, he concerned himself less and less with electrical manufacturing activities, and soon devoted his entire time to his laboratory in West Orange to perfect a modernized phonograph, a motion picture camera, and an electrical storage battery.

During World War I Edison experimented on many war problems for the U.S. Government, among them the sound detection of guns and submarines, airplane detection, increasing power and effectiveness of torpedoes, improving submarines, and mining harbors. But some of Edison's greatest contributions to America's war efforts were in developing chemicals and synthetic products for goods we could no longer get from Europe.

Honors and awards were bestowed lavishly on Mr. Edison by persons, societies, and countries throughout the world. His greatest honor, perhaps, was the Congressional Medal of Honor, the nation's highest recognition of service. Edison died October 18, 1931, in Llewellyn Park, New Jersey, at the age of eighty-four.

Edison in the 1920's.

1876

Company Evolution

Thomas A. Edison moves into his new laboratory at Menlo Park, New Jersey. A year earlier he had decided to give up his telegraphic machine manufacturing interests and devote all of his time to invention in a peaceful setting away from the bustle of the city (Newark, New Jersey).

Power Generation

Charles F. Brush constructs his second hand-built dynamo. He successfully demonstrates the development to his employer and sponsor, George W. Stockly, Manager of the Cleveland Telegraph and Supply Company, founded in 1872. The Brush dynamo was one of the first to show that electric power could be put to practical use.

Communications

Alexander Graham Bell demonstrates his telephone at the Philadelphia Centennial.

Edison invents the carbon telephone transmitter improving on Bell's earlier telephone which had limited transmission ability. Patent rights to the Edison transmitter were purchased by the American Speaking Telephone Company, a subsidiary of the Western Union Telegraph Company.

Edison patents his mimeograph machine. It consisted of an electric pen that made 8,000 punctures per minute on a sheet of waxed paper which served as the stencil. An inked felt roller transferred the ink supply through the perforated sheet onto the blank sheet below.

The Western Union Telegraph Company completes installation of the Edison quadruplex telegraph system on its lines. The system, which permitted four messages to be sent simultaneously over a single circuit, doubled the capacity of existing wires and revolutionized the telegraphic communications industry.

Charles Brush's dynamo.

Edison's electric pen - the forerunner of the mimeograph.

The grounds at Thomas Alva
Edison's Menlo Park, New Jersey
Laboratory facility.

Edison & his Menlo Park staff, 1880

Charles Francis Brush
1849-1929

The first important commercial product of the fledgling electrical industry of the 1870's was the arc light, and the pioneer innovator of that product was Charles F. Brush. Not long after graduating from the University of Michigan with a degree in chemistry, Brush opened a consulting office in Cleveland and worked for several years as an analytical chemist. In his spare time he studied electricity and set up a laboratory and workshop at the family estate at Wickliffe, Ohio. Brush believed that if he could make improvements to the basic elements of the arc lighting system, the dynamo and the carbon rods and the rod feeding mechanism, he could displace gas as a means of lighting streets and commercial establishments. It is said that the first arc light dynamo that he designed was driven by a team of horses operating a treadmill. It supplied enough current for one arc lamp generating 10 amperes at about 45 volts. George W. Stockley, vice president of the Cleveland Telegraph Supply Company, and a friend of Brush was also impressed with the potential of arc lighting and agreed to furnish him with facilities, manpower, and funds so that he could expand his work. In 1876 the Telegraph Supply Company became the exclusive outlet for all of Brush's inventions.

Well publicized tests at the Franklin Institute during the following year demonstrated that the Brush arc light dynamo was the most desirable of those compared, not to mention the fact that a Brush arc lamp was chosen as the standard with which all of the test dynamos were operated.

While working to improve the efficiency and reliability of the dynamo, Brush used his chemical expertise to improve the composition of the carbon electrodes. He searched for a source of carbon that would contain a lower level of impurities than the illuminating gas coke then in use. He found such a source at a Standard Oil Company oil distillation plant within a mile of his Cleveland workshop. The new material produced a more steady light and extended the life of the arc carbons. By copper plating the carbons he improved the electrical contact with their holders and decreased the circuit resistance. Other innovations include the double-carbon lamp which could give light for up to sixteen hours without attention, an automatic constant current regulator and a simple and reliable carbon feed mechanism. With the elements of his system far superior to those offered by the competition, Brush arc lights found widespread acceptance across the country. In 1879 Brush was able to promote the formation of the California Electric Light Company of San Francisco, the first electric central station in the world. It had two Brush dynamos supplying a total of twenty-two arc lamps.

By 1880 over 5000 Brush arc lights and dynamos were in operation, and represented over 80 percent of all arc lights in use at the time. The Telegraph Supply Company became the Brush Electric Company and again expanded to meet demand. By 1890, 20,000,000 arc carbons were produced annually.

In 1889, a law suit led to the loss of Brush's patent protection on certain key elements of arc-lighting systems. The need for additional capital and technological developments by the competition induced Brush Electric to accept an acquisition proposal from the Thomson-Houston Company. Brush retired from the manufacturing portion of the business and devoted his time to experiments in his private laboratory. The flow of inventions continued to be prolific up to the time of his death in 1929. One of his last notable deeds was the establishment of the Brush Foundation for population study and the betterment of humanity.

A Brush arc lamp and arc lamps
in the Brill Brothers Store
in New York City.

A Brush dynamo room
in South America

1877

Lighting

Edison increases his Menlo Park staff and begins his incandescent lamp experiments. At the same time, he starts development of what he envisions as a complete electric lighting system.

Brush is granted patents on his copper-coated carbons for arc lamps and the first open-coil arc dynamo.

The Cleveland Telegraph Supply Company receives the sole right to manufacture Brush's dynamos and arc lamps. After several months of testing, the Franklin Institute of Philadelphia decides to purchase a Brush dynamo, citing it as one of the most efficient and the best engineered of its type.

Electricity

Elihu Thomson, Assistant Professor of Chemistry at the Central High School in Philadelphia, demonstrates that by passing sufficient current through a coil of German silver it can be used as a heating element. Two years earlier, he demonstrated the production of "electric waves" and the ability to detect them. In 1887, Heinrich Hertz demonstrated electromagnetic waves, and in 1895, Marconi put them to practical use in the first wireless transmission of messages.

Communications

Edison invents the phonograph. A grooved cylinder, covered with tin foil, was turned by hand with a stylus attached to a diaphragm resting against it on either side. The tin foil recorded the vibrations of the diaphragm which were caused by the voice. When the stylus was returned to its original position and the cylinder was rotated again, the original vibrations were reproduced with the sound playing through the diaphragm on the other side.

Elihu Thomson

Edison's original tin foil phonograph
played the first recorded
words of its inventor:

> *Mary had a little lamb,*
> *Its fleece was white as snow,*
> *And everywhere that Mary went*
> *The lamb was sure to go.*

1878

Company Evolution

The Edison Electric Light Company is founded to support Edison's lighting research. Organizational and financial backing for the company was provided by Grosvenor P. Lowrey, Edison's patent attorney; J.P. Morgan, financier; and others. The founding of this company marked the beginning of the General Electric Company lineage.

Lighting

Brush is granted a patent on the first series arc lamp, marking the beginning of the arc lighting industry.

Five Brush dynamos power twenty arc lamps in the front windows of Wanamaker's Philadelphia store.

Thomson demonstrates his alternating-current dynamo and transformers at the Franklin Institute. He and Edwin J. Houston devise a vibrating arc lamp powered by the Thomson dynamo.

Thomson's first dynamo.

LITTLE KNOWN FINANCIAL PIONEER

WHEN the Edison Electric Light Co. was organized in October, 1878, to found the succession which was eventually to become the General Electric Co. as it is today, its moving spirit was not Thomas A. Edison but a man little known in the electrical industry. He was Grosvenor Porter Lowrey, a Wall Street lawyer associated with many of the big banking houses of the day. In sponsoring the "wizard of Menlo Park" and forming a company, Lowrey was first to establish a research laboratory by capital—a workshop devoted solely to the solution of problems which had baffled scientists for years. It was a daring speculation, for the ledger showed rather large expenditures balanced only by the brains and imagination of a single man with a revolutionary idea for a new system of illumination—a system which not only the gas and arc light interests bitterly opposed but which many declared to be utterly impossible.

Lowrey was actuated not alone by his great admiration for Edison but also by a new light, the Jablochkoff arc light candle, exhibited in 1878 at the International Exposition in Paris. Feeling there were greater possibilities in electric lighting than offered by the outdoor arc already in use in this country and Jablochkoff's candles, he approached Edison and was delighted to learn that the inventor had already experimented in a small way with a new type of lamp and had also conceived a plan for the distribution of electricity. But, if the work was to continue, Edison would need financial assistance, and Lowrey determined to raise money so the wizard might continue his work. Among his numerous friends were some of the most influential financiers of the country, including Drexel, Morgan and Company. Before them he laid his plans for the Edison Electric Light Co., and J. Pierpont Morgan agreed to join with the others in backing Edison.

At this time Edison had only a one-story frame building at Menlo Park, erected in 1876 for the purpose of experimenting on telegraphy, telephony, and the phonograph. The equipment was meager, and his staff consisted of a few men. With the $300,000 of new capital furnished by the Edison Electric Light Co., Edison placed $250,000 in much-needed additions to his plant and staff and kept the remaining $50,000 for working capital.

The new company grew rapidly. Stockholders subscribed loans of $78,000 in 1880, receiving certificates of indebtedness to be exchanged for new stock when authorized. In November of that year the capital was increased to $480,000, in the following year to $720,000, and in 1883 to $1,080,000. As time went on and the industry grew, further increases were made. By 1889, when the first report of the Edison General Electric Co. (which had acquired the Edison Electric Light and other Edison companies) was issued, the capital had increased to $9,026,200; in 1892, when this company was merged with Thomson-Houston to form the General Electric Co., its capital had increased to $14,970,300.

Grosvenor P. Lowrey and his law firm
associates (Lowrey is third from left.)

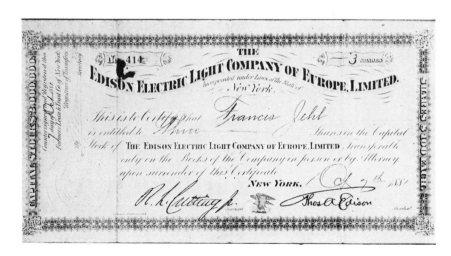

A stock certificate for the
Edison Electric Light Com-
pany of Europe — signed to
Edison's associate, Francis
Jehl.

*Edison and Francis Jehl demonstrating
the electric incandescent lamp to their
associates in the main Menlo Park lab.*

*Menlo Park
Laboratory.*

1879

Lighting

Edison invents the carbon filament incandescent lamp. On October 21, the first commercially practical incandescent lamp completes a 40 hour duration test at the Menlo Park Laboratory.

On December 31, Edison gives the first public demonstration of his electric lighting system in the streets and buildings at Menlo Park. The entire system was interconnected using underground mains.

Edison installs a small dynamo for lighting on the "Jeanette", the James Gordon Bennett arctic exploration ship. Although the lighting system was a success, the exploration was not, and the ship was lost in the Arctic.

Brush promotes the formation of the California Electric Light Company of San Francisco, the first electric central station for arc lighting in the world.

Brush receives patents on compound wiring and secondary distribution systems for arc lighting.

The first large-scale installation of arc lighting is made in Monumental Park, Cleveland using Brush lights on a 250-foot mast.

Niagara Falls is illuminated for the first time on July 4th, using 16 Brush arc lamps powered by a Brush dynamo.

James J. Wood constructs a spark-free dynamo and arc lamp. His employer, James Brady, owner of the Brady Manufacturing Company, agrees to build the dynamos in return for a half interest in the patent.

Thomson and Houston install their first commercial arc lighting system in Fuller's Bakery in Philadelphia. The three-phase alternating current winding used in the dynamo was later to become fundamental to the design of electric power systems.

Model of Edison's incandescent lamp.

James J. Wood and his spark-free dynamo.

1880

Company Evolution

Sigmund Bergmann, a good friend of Edison's, organizes Bergmann & Co. in New York for the manufacture of light fixtures, meters, junction boxes, and other accessories to complete the production of Edison's lighting systems.

Brush Electric Company of Cleveland is formed from the Telegraph Supply Company to continue the production of Brush's dynamos and arc lights.

Lighting

Edison is granted his main lamp patent, no. 223,898, on January 27, covering the fundamental features of the carbon filament lamp. Edison adopts carbonized bamboo filaments for his lamps and increases their rated life to 600 hours.

Edison establishes the first incandescent lamp factory at Menlo Park, New Jersey.

The first commercial installation of incandescent lights in the world is completed by Edison on the Steamship "S.S. Columbia".

The first municipally owned electric light plant is put into service at Wabash, Indiana, using four Brush arc lamps above the courthouse. An installation of Brush arc lamps is also made on Broadway, New York City.

Brush receives a patent on his automatic cutout for arc lamps.

Edison files his first patent for a large-scale public electric distribution system. (The patent was not issued until 1887.)

The Thomson-Houston arc dynamo is patented. Its manufacture, along with a line of arc lights, is begun by the American Electric Company, New Britain, Connecticut.

Transportation

Edison's electric railway undergoes trials at Menlo Park. It uses many of his new inventions for drive and braking systems.

First incandescent lamp factory at Menlo Park.

Edison's electric railway on a trial run at the Menlo Park laboratories.

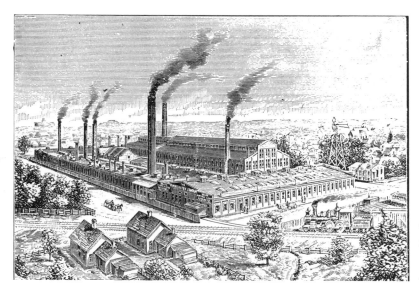

*The Brush Electric Company —
formed from the Cleveland Telegraph Supply Company to
manufacture Brush dynamos and
arc lights.*

*The "S.S. Columbia" — the first commercial
installation of the Edison lighting system.*

Elihu Thomson
1853-1937

Two days after the death of Elihu Thomson on March 13, 1937, the River Works News of the General Electric Company plant at Lynn, Massachusetts published a special four page edition carrying tributes to him from around the world. Reprinted below is a portion of General Electric's final tribute to one of its founders.

| 1853 — 1937 | # GENERAL ⊕ ELECTRIC | 1853 — 1937 |

RIVER WORKS NEWS

| Vol. 4 | MONDAY, MARCH 15, 1937 | Special |

Final Tribute Is Paid Prof. Thomson

Genius Won High Honors In Lifetime

Elihu Thomson Was Only Scientist Who Received Great Britain's Three Most Notable Medals

Elihu Thomson, teacher, engineer, inventor, scientist, pioneer in the electrical field, and benefactor of humanity, received many government, scientific, and academic honors as well as numerous medals and prizes during his lifetime of service.

No other scientist in the world received the unique distinction given Professor Thomson when he was awarded the three most notable medals of Great Britain. In 1916 he was the recipient of the Hughes medal, bestowed by the Royal Society. He was honored by the award of the Lord Kelvin medal, given by all technical and engineering bodies of England with the concurrence of leading engineering societies of America, in 1924. The Faraday medal was presented to him in 1927 by the Institution of Electrical Engineers of England in commemoration of the founding of the Institution.

Professor Thomson was decorated by France in 1889 with the red rosette of the Legion of Honor. He was a chevalier and an officer of this distinguished body.

Awarded Many Medals

Twice Professor Thomson received the John Scott Legacy medal and premium of the Franklin Institute. He was awarded the Rumford medal of the American Academy of Arts and Sciences in 1902, the first Edison medal of the American Institute of Electrical Engineers in 1910 the Elliot Cresson gold medal of the Franklin Institute in 1912, the John Fritz medal given by the four principal American engineering societies in 1916, the Franklin medal of the Franklin Institute in 1925, the Grand Prix at the Paris expositions of 1899 and 1900.

On his 82nd birthday, March 29, 1935, Professor Thomson was awarded the medal of honor of the Verein Deutscher Ingenieure of Germany. Up to that time, the late Calvin W. Rice was the only other American on whom this medal, of what is considered the oldest and largest engineering society in the world, had been conferred.

Although he never attended a college, Elihu Thomson held the following honorary academic de-

Continued on Page 2, Column 3

ENTIRE WORLD MOURNS HIS DEATH

Professor Elihu Thomson

President Swope And Other G. E. Officials Pay Professor Tribute

(From his office in New York, President Gerard Swope of the General Electric Company sent the following telegram to Mrs. Elihu Thomson last Saturday morning.)

After our conversation of Thursday, you know how deep is my feeling and the feeling of 60,000 General Electric employees in the loss of dear Professor Thomson. His contributions were of the greatest value to the General Electric Company and the industry and his life was an inspiration to his associates and will long remain a tradition in the General Electric Company.

Very cordially,

GERARD SWOPE

Established Tradition

"General Electric's earliest products were, for the most part, the offspring of Professor Thomson's brain. He was a true scientist and by example and precept established the tradition of scientific research in the General Electric Company. I feel the loss of a great and good friend."

DR. W. D. COOLIDGE

All-round Scientist

"Chemists knew him as an expert in their field just as electrical engineers recognized him as preeminent in their field and mechanical engineers as the leader in theirs. Astronomers also knew he was one of their group. He was an all-round scientist. In his death I feel a great personal loss."

DR. W. R. WHITNEY

Famed Inventor Helped Found General Electric

One Of Most Far-sighted Inventors, Elihu Thomson Held Over 700 American Patents, Third Largest Number Held By Any Man, And Was Considered One Of The "Big Four" Of Electricity In America

Officials and employees of the Lynn Works join with leaders of industry, science and government today in paying a final tribute to Professor Elihu Thomson, world famous scientist and inventor, at funeral services held this afternoon at the First Unitarian church in Lynn.

While the simple but impressive service is in progress at the church, several thousand workers in the two Lynn plants of the company will pause from work for a minute of silent tribute to the last surviving founder of General Electric Company. Meanwhile, messages of sympathy continue to arrive with tributes to the noted scientist who passed away peacefully at his Swampscott home Saturday morning after a long illness. Had the Professor lived, he would have celebrated his 84th birthday March 29.

At an early age, Professor Thomson's inventive genius asserted itself. When he was only 11 years old, he constructed the first crude friction electric machine using a wine bottle for a cylinder. Throughout the 73 years following this invention, he devoted his life to mechanical, electrical, and optical experiments and inventions for which he received the third largest number of patents ever granted to any man.

Funeral Today For Professor Thomson

Funeral services for Professor Thomson who died Saturday morning at his home in Swampscott, will be held at 2:30 o'clock this afternoon at the First Unitarian church of Lynn. Reverend Dr. Cloyd Valentine, pastor of the church, will conduct the service assisted by Reverend Doctor William Wallace Rose, pastor of the First Universalist church. Burial will be at the Pine Grove cemetery in Lynn.

While many employees of the two Lynn Works will attend the funeral as representatives of the numerous departments and organizations, all will pause in their work at 2:30 o'clock and observe a minute of quiet in respect to Professor Thomson. The plant whistles will blow to signal this pause of respect for the last surviving founder of the General Electric Company.

When word of the Professor's death was received, flags at all works and offices of the Company were lowered to half-mast where they will remain until after the funeral this afternoon.

All Lynn Works employees will be represented at the services this afternoon when representatives of the engineering and manufacturing

Continued on Page 3

Professor Thomson was born in Manchester, England, on March 29, 1853, the son of Daniel and Mary Rhodes Thomson. When he was five, the family came to the United States, settling in Philadelphia, where he was educated in the public and at Central High school.

Making unusually rapid progress in his studies, Elihu Thomson was ready for high school at 11 and had to wait two years before he could enter. Instead of playing with other boys during this time, he spent his spare time making electrical and mechanical experiments.

Graduating from high school at the age of 18, he became an instructor, his students being boys his own age or older. His work was so outstanding that he was made an assistant professor at 20 and a professor at 23.

During these years his chief interest was in the field of electricity. Outside of his school work he gave a series of lectures at the Franklin Institute in Philadelphia, where he held audiences spellbound with his electrical experiments. It was here that he demonstrated his first dynamo in 1876.

Professor Thomson made two friends during his ten years at Central High who were destined to play an important part in his later life. Edwin J. Houston, the first of these, later assisted Thom-

Continued on Page 4, Column 1

Final Tribute Paid

Continued from Page 1

son in forming the Thomson-Houston Electric Company. The second was Edwin Wilbur Rice, Jr., who was associated with the Thomson-Houston Company in its early years and later became president and honorary chairman of General Electric Company.

Perfected Separator

Working with Houston while they were both teaching in Central High, Professor Thomson perfected his machine for the continuous separation of substances of different densities. This machine was immediately recognized and soon put to general use in separating cream from milk in creameries.

Another early experiment which was successfully demonstrated in 1875 was the transmission of wireless waves to a distance through walls, solid floors and space. Because of other work and interests Elihu Thomson did not follow this lead which was later developed by others to our present radio and wireless transmission systems.

Important Inventions

Professor Thomson showed his first bi-phase dynamo in 1878 and his second in 1879. These were important because the first contained characteristics essential in modern generators while the second was the basis for the Thomson-Houston arc lighting system which only recently gave way to more modern methods of lighting.

In 1880, Professor Thomson gave up teaching and went to New Britain, Connecticut, as electrician for the American Electric Company and two years later, in 1882, organized the Thomson-Houston Company to take over his business.

Thomson Electric Meter

A year later the work was moved to Lynn where it grew to cover all branches of the electrical industry through Elihu Thomson's inventions and genius. Invention of the Thomson electric meter and electric welding contributed to this growth.

With the merger of the Thomson Houston Company and the Edison Electric Company to form the General Electric Company in 1892, Professor Thomson was made head of the Lynn Works' research laboratories which soon became world famous as the Thomson Research laboratory.

Continued His Research

As General Electric grew and become the leader in the electrical industry, Professor Thomson continued his research and inventions, winning world-wide fame. Important discoveries which contributed to his greatness and the Company's growth during this period were the principle of dynamic repulsion between primary and secondary coils, the development of a full capacity electric locomotive, his method to control electric cars and trains, and the Thomson-Houston street railway system which was adopted throughout the world.

Other inventions made by Professor Thomson include many of the safety devices now compulsory in the distribution of alternating current power, and forms of lightning arresters which made possible great savings to power systems by eliminating damage from lightning.

Made Many Contributions

Professor Thomson made many contributions too numerous to mention to the electrical industry as well as along other lines during the busy years. He invented the first stereoscopic methods in X-ray photography; a uniflow engine, a steam engine of very high efficiency, and a steam engine for automobiles, one of which he used in his own car for many years. His electric meter proved the forerunner of over 30 millions of these instruments now in use by industry as well as in private homes. His alternating current repulsion motor was probably his most important single contribution to industry. Over 1,000,000 of these are now in operation.

Astronomy His Hobby

Through Elihu Thomson's long life, astronomy was his hobby. At his home in Swampscott he built an observatory equipped with two telescopes which he designed and built in his own laboratory. He spent many enjoyable hours of leisure time there studying the stars.

Toward the close of his life, Professor Thomson devoted much effort to the construction of a 200-inch fused quartz mirror for the world's largest telescope planned for the Mt. Wilson observatory. While it was eventually decided to use a glass mirror, he had already secured patents on a process for making quartz mirrors which will be of great value in future work along this line.

While Professor Thomson first lived in Lynn, he later moved to Swampscott, where he lived at the estate on Monument avenue until his death. Not confining his interests to science and invention, he took a part in town affairs which won the devotion and respect of Swampscott people. He aided many civic interests in Greater Lynn which included giving the land for Swampscott's public library and serving that institution for many years as a trustee.

Received Many Honors

Professor Thomson was also closely associated with scientists at Harvard and M. I. T. He lectured at various colleges and later became a faculty member at Tech, and acting president of that institution from 1920 to 1922.

Elihu Thomson has been honored throughout the world by government recognition and by leading scientific societies and universities who have conferred on him numerous medals, honors, and degrees. Dr. Karl T. Compton, president of Massachusetts Institute of Technology, has said of him, "More than any man now living, or in fact, more than any man in history, it seems to me that Professor Thomson has combined in a most remarkable way the constructive powers of the inventor, the thoroughness and soundness of the man of science, and the kindly balance of the ideal philosopher, teacher, and friend. Because of these qualities he is held in equally high esteem by engineers and in the most highbrow academic circles. He has always shunned publicity, and because of this, his achievements have not been highly advertised or made common objects of front-page newspaper publicity."

Married Clarissa Hovey

On May 1, 1884, Professor Thomson married Mary I. Peck of New Britain, Connecticut. They had four sons, the late Captain Stuart Thomson, who died of war injuries in 1919, Roland D. Thomson of Schenectady, N. Y., Malcolm Thomson of Swampscott who is a welding engineer in the Works Fabricating department, and Donald T. Thomson of Rye, New York. Mrs. Thomson died in 1916, and on January 4, 1923, Professor Thomson married Miss Clarissa Hovey, the daughter of Theodore Hovey of Boston, who survives him.

PROFESSOR THOMSON AT WORK IN HIS STUDY AT HOME

Until the last few months of his life, Professor Elihu Thomson spent much time working in the study of his Swampscott home. Taken on his 80th birthday, this picture shows him reading some of the large number of congratulatory letters which came to him from all parts of the world on that occasion.

THOMSON LIKED FRIENDLY TITLE OF PROFESSOR

Although Elihu Thomson held doctors' degrees conferred by the world's leading colleges and universities, he always preferred to have his friends address him as "Professor", the title given him over 60 years ago by the Philadelphia Central High School. He liked this title because to him, it was more endearing and friendly than "Doctor".

Thomson Was "General" To A Small Boy

Charles A. Coffin Selected Late Professor As One Most Worthy Of Title "General" Electric

The late Professor Thomson received many formal honors during his lifetime, but the only military rank he held was in the heart of a small boy whose own engineering career was later cut off in action at St. Mihiel. That was a general's rank, and how it came about was revealed in a letter from the boy's father, Ira Walton Henry, a New York consulting engineer.

Henry took a short "Expert" course here under Professor Thomson in 1887 and was later sent to a New York City power station as an electrical engineer.

Years later, he stopped in Schenectady with his wife and five-year old son. The boy had spent the previous day at an army review and was still much impressed by his introduction to Generals Merritt and Greeley. Without his father's knowledge he expressed a desire to meet "General" Electric in the hearing of Charles A. Coffin, then president of the company. With some ceremony, the latter presented him to Professor Thomson as the one most worthy of that title.

Later young Henry studied engineering at Harvard and always spoke of the famous Professor to his fellow students and instructors as "General" Electric.

Genius Is Lauded By J. A. McManus

(As Professor Thomson's secretary for the past 34 years, John A. McManus has been privileged to know him intimately during this long period and is, therefore, well qualified to know his unusual abilities.)

The death of Professor Thomson marks the passing of the last of the great pioneers in the electrical industry in America. But, Professor Thomson was more than this, and time will enhance his stature in the firmament of the great. His colossal attributes of genius are too little known to the lay world for immediate appraisal by it, but his fellow scientists and engineers have appraised them in superlative terms on many occasions. I have been closely associated with Professor Thomson since his prime of life in an intimate and delightful relationship, and privileged to observe first-hand his great tolerance, his kindly sympathy, his eager desire to pass along to others the wealth of his information, and his love for and interest in youth. These were among his outstanding qualities. I am naturally deeply grieved by a loss which, to me, is irreparable.

JOHN A. McMANUS.

The Edison Installation at Blue Mountain Lake.

Regarding the plant in the Prospect House, Blue Mountain Lake, Adirondack Mountains, N.Y., Mr. G.W. Waters, the engineer in charge, has just made the following report:

"The Edison incandescent electric light plant installed here was started by me June 16th, 1882, and has run without any interruption every evening since. It has run all this season on an average of about five hours per night. The plant consists of two Z dynamos, 230 A lamps, and 102 B lamps run in series. Although there is a total of 332 lamps in the building we do not have occasion to run over 125 lights at any one time. The engine runs them easily with seventy pounds indicated steam pressure. The boiler burns wood, and on a careful test has consumed only one quarter of a cord during a six hour run. As to breakage of lamps, as near as I can get at the number of hours that the lamps are burned, I think it will average fifty lamps for the whole evening, showing an average life of the lamps thus far of about eight hundred hours. The lamp which I placed in the elevator car, July 12th, has been lighted every night since successfully. The plant has given complete satisfaction to Mr. Durant, and every one who sees the light is delighted with it."

Prospect House, Blue Mountain Lake in the Adirondacks, New York

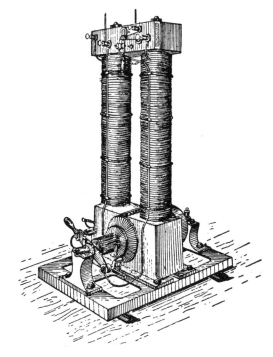

Edison's "long-legged Mary Ann" lighting dynamo.

1881

Company Evolution

The Edison Machine Works is established on Goerck Street, New York City. Later, it was moved upstate to become the Schenectady Works of the General Electric Company.

Edison opens business offices at 65 Fifth Avenue, New York City, to exploit his electric lighting systems.

The Fort Wayne Electric Light Company is formed by Ronald T. McDonald, a clothing manufacturer, to produce the James Jenney System of arc lighting.

The Edison Lamp Company of Menlo Park, the Edison Tube Company of New York, and the Edison Shafting Company of New York are formed.

Lighting

Edison receives patents on his current regulator for dynamos, apparatus for producing high vacuum, and a method of treating carbon for use in electric lamps. All of these patents are related to his new system of incandescent electric lighting.

The Edison"Jumbo", the largest dynamo ever built, with a 1200 light capacity is exhibited at the Paris Exposition.

The first commercial incandescent light installation on land is installed at the lithography shop of Hinds, Ketchum & Company, New York City.

Prospect House at Blue Mountain Lake in the Adirondacks of New York becomes the first hotel lighted by electricity.

Electricity

Elihu Thomson develops the constant-current regulator.

The first generating plant in a mill is installed at James Harrison's woolen factory in Newburgh, New York.

Office of the Edison Electric Light Company, 65 Fifth Avenue, New York City. (Edison is at the extreme left.)

Edison's "Jumbo" dynamo — built at the Edison Machine Works, Goerck Street, New York.

1882

Company Evolution

The Edison Company for Isolated Lighting is formed in Harrison, New Jersey. Its purpose is to make direct installations on the premises of commercial and industrial firms, providing complete systems from dynamos to lamps. By the end of the year there are 150 such installations with 30,000 lamps. Within five years the totals increase to 700 installations and more than 180,000 lamps.

The Schuyler Electric Light Company is incorporated for the manufacture of arc lighting systems.

Lighting

Edison applies for a patent on the three-wire electric distribution system. This development, resulting in an almost two-thirds reduction in the amount of copper used in wiring systems, is an important factor in making incandescent lighting and central stations economically feasible.

Electricity

The world's first hydroelectric plant is placed in operation at Appleton, Wisconsin, using an Edison bipolar generator.

Two Edison "Jumbo" dynamos are installed in the central station at Holburn Viaduct, London.

The first incandescent lamp central station in the United States, the Pearl Street Station, built by Edison and staff, begins operation in New York on September 4. Employing six "Jumbo" dynamos, the installation supplies 7,200 16-candlepower lamps over an area of one-sixth of a square mile. All power lines are laid in underground mains.

Thomson develops the air blast arc arrester for the protection of high current switching components.

Transportation

Frank J. Sprague develops the underrunning trolley for street railways. Sprague conceived the idea of using an overhead conductor cable and an upward pressing contact arm mounted on the roof of the car to transmit electricity to a motor-drive system underneath the car.

Edison's generating station at Appleton, Wisconsin.

Sprague-designed freight car using third rail system at New York sugar refinery.

Drawing of Edison's Pearl Street Station in New York City.

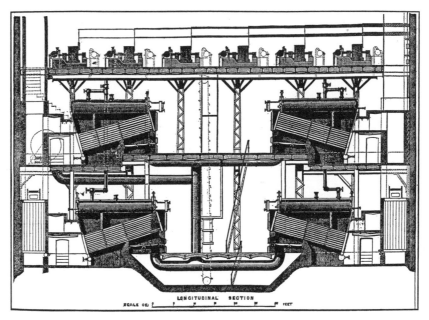

An 1882 drawing of the arrangement of engines and dynamos in the Pearl Street Station. Six "Jumbo" dynamos are on the upper level and the boilers and steam engines are on the two levels below.

Frank Julian Sprague
1857-1934

"In the roster of men who have been the foremost energizers of electrical invention and industry will be found the name of Frank J. Sprague"

T.C. Martin, S.L. Coles

One of the pioneers in electric railway transportation started his career at sea as a graduate of the U.S. Naval Academy and an ensign in the U.S. Navy. In 1877 he was assigned to duty off the coast of China on the USS Richmond during President Grant's Far Eastern tour. On his return, he worked at the Brooklyn Navy Yard and Stevens Institute making plans for the introduction of incandescent electric lamps on U.S. Navy vessels. His investigations caused him to be so enthusiastic about Thomas Edison's work that he resigned from the Navy to join Edison at Menlo Park. His interest focused on the design of electric motors and the possibilities for their use on electric railways. In 1884, he organized the Sprague Electric Railway and Motor Company. Almost immediately the company was offered a contract to build an electric street railway at Richmond, Virginia. It consisted of 40 cars propelled by 80 motors, a complete overhead system and a central power plant. This constituted the first sizable commercial electric road in the world. It was followed by 110 Sprague-built railways before his company merged with the Edison General Electric Company in 1890.

Sprague's interests included vertical as well as horizontal transportation. In 1886 the first 220-volt Sprague motor was installed in a building in Boston for the purpose of running a freight elevator. In 1892, the Sprague Electric Elevator Company was formed and was a spawning ground for his numerous inventions in the area of remote control and other equipment for elevator operation. The development of control circuits found its most widespread use in Sprague's "Multiple Unit" system of train control, which permitted the assembly of any desired number of cars into a train, with control over the train made possible with each car's motor and controller from any point in the train. The invention, first installed on the South Side Elevated in Chicago in 1897, paved the way for the construction of electrically powered elevated roads and subways throughout the world. General Electric's President Charles Coffin negotiated with Sprague to acquire the multiple unit patent and, in 1903, the Sprague Electric Company was acquired. Sprague's first large task was the electrification of Grand Central Terminal and the replacement of the old steam locomotives with General Electric locomotives coupled together by means of the multiple unit system.

Although Sprague's varied interests led him to the formation of a number of independent businesses including the Sprague Development Corporation and the Sprague Safety Control and Signal Corporation, he remained for many years, a consultant to the General Electric Company.

1883

Company Evolution

The Thomson-Houston Company, a reorganization of the American Electric Company, is formed by a group of Massachusetts shoe manufacturers headed by Charles A. Coffin. Its operations are later moved to Lynn, Massachusetts.

The Bentley-Knight Electric Railway Company is formed through the aid of the Brush Electric Company in Cleveland, Ohio.

Lighting

Thomson patents the magnetic blowout for the protection of arc lighting circuits from current surges.

San Francisco makes its first use of electric street lighting with the Brush system.

The first night baseball game is played in Fort Wayne, Indiana, using seventeen arc lights of 4,000 candlepower each.

The first photograph ever made using incandescent lamps is taken at Menlo Park, New Jersey.

Electricity

Edison discovers that electric current can flow through an evacuated space from a filament to a plate in an incandescent bulb. This phenomenon, later called the "Edison Effect", was patented by him and became the forerunner of electronics.

The first central station to use Edison's three-wire system begins operation at Sunbury, Pennsylvania. The Edison Electric Light Company inaugurates the first underground three-wire system at Brockton, Massachusetts.

Transportation

The first elevated electric railway in the United States is operated at the Chicago Railway Exposition by the Electric Railway Company.

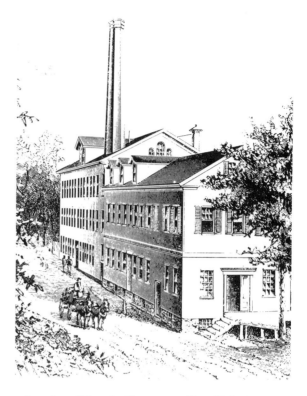

American Electric Company, New Britain, Connecticut — forerunner of the Thomson-Houston Company.

The first incandescent lamp photo, Menlo Park.

1884

Company Evolution

Edison's lamp manufacturing business at Harrison, New Jersey becomes the Edison Lamp Company.

Frank Sprague demonstrates his invention of a DC motor. He forms the Sprague Electric Railway and Motor Company to exploit this and his other inventions.

Transportation

The Bentley-Knight Company demonstrates the first electric street railway in Cleveland, Ohio, using an early form of the third-rail system with Brush dynamos and motors.

The first electric submarine in America, "The Peacemaker", is built by the Delameter Iron Works of New York City. The vessel used Brush storage batteries and a Brush 12-hp motor for propulsion.

Electricity

George Westinghouse forms the Westinghouse Electric and Manufacturing Company in Pittsburgh, Pennsylvania, after purchasing William Stanley's incandescent lamp and DC dynamo patents from the Swan Incandescent Electric Light Company.

Industrial Products

Alfred and Eugene Cowles produce the first electric industrial furnace using a Brush dynamo for current. With this furnace, they produced the first alloy of aluminum; and later, synthetic rubies and sapphires.

From an Edison Electric Light Company circular to its licensee central stations in 1885.

"A practical motor has been a want seriously felt in our system . . . The Sprague motor is believed to meet . . . all the exigencies of the case and the Edison Electric Light Company feels that it can safely recommend it to its licensees as the only practical and economic motor existing today."

Walter H. Knight and Edward M. Bentley — pioneers in the development of electric railways and public transportation.

*A Thomson-Houston central station
in Boston, Massachusetts.*

*A Bentley-Knight street railway
powered by contact with an electric
conduit between the tracks.*

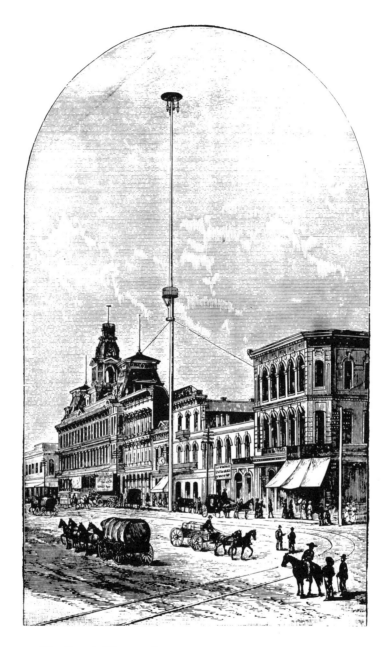

*The Brush Electric Company arc lighting system for the
Los Angeles, California light tower.*

1885

The Thomson-Houston Company's manufacturing machine shop at Lynn, Massachusetts.

Company Evolution

The Van Depoele Electric Light Company is merged into the Van Depoele Electric Manufacturing Company.

Lighting

Thomson devises the use of the grounded secondary for transformers. This development provided a means for coping with the possibly dangerous effects of insulation breakdown in a transformer and, in so doing, gave impetus to the use of AC distribution systems.

Thomson develops a DC dynamo for incandescent lamps.

Thomson adopts the magnetic blowout as a lightning arrester for the protection of arc lighting and other circuits. The principle of the magnetic blowout has since been employed in the design of modern high-current switching devices.

The Statue of Liberty is floodlighted by the use of arc lights from the Fort Wayne Electric Company.

The Thomson-Houston Company begins to manufacture incandescent lamps at Lynn, Massachusetts.

Dr. Edward Weston develops the hydrocarbon flashing process for making uniform carbon lamp filaments.

Industrial Products

Weston patents a magnetic drag-type speedometer — an early automobile speedometer.

An electric drill is invented by Charles J. Van Depoele, and its manufacture is begun by the Thomson-Van Depoele Electric Mining Company, a subsidiary of Thomson-Houston for the production of mining equipment.

Servicing an arc lamp in Hartford, Connecticut.

1886

Company Evolution

The Edison Machine Works moves to Schenectady, New York, following a strike in New York City. In December, the two unoccupied buildings erected by the McQueen Locomotive Company are purchased for $45,000. Of this sum, Edison paid $37,500, and $7,500 was supplied by a group of Schenectady citizens and businesses interested in attracting his company to the city. These buildings, Shop 10 and part of Shop 12, formed the nucleus around which the present extensive Schenectady Works has grown.

The Edison Tube Company and the Edison Shafting Company merge with the Machine Works. John Kruesi, General Manager of the Machine Works, was later to become Chief Mechanical Engineer of the General Electric Company.

The Edison Electric Light Company absorbs all the business previously handled by the Edison Company for Isolated Lighting.

Electricity

Thomson receives patents for the first electrical resistance welder and welding transformer.

William Stanley develops a commercially practical transformer that he uses in the first AC lighting installation in the United States at Great Barrington, Massachusetts. The overall distance spanned by the system was 4,000 feet. Stanley also demonstrated that transformers could be connected in parallel and designed as self-regulating.

John Kruesi, General Manager of Edison's Schenectady Machine Works.

Buildings 10 & 12, Schenectady, New York.

*William Stanley and his transformer —
an important step in the establishment
of AC power systems.*

Charles Joseph Van Depoele
1846-1892

During his early experiments with arc lighting, Charles J. Van Depoele so frightened his neighbors with the eeriness of the glows that were emitted from his laboratory that they called the local fire department. But Van Depoele would not be deterred either from his construction of lighting systems or from his work with dynamos and motors and other equipment that could be used to support the development of electric traction. The latter efforts were to be so successful in demonstrating the feasibility of the electric street railway that they would earn for him the designation "Father of the Trolley."

Van Depoele was born in Lichtervelde, Belgium in 1846. He was educated at the College of Poperinghe, Belgium and the Imperial Lyceum, Lille, France. His father's position as master mechanic at the East Flanders Railway shops undoubtedly influenced his interest in machinery and transportation, but he was even more interested in physics and electricity — so much so, that at the age of fifteen, he succeeded in generating his first electric light through the use of about forty Bunsen cells. Although the faculty members at the schools that Van Depoele attended were enthusiastic about his work, his family's attitude was discouraging and he left home for America in 1868, settling in Detroit. There he built a successful business manufacturing church furniture and used the earnings to finance his electrical studies.

In 1877 he decided to commit himself completely to a career in the electrical industry. He turned his furniture business over to his father who had joined him in America and organized the Van Depoele Electric Light Company, with shops at Hamtranck, a suburb of Detroit. Two years later the business was moved to Chicago and Van Depoele arranged to demonstrate the potential use of electric propulsion for an elevated railway that was being planned for the city. The test track, which was 500 feet in length with a five percent grade toward the center of its length, was equipped with an overhead wire supplying electricity to an underrunning wheel attached to a trolley pole mounted on the roof of the 25-passenger car. After several weeks of successful operation, the car was moved to an elevated track built on the grounds of the Chicago Inter-State Fair. It operated for fifty days without any problems. Many of those who doubted the future of electric traction were convinced and orders came in from across the country. By 1887, the Van Depoele company had installed over a dozen electric street railways which used nearly a hundred cars over sixty miles of track.

The pace of business was so great that Van Depoele turned to the Thomson-Houston Company to supply additional manufacturing facilities and working capital. In 1888, Thomson-Houston purchased the business and agreed to pay the inventor a royalty of $5 per car. He moved to Lynn, Massachusetts where he joined the engineering staff of Thomson-Houston's Railway Department.

Van Depoele died on March 18, 1892, shortly before the consolidation of the Thomson-Houston Company and the Edison General Electric Company. In the fifteen years that he had devoted to work on things electrical he had been credited with nearly 250 patents touching on a wide range of applications from electric lighting to electric mining machinery. His invention of the carbon brush not only brought a revolution in the operating capabilities of railway motors but of DC electric motors of virtually every kind. One can only wonder what an additional twenty years might have produced in this short but fruitful career.

1887

Company Evolution

The Schuyler Electric Manufacturing Company, which went into receivership in 1886 after great financial difficulty, becomes the Schuyler Electric Company and is acquired by Thomson-Houston.

Edison moves his residence from Menlo Park to West Orange, New Jersey, where he reestablishes his laboratory. The new laboratory was ten times the size of Menlo Park, with 60,000 square feet of floor space and a staff of 45 to 60. It was considered the largest industrial research facility in the world.

Industrial Products

Elihu Thomson builds the first repulsion-induction motor. The first Thomson alternator is shipped by the Thomson-Houston Company to the Lynn Electric Company.

Power Transmission

Thomson receives a patent on the use of oil to insulate and cool transformers.

The Bentley-Knight Electric Railway Company starts operation of the Woonsocket Electric Railway, the first in New England. Tracks for an electric railway are laid on Fulton Street, New York City.

Communications

Edison inventions improve his wax cylinder phonograph. Between 1887 and 1890 he received more than eighty phonograph-related patents and established an extensive commercial business in the manufacture and sale of phonographs and records.

Lighting

Thomson-Houston begins production and sale of an AC incandescent lighting system.

"I will have the best equipped and largest Laboratory extant, and the facilities incomparably superior to any other for rapid and cheap development of an invention and working it up into Commercial shape with models patterns and special machining. In fact there is no similar institution in Existence. We do our own castings, forgings and can build anything from a lady's watch to a locomotive... Inventions that formerly took months and cost large sums can now be done 2 or 3 days with very small expense, as I carry a stock of almost every conceivable material." From Edison's notebook.

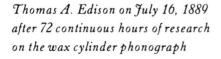

Thomas A. Edison on July 16, 1889 after 72 continuous hours of research on the wax cylinder phonograph

1888

The basement of Factory A of the Thomson-Houston Company's plant at Lynn, Massachusetts...In the left foreground — the first alternator ever shipped by the company.

Company Evolution

The Edison Machine Works begins to expand its operations in Schenectady.

The Weston Electrical Instrument Company is formed by Edward Weston. During the '70s, Weston had developed highly efficient dynamos and arc lighting systems.

To commercialize the transformer for electric resistance welding which he developed in 1885, Elihu Thomson organizes the Thomson Welding Company.

Lighting

Edison's lamp factory at Harrison, New Jersey, improves his filament by coating it with asphalt.

Transportation

In January, the Thomson-Houston Company installs the first industrial electric locomotive at the Tremont & Suffolk Mills, Lowell, Massachusetts.

The Thomson-Houston Company enters the electric railway field by acquiring the Bentley-Knight, Van Depoele, and Sprague patents, which give the company control of virtually all important patents in this field. By the end of 1888, it had on order or had constructed 16 complete street railway installations.

Charles J. Van Depoele invents carbon brushes for the electric railway motor. One of the most important inventions in the electric railway field, his carbon brushes also had much to do with the success of the direct-current motor.

Railway streetcar scene on the Ansonia, Derby & Birmingham line.

A view of the wire insulating department at Schenectady, Shop 1, Building 10.

M.M.M. Slattery, Chief Electrician of the Ft. Wayne Electric Light Company, demonstrated an electrically driven, battery powered tricycle in 1887.

Streetcar armature winders at the
Schenectady Works, late 1880's.

A display of Edison telephones and phonographs
attracted over 30,000 people at the Paris Exposi-
tion this year.

1889

Charles P. Steinmetz—in Yonkers, New York after his arrival in the United States.

Company Evolution

The Edison General Electric Company is formed by consolidating the Edison Electric Light Company, the Edison Lamp Company, the Edison Machine Works and Bergmann & Company.

The Edison United Manufacturing Company becomes the United Edison Manufacturing Company and is acquired by the Edison General Electric Company.

The Sprague Electric Railway and Motor Company is absorbed by the Edison General Electric Company.

The Thomson-Houston Company buys the Brush Electric Company, although the Brush Company continues as a separate organization.

The Bentley-Knight Electric Railway Company merges with the Thomson-Houston Company.

Charles Proteus Steinmetz (1865-1923) of Germany arrives in the United States and starts work in Yonkers, New York, as a $12-a-week electrical draftsman for Eickemeyer and Osterheld.

Transportation

The first official commercial run of an electrified street railway is made on the Beacon Street-Brookline Division in Boston along 13 miles of track powered by the Sprague Company.

Lighting

The Paris Exposition is the first to be kept open successfully during the evening with the extended use of electric lighting. More than 10,000 incandescent lamps, ranging from 4 to 50 candlepower, were used for lighting purposes.

Power Transmission

The first alternating-current power transmission system to be installed in the United States is placed in operation between Portland and Willamette Falls, Oregon — a distance of 13 miles.

Electricity

Thomson invents the integrating wattmeter. This meter was the forerunner of the watt-hour meter used almost universally for the automatic measurement of power utilization by electric utility consumers.

Soldering wattmeter housings at Lynn, Massachusetts.

1890

Company Evolution

The Edison Electric Company sets up a district sales organization of seven zones across the United States.

Charles A. Coffin of Thomson-Houston organizes the United Electric Securities Company in an effort to combat the effects of the nation's faltering economy.

Charles A. Coffin and Henry Villard, President of the Edison General Electric Company, conduct negotiations aimed at a possible merger of their two companies.

The Stanley Electric Manufacturing Company of Pittsfield, Massachusetts is formed by William Stanley, after leaving the Westinghouse Company. He begins the manufacture of a polyphase motor for AC power systems. Later this company was to become the Pittsfield Works of General Electric.

Industrial Products

Edison builds a large plant near Ogdensburg, New Jersey for the magnetic concentration of low grade iron ore. With the formation of the Edison General Electric Company the previous year, Edison had received a large sum of money. He decided that the best use for this money was the financing of an independent venture into the field of ore production. In spite of his numerous technological innovations, the project was a financial disaster because of a sharp drop in the price of ore concentrations newly discovered in the West.

Thomson receives several patents covering devices and processes for electric soldering and pipe welding.

Electricity

The first electrocution of a prisoner takes place at Auburn Prison, New York. Alternating current at 2,000 volts was employed for the execution, and Edison, who opposed the development of AC, used this event to support his arguments about the dangers of the system.

Charles A. Coffin, Thomson-Houston Company executive and the first President of the General Electric Company.

Edison in his West Orange chemistry laboratory.

The earliest type of AC generator — constructed by the Thomson-Houston Company.

Making porcelain insulators at the Schenectady Works in the 1890's

General view of Building 12, Schenectady Works.

*Correspondence Department, Schenectady
Works in early 1890's.*

1891

Lighting

Edison wins a court victory — gaining all patent rights on the incandescent lamp.

The manufacture of incandescent lamps in Europe is begun in Eindhoven, Holland, by the Philips Holland Company.

Communications

Edison invents the motion picture camera. With the continuous tape-like film that he originated for this mechanism, it became possible to take and reproduce motion pictures.

Transportation

Edison invents a number of devices for use in electric railway overhead-wire systems. Such systems were used in areas where third rails could not be conveniently installed.

Industrial Products

The Westinghouse Electric and Manufacturing Company installs the first electric equipment for steel mills in the Edgar Thompson Works of the Carnegie Steel Company, Bessemer, Pennsylvania.

Power Transmission

Westinghouse introduces the 60-cycle frequency, which later saw almost universal use in the United States.

The first alternating-current power transmission installation in the United States for industrial use is made at Telluride, Colorado, by the Westinghouse Electric and Manufacturing Company.

Steinmetz publishes his first paper on hysteresis while working for Eickemeyer & Osterheld in Yonkers, New York.

A section of the buildings of the Stanley Electric Manufacturing Company at Pittsfield, Massachusetts.

The world's first motion picture camera — strip kinetograph by Thomas Edison.

1892

State of New York.

No. 684.   Int. 652.

IN SENATE,

March 15, 1892.

Introduced by Mr. CANTOR (by request) — read twice, and ordered printed and when printed to be committed to the committee on miscellaneous corporations.

AN ACT

To incorporate the general electric company.

The People of the State of New York, represented in Senate and Assembly, do enact as follows:

1 SECTION 1. Joseph P. Ord, S. Endicott Peabody, Frank S. Hastings, James

2 Jackson, S. Dana Green and Eugene Griffin, their associates and successors

3 and assigns, are hereby constituted a body corporate under the name of

4 " general electric company," and as such, are authorized to carry on business

5 for the following purposes, or any of them: The manufacturing, buying,

6 selling, leasing and using of machinery, generators, motors, lamps, apparatus,

7 devices, supplies, and articles of every kind appertaining to or in any wise

8 connected with the production, use, distribution, regulation, control or

9 application of electricity or electrical apparatus for the purpose of light, heat,

10 power, locomotion, telephony, telegraphy, metallurgy, or for any other use

11 or purpose; of constructing, acquiring, using, selling, buying or leasing any

12 works, construction or plant, or part thereof, connected with or involving

13 such use, distribution, regulation, control or application of electricity, or the

Correction marks by Joseph P. Ord, Comptroller of the General Electric Company.

*Schenectady Tube Works
destroyed by fire in 1892
(litho 1888)*

Company Evolution

The General Electric Company is formed by merging the Edison General Electric Company and the Thomson-Houston Company on April 15. The Edison Company contributed to the new company such major assets as the fundamental incandescent lamp patents, the Edison system of distributing electrical energy, and a growing electric traction business. Thomson-Houston contributed its profitable arc lighting business and valuable developments in alternating-current systems. Together, they accounted for about $20 million in gross sales and employed about 10,000 people.

The General Electric Tube Works in Schenectady is destroyed by a fire.

Eickemeyer & Osterheld is acquired by the General Electric Company. In this acquisition the prize was Charles Proteus Steinmetz, who now goes to work for General Electric at Lynn, Massachusetts.

Lighting

Machine-molded bulbs replace the old hand-blown type.

Thomson-Houston Company begins experiments with the squirted cellulose filament in an effort to improve the productivity and properties of its carbonized filament lamps.

Industrial Products

The first automatic push-button controlled elevators are installed in the Postal Telegraph Building in New York using six Sprague-Pratt passenger elevators.

Thomson-Houston Company develops the waterproof motor.

Transportation

The Baltimore & Ohio Railroad becomes the first steam railway in the United States to use electric locomotives and power equipment.

General Electric Type LRR electric locomotive.

Armature shop at the Schenectady Works in the 1890's.

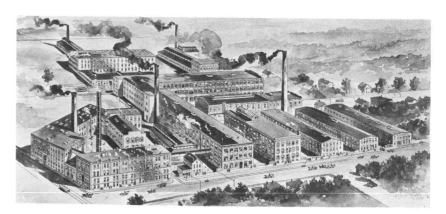

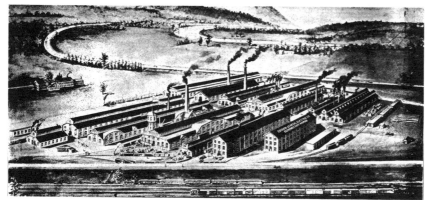

The Edison General Electric Company, Schenectady in 1891 (left) and the Thomson-Houston Plant at Lynn in 1892 (above).

Edison's lamp manufacturing factory in Harrison, New Jersey.

THE ORGANIZATION OF THE GENERAL ELECTRIC COMPANY 1892

Executive Officers

Charles A. Coffin - President
Eugene Griffin - First Vice President
Samuel Insull - Second Vice President
Frederick P. Fish - General Counsel
E.I. Garfield - Secretary
Benjamin F. Peach, Jr. - Treasurer

Departments - General Managers

Lighting - S.Dana Greene
Railway - O.T. Crosby
Power - John R.McKee
Supply - Jesse R. Lovejoy

Board of Directors

H.M. Twombley - Chairman

F.L. Ames	Eugene Griffin
C.A. Coffin	F.S. Hastings
T.J. Coolidge, Jr.	H.L. Higginson
C.H. Coster	D.O. Mills
T.A. Edison	J.P. Morgan

Works Managers

Manager - Schenectady Works - John Kreusi
Manager - Harrison Works - Francis R. Upton
Manager - Lynn Works - George E. Emmons

* * *

Technical Director - Edwin W. Rice,Jr.

The formation of the General Electric Company by the consolidation of the Edison General Electric Company and the Thomson-Houston Company on April 15, 1892 brought together many of the most inventive minds in the electrical industry - Edison, Thomson, Van Depoele, and Wood; and it provided the new company with the outstanding administrative capabilities of Charles A. Coffin, who had been so successful in building the Thomson-Houston Company. Coffin was elected President of General Electric, with Eugene Griffin, an expert salesman and former Thomson-Houston man, as Executive Vice-President. Edwin W. Rice, Jr., Thomson's assistant after his departure from Central High School and later general superintendent of Thomson-Houston operations, was named Vice-President and Technical Director.

Thomson, more interested in research than in the day-to-day operations of the company, chose to continue his work at the Engineering Laboratory at Lynn, Massachusetts. During his career he was to receive a total of nearly 700 patents, the first granted in 1876 and the last in 1932 - five years before his death.

Edison, who initially opposed the merger, joined the General Electric Board of Directors but became more involved with independent ventures. He turned his attentions to such things as his mining projects, motion pictures, the perfection of his phonograph, and even the development of new types of cement and a system for the construction of poured concrete homes which could be mass-produced and assembled in less than three days. He was to receive a total of some 1,300 patents in the course of his lifetime, and leave in the pages of history a name which has become synonomous not only with elecricity but with inventive genius.

At the end of its first seven months of operation - from June 1 to December 31, 1892 - the General Electric Company had earned nearly $3 million. But within months the country was faced with a severe economic depression which would continue for five years. Many companies failed and the young electrical industry was hard pressed for survival. Coffin would subsequently prove that he could provide the leadership to meet the challenge; and the innovators who had created the products and ideas which were the foundation of the company would be joined by Charles P. Steinmetz, William Stanley, Willis R. Whitney and numerous others who would make their contributions to its growth.

EDISON'S LATER YEARS

Thomas A. Edison seated in his library.

Edison in the New York Edison Company office.

Presentation of Edison's "Glass House" to Henry Ford, June 1929. Edison and Ford autographing board from building.

Edison with his "Edison Effect" lamps.

Edison Day window display 1915 at Rikers Drug Store 200 Broadway, New York City.

Thomas A. Edison on tour of the Schenectady plant in 1922.

Dr. W.D. Coolidge, Dr. W.R. Whitney, Thomas A. Edison, Dr. Charles P. Steinmetz and Dr. Irving Langmuir on the steps of the Research Laboratory, General Electric Company, Schenectady, N.Y., October 18, 1922.

*Edison and
Steinmetz before
lightning generator.*

*Edison in front
of his home
at Orange, N.J.*

*Edison at the office of the
ore-concentrating plant at Edison,
New Jersey, in the nineties.*

Steinmetz and Edison during a moment of contemplation.

CHAPTER TWO

STEINMETZ AND THE DAWN OF INDUSTRIAL RESEARCH
1893-1923

In 1892, America celebrated the quadricentennial of its discovery by Christopher Columbus. The Great Chicago Columbian Exposition and World's Fair was described as the most elaborate spectacle of the use of electricity ever presented. One of the exhibitors at the Columbian was the General Electric Company, the new corporate enterprise whose presentation at the Fair was described as "an almost perfect epitome of the electrical art as it then existed." That might have been expected, considering the wealth of inventive genius that was represented by Thomas Edison, Elihu Thomson and the other electrical "wizards" who had brought together by the merger of the Thomson-Houston Company and the Edison General Electric Company. Joining them, in 1892, was Charles P. Steinmetz, a brilliant young mathematician and engineer who was to become "Chief Consulting Engineer" of the company and a magnetic force for the attraction of other creative giants such as Willis R. Whitney, William Stanley, Ernst F. W. Alexanderson, William D. Coolidge and Irving Langmuir. Under the leadership of Charles A. Coffin, the founder and first President of General Electric, these men and others who would join them would transform the development and application of electricity from an art to a science and pioneer new paths in industrial research.

Continuing the tradition of Edison (center) in the Steinmetz era: left to right, William D. Coolidge, Willis R. Whitney, Charles P. Steinmetz, Irving Langmuir.

Extracts from President C.A. Coffin's Message to Stockholders in 1st Annual Report - April 11, 1893

"The General Electric Company was incorporated April 15th, 1892, and began active business the first day of June, 1892...

"As you know, the General Electric Company acquired in exchange for its stock practically all the capital stock of the Edison General Electric Company, of the Thomson-Houston Electric Company and of the Thomson-Houston International Electric Company ...

"The difficulties inherent in such a reorganization were many and serious, and we feel that the stockholders are to be congratulated that, largely because of the zeal and hearty co-operation of the former officers and employees of the Edison General and Thomson-Houston Companies, it has been carried through to a complete and successful issue...

"While your Company has about 6000 customers included in the different departments of its business, the interesting and important development is in the direction of local lighting and railway enterprises."

Charles A. Coffin
1844-1926

"A man born to command, yet who never issued orders." This phrase sums up the leadership qualities of *Charles A. Coffin,* General Electric's first president. His executive skills helped establish GE's place in the front rank of American corporations.

Electrical manufacturing was Coffin's second career. At 18, he moved from Fairfield, Maine, where he had been born in 1844, to enter his uncle's shoe business at Lynn, Massachusetts. He later founded his own shoe manufacturing firm, and by 1883 had established himself as an outstanding success in this line.

In that year, Silas A. Barton, a Lynn businessman, proposed bringing to the city the struggling young American Electric Co. of New Britain, Connecticut, whose major asset was the inventive genius of Elihu Thomson. A businessman was needed to supplement Thomson's technical skills. Coffin was prevailed upon to take the post.

He led the new company, Thomson-Houston, to parity with Thomas Edison's companies, the previous leaders in the field. When negotiations in 1892 led to the formation of General Electric, a key step in creating a viable enterprise was the installation of Coffin as its first chief executive officer.

Coffin's associates (and he always made a point of calling them "my associates," not "my subordinates") knew him as a gracious gentleman and delightful companion. He never ordered one of them to do anything, preferring to rely on his powers of suggestion. In his turn, he graciously sought and welcomed suggestions from those around him — and then decisively made up his own mind on key questions.

Customers and competitors knew him as both the outstanding statesman and the outstanding salesman of the electrical manufacturing industry. He took a personal interest in major negotiations, often writing business proposals to important customers in his own hand. At tense meetings, he knew how to relieve the pressure with an appropriate anecdote, and how to add the key words to bring matters to a successful conclusion.

His greatest test came in the depression of 1893. A cash shortage threatened GE's existence. He cooly negotiated a deal with J.P. Morgan whereby New York banks advanced the needed money as payment for utility stocks which GE held. The tactic saved the company and made possible its rapid recovery and growth during the remainder of his tenure. The strength and wide-ranging excellence of the company he passed on to Owen D. Young and Gerard Swope when he retired from the board chairmanship in 1922 was — and remains — his greatest monument.

STEINMETZ ... *BEGINNINGS*

Carl August Rudolph Steinmetz, born April 9, 1865, was the son of Carl Heinrich Steinmetz, an official with the state-owned railroad. Barred from strenuous physical activity by disability, young Carl's pleasures were mainly intellectual ones, such as the study of pure mathematics at the university in his home town of Breslau, Germany.

Right: Carl Heinrich Steinmetz. Below: Charles Proteus Steinmetz in 1890.

In this letter to his father, (extracted and translated from the original German), Steinmetz reflects some of his positive feelings about America. Father Steinmetz probably never read it since he died on June 26, 1890, and the mail was not that fast in the nineties.

Yonkers, June 7, 1890

Dear Dad:

So much time passed since my last letter; I should have written earlier; but you know how it is, something always interferes, a new analysis, an improvement to be found and other things, and the letter has again to wait for the next steamer.

... It was two years last week that I left Breslau, one year that I am here. Result: I am very satisfied to have left the narrow living conditions of Germany and to have come here where a reasonable man can live reasonably and succeed. It is infinitely better here than at any place where I ever was — even if certain things could be still better. Nobody interferes with your freedom; you can go where you want to and do what you want; there is no war, no soldiery, no possible danger of war, no taxes (except for real estate), you can travel where you want without notifying the police or similar nonsense, you can change your name, the income is several times higher, life is not significantly more expensive, and you have much more time for yourself. On Sunday, for example, nobody works anywhere; even railroad traffic is cut down to only a few trains. This is somewhat inconvenient if one forgot to buy cigars on Saturday and has nothing to smoke on Sunday since all shops are closed. But, objectively spoken, it is of great advantage because one has the entire Sunday for oneself.

... This is all for today! Write me soon how everything is at home and urge Mache to write a letter!

Cordial regards,

Karl

Arriving penniless in New York in 1889, he made two major decisions: to change "Carl August" to "Charles Proteus" and to accept employment with Eickemeyer and Osterheld, a Yonkers based electrical manufacturer. Rudolph Eickemeyer and his plant are shown below. In 1892 General Electric purchased this plant and Steinmetz began his 31-year GE career.

Prior to the automobile age, Steinmetz was an ardent bicyclist. This photo was taken in 1895.

An enthusiastic amateur photographer, Steinmetz especially enjoyed trick shots, such as this.

63

1893

Lighting

J.W. Howell, of the Harrison Lamp Works, develops an automatic filament treating machine for incandescent lamps. His improvement of the Sawyer-Mann process for applying a graphite coating to the filaments results in more uniform electrical properties, improved lamp efficiency and increased production rate.

The first commercially practical enclosed arc-lamp is manufactured by the Lighting Dept. for street and open area lighting. The lamps' carbon electrodes, now housed in sealed glass globes, last over 100 hours, ten times longer than the unsealed variety.

Transportation

The Transportation Dept. displays a 30-ton electric locomotive and operates a complete electric elevated railroad, hauling passengers around the fairgrounds of the Chicago Columbian Exposition. A summer worker at the service shops is Gerard Swope, MIT undergrad, who is paid $1 per day for his labor.

The Tower of Light - symbol of a new era in lighting - Columbian Exposition.

The Intramural Railway - a complete electric railway at the Columbian Exposition.

Generation and Transmission

The world's first commercial polyphase generating system is built at Mill Creek, California, to supply the town of Redlands. It consists of two three-phase hydroelectric generators rated at 250-kw, 2400 volts, each.

The first full scale electrification of a textile plant occurs at Columbia Mills, Columbia, South Carolina. Two water driven 500-kw three-phase generators power fourteen 65-hp alternating current motors, the largest yet built by the company.

William Cermak develops the "petticoated" porcelain insulator capable of withstanding over 10,000 volts for transmission line use.

The largest direct current generator in the world, at 2000-hp, is operated as part of the General Electric exhibit at the Chicago World's Fair.

Charles S. Bradley, an early associate of Edison, invents the rotary or synchronous converter for changing alternating to direct current.

Direct-coupled generators are built with a capacity of 12,000 incandescent lamps, replacing belt driven types which could power only 2000 lamps. Edison's "jumbo" dynamos were the forerunner of this new type of generator.

First full scale electrification of a textile mill - Columbia Mills, South Carolina.

Power station for the Intramural Railway - Columbian Exposition.

1894

Lighting

The Harrison Lamp Works substitutes "squirted" cellulose for bamboo in its carbonized filament incandescent lamps. The extruded filaments are more uniform, less costly, and more adaptable to large scale production than the hand-processed bamboo fibers.

Transportation

A five-mile-long underground electric conduit is installed on the Lenox Avenue Line of the New York City Metropolitan Street Railway Company. The newly developed, GE-800 traction motors of 25-hp are used in the passenger cars.

Work is begun on the first complete electrification of an American transit line, the Chicago Metropolitan Elevated Railway. The installation includes 110 GE-2000 motors, of 100-hp, two of which are used on each locomotive passenger car.

Generation and Transmission

Construction starts on the first Niagara Falls hydroelectric plant, the largest such installation in the country, with a power output of 15,000 kw. A team under the direction of W.L.R. Emmet undertakes construction of a 10,000-volt transmission line stretching twenty-six miles from Niagara Falls to Buffalo, New York.

E.W. Rice, Jr. and E.M. Hewlett develop the high voltage, oil immersed switch or circuit breaker.

10,000 volt transmission line at Niagara Falls, New York.

Adjusting arc lamps at Lynn, Massachusetts.

The first practical enclosed arc lamp - no longer need electrodes be adjusted every 10 hours.

The world's first commercial polyphase power generating station - Redlands California.

1895

Lighting

The Lighting Department adopts the phosphorous vapor exhaust process in the manufacture of its incandescent lamps. Developed by Arturo Malignani of Italy and improved upon by John Howell, the process removes air from the bulbs more effectively and greatly reduces lamp preparation time.

Transportation

The first major conversion of a steam railway to electricity occurs with the electrification of the Baltimore and Ohio's Mount Royal Tunnel on its N.Y.-Washington line. GE locomotives, the world's largest at 96 tons, are propelled by four gearless motors rated at 360 hp each. The use of the new locomotives eliminates the hazards of operation in smoke-filled tunnels.

Generation and Transmission

Niagara Falls Power Station No. 1 is placed in operation to supply the electrochemical plants which are being built to take advantage of the low cost source of electricity.

In California, a power station housing four 750-kw, three-phase hydroelectric generators is built at the American River to serve the city of Sacramento. The twenty-five mile distance is spanned by an 11,000-volt transmission line.

Organization

The Standardizing Laboratory is organized to insure the accuracy of instruments used to measure the performance of electrical equipment. Its first director is Lewis T. Robinson, former employee of the Thomson-Houston Co.

Steinmetz Contributions

"Notes on the Theory of Oscillating Currents", Physical Review 3, 335-350 (1895). Applies complex imaginary mathematics to current-voltage behavior of oscillating currents.

Laboratory Building 19. First home of the Standardizing Laboratory.

LOCOMOTIVES LARGE AND SMALL

Two-ton electric mining locomotive.

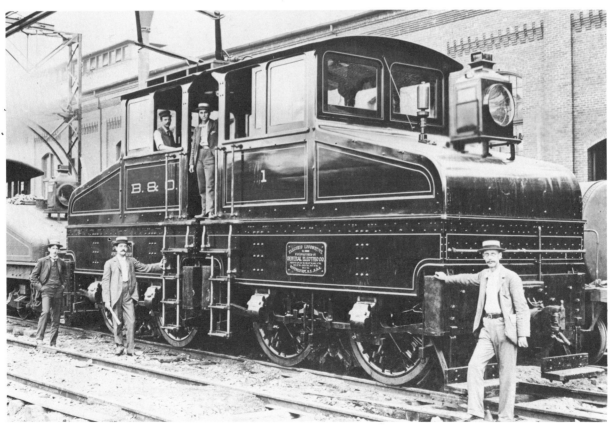

Ninety-six ton electric locomotive for the Baltimore & Ohio Railroad.

1896

Lighting

Howell perfects the first modern glassworking machine used for lamp making. The four-headed machine permits a factory worker to seal the lamp assembly to the bulb at the rate of 600 units per day — twice the previous output.

Transportation

The first use of electric motors and controls for turning gun turrets is demonstrated on the U.S. Navy cruiser, "Brooklyn". The 50-hp motors are the largest ever installed on a ship for any purpose.

Generation and Transmission

The Niagara Falls-Buffalo transmission line is completed. At Niagara Falls the 2000-volt, 25-cycle output of the Westinghouse alternators is stepped up to 10,000 volts and converted to three-phase by 800-kw GE transformers, the largest yet built. At the Buffalo substation, the voltage is stepped down to 2000 volts for distribution to the transportation and electric power facilities of the community.

A thirty-six mile, 15,000-volt, transmission line is built from the Ogden River to Salt Lake City.

Medical Equipment

Elihu Thomson builds electrical equipment for the production of X-rays and demonstrates the use of stereoscopic "roentgen" pictures, for diagnosing bone fractures and locating foreign objects in the body. A year earlier Wilhelm Konrad Roentgen of Germany had announced his discovery of X-rays to the world.

Elihu Thomson's X-ray machine.

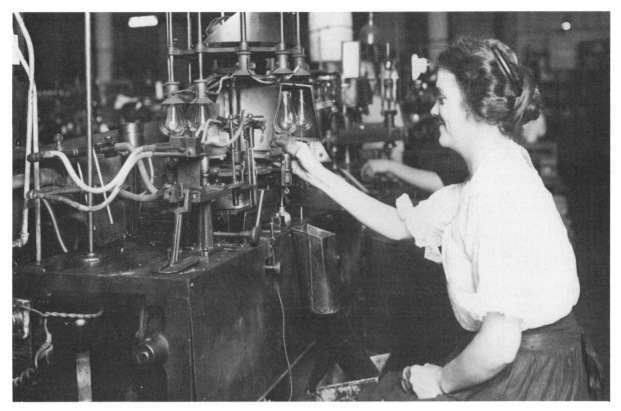

Automatic exhaust machine for lamp bulbs.

Elihu Thomson

Transformer for the Niagara Falls hydroelectric station — 800 k.w, 10,000 volts.

1897

Transportation

Frank Sprague operates the first multiple unit control system on cars of the Chicago South Side Railway at GE's Schenectady test track. The system makes possible centralized control of the operation of a number of interconnected, electrically propelled cars.

The "Wagonette" electric carriage is built at Lynn by Thomson and Hermann Lemp, long time collaborator with Edison and Thomson. The 3-hp, 75-volt, 30-ampere battery-supplied motor can propel the car to a top speed of 18 mph.

The "Uniflow" engine steam automobile is developed by Thomson and Lemp and built by General Electric. Its new "flash" tube boiler design and improved steering and braking mechanisms represent important advances in steam vehicle technology.

Generation and Transmission

Charles G. Curtis starts work at Schenectady aimed at developing the commercial potential of the steam-driven turbine. About 15 years earlier, Charles A. Parsons and Gustaf de Laval had built their first turbines in Europe.

Construction is begun on the longest, highest voltage transmission line ever attempted, a 33,000-volt line stretching 81 miles from Santa Ana Canyon to Los Angeles, California.

Thomson invents the constant current transformer, which make it possible for parallel wired arc lamps to operate efficiently from ordinary AC circuits. Previously, satisfactory performance could be obtained only with series wired circuits.

Steinmetz Contributions

The epic work "Alternating-Current Phenomena" outlines the theory of alternating current technology. It runs through several editions.

The "Uniflow" engine steam carriage developed by Thomson and Lemp.

The "Wagonette" electric carriage built at Lynn by Thomson and Lemp.

LORD KELVIN VISITS SCHENECTADY

Lord Kelvin and party on visit to GE Schenectady Works in 1897. Front row, left to right are A.L. Rohrer, G.E. Emmons, Dr. C.P. Steinmetz, Prof. Elihu Thomson, Lady Kelvin, Lord Kelvin, Spencer Trask, Jr., and Spencer Trask, Sr. Second row: J. McGhie, T.C.Martin, J.R. Lovejoy, E.W. Rice, Jr., W.B. Potter, E. Griffin, E.M. Hewlett, E.A. Carolan, S.D. Greene, J.P. Ord, and G.F. Peabody. Third row: unidentified.

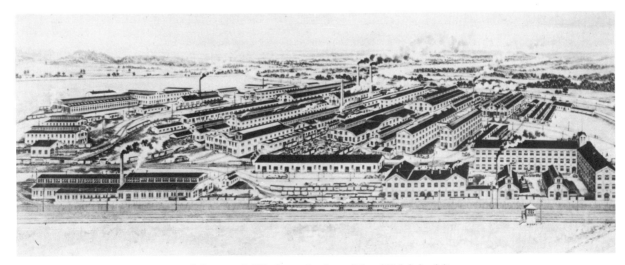

Schenectady Works at the time of Lord Kelvin's visit.

1898-1899

Lighting

Walter D'Arcy Ryan opens an illuminating engineering laboratory at Lynn and embarks on the development of methods for the scientific planning of lighting installations.

Organization

The assets of the Fort Wayne Electric Corp. (James J. Wood, principal inventor) are purchased from its trustees by General Electric and the formerly bankrupt company becomes the Fort Wayne Electric Works.

Frank Sprague organizes the Sprague Electric Co. by merging the Interior Conduit Co. with the Sprague Electric Co. Sprague, pioneer in railway electrification and electric elevators has often been referred to as the "father of electric transportation-both vertical and horizontal."

Fort Wayne Electric Corporation-site of James J. Wood's accomplishments.

James J. Wood
1856-1928

Edison epitomizes the pioneering era of electricity; Steinmetz epitomizes the era when it became a science and an industry. James J. Wood represents a link between the two epochs. As an electrical pioneer, he contributed to the development of electric motors and generators. As a leader of the General Electric Company, he played a major role in the success of the GE works at Fort Wayne, Indiana.

Wood's career extends wider than the electrical industry, through such technologies and events as lockmaking, the development of the submarine, the construction of the Brooklyn Bridge, and the design of the modern refrigerator. To these fields he brought his remarkable skills at envisioning new inventions, designing them, building models by hand at the bench, and managing their manufacture and introduction.

Born in Kinsale, Ireland, in 1856, Wood came to New York City in 1864. At the age of 11 he began his working career with a lock company at Branford, Connecticut. In 1874 he entered the employ of the Brady Manufacturing Company of Brooklyn, rising swiftly to the posts of superintendent and chief engineer. Among his achievements there were design of the engine used on John Holland's submarine, and of construction machinery used to make the main cables of the Brooklyn Bridge.

Concurrently, he found time to gain an education, eventually graduating from the Brooklyn Polytechnic Institute as a mechanical engineer. He also found himself drawn into electrical design in 1879, with the aim of increasing the output while decreasing the size and weight of arc-light generators. At this he succeeded brilliantly — the machine he designed in 1880 remained a highly successful product for 35 years.

In 1890, the general manager of the Fort Wayne Electric Corporation, R.T. McDonald, purchased Wood's electrical company, and brought him to work at Fort Wayne. After McDonald's death in 1898, the company became part of the General Electric Company. Wood became factory manager of the Fort Wayne Works.

He continued active at invention and design. His total of 240 patents places him behind only Edison, Elihu Thomson, and E.F.W. Alexanderson on the list of the company's most prolific inventors. He was also one of the first to recognize the business potential of the household refrigerator. Partly through his influence, Fort Wayne played a major role in the creation of GE's refrigerator business — a development whose success he was able to see before his death in 1928.

STEINMETZ...
THE ENGINEER

My Three Most Important
Works:

1. Law of Hysteresis
2. Symbolic Method
   of A-C Current
   Calculations
3. Theory of Electrical
   Transients

Charles P. Steinmetz

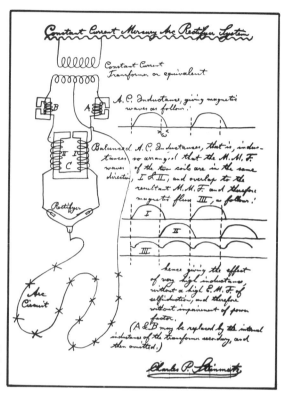

Steinmetz became intensely interested in the mercury-arc rectifier, and his inventive mind was soon at work to utilize it. This is one of his original 1903 sketches on circuits for charging storage batteries.

Among Steinmetz's distinguished visitors was Marchese Guglielmo Marconi, inventor of the first practical radio-signaling system and recipient of the Nobel Prize for Physics in 1909.

Called an engineering wizard by the engineering profession at GE in Schenectady, Steinmetz in 1892 presented a major paper on the Law of Hysteresis to the AIEE, and this gave him world-wide professional recognition.

Hailed as a "forger of thunderbolts," Steinmetz was first to create artificial lightning. Here (above) in 1922, Steinmetz demonstrated his 120,000 volt lightning generator to Thomas A. Edison and other notable guests. "The man who made lightning" (right) examines the fragments of a tree branch splintered by a bolt of lightning from his generator. Steinmetz's studies enormously increased the reliability of electric power transmission.

Even when Steinmetz went out in his canoe, paper, pencil, and slide rule accompanied him. In his diary he wrote, "It was a hot, sunny day with almost no wind, and I sat in the sun and calculated instances of condenser discharge through an asymmetrical gas circuit."

1900

Transportation

The Transportation Dept. places a standard line of mine locomotives on the market. As early as 1895, its 2-ton locomotives were replacing mule driven carts in the mines of Pennsylvania and Ohio.

The Manhattan Elevated Railway is electrified. The installation includes 1700 motors and the largest generators ever built.

Organization

E.W. Rice, Jr., Thomson, Steinmetz and A.G. Davis, manager of the Patent Department propose the formation of "a laboratory where scientific investigation can be made on the incandescent lamp and other problems" (Davis).

The General Electric Research Laboratory is established. Willis R. Whitney, assistant professor at MIT is selected as its director.

Registration of the GE trademark (monogram) is granted.

Steinmetz Contributions

Steinmetz develops the magnetite arc lamp. By substituting electrodes made from a mixture of magnetite (iron oxide) and titanium for carbon electrodes, the light output and life of the arc lamp are significantly increased.

"Systems of Electric Transmission and Distribution", a lecture to the New York Electrical Society, gives the pros and cons of AC and DC systems. This presentation is considered a key to acceptance of the power system which evolved worldwide.

Albert G. Davis
Head of the Patent
Department

The staff of the new Research Laboratory - (from left) Charles P. Steinmetz, John T.H. Dempster and Willis R. Whitney, Director.

First site of the General Electric
Research Laboratory.

Generator room of the Manhattan Elevated Railway.

1901

A.L. Rohrer

Lighting

The National Electric Lamp Company is organized under the leadership of J.B. Crouse, Franklin S. Terry and Burton G. Tremaine, with financial assistance provided by GE. Marketing, manufacturing and research activities are centered in Cleveland, Ohio.

Peter C. Hewitt develops a mercury vapor arc lamp having high light output efficiency and long life. The 385-watt lamp is four feet long, and its greenish-blue light makes it suitable primarily for industrial applications.

Transportation

The oil impregnated baked carbon brush is developed by Peter J. Mulvey, foreman in charge of railway motor testing. His improvement on Van Depoele's brush permits operation of these motors at high currents without danger to the commutator from sparking.

Generation and Transmission

Curtis and Emmet, assisted by Oscar Junggren, design and supervise the construction of two horizontal shaft steam turbines of 500 and 1500 kw. With the successful operation of these machines, an order is placed for two 5000-kw vertical shaft turbines to be built for the Chicago Edison Co. headed by Samuel Insull (former secretary to Thomas Edison, Vice President of the Edison General Electric Co., and later Second Vice President of the newly organized General Electric Co., in 1892.)

Transformers capable of operating at 80,000 volts are demonstrated.

Organization

The Apprentice Course is organized by Albert L. Rohrer who, in 1894, had initiated the Test Course and was responsible for recruiting virtually all of the technical graduates joining the Company.

One of Charles G. Curtis's
first steam turbines — 50 kw.

500-kw steam turbine designed by Curtis and Emmet.

1902

Lighting

A mercury vapor arc lamp is constructed at the Research Laboratory by Ezekiel Weintraub, who almost simultaneously with Hewitt discovers that the mercury vapor causes the conversion of alternating current to direct current. Steinmetz first adapted this rectifier for use with his magnetite arc lamp.

W.D'Arcy Ryan's Illuminating Engineering Laboratory is transferred to Schenectady from Lynn.

The "Meridian" lamp is developed to meet the demand for high light output without the maintenance required of the arc lamp.

Appliances

James J. Wood, now consulting engineer at the Fort Wayne Works, receives patents for stationary and revolving fans. The first of these fans were built in the 1890's.

Steinmetz Contributions

"Notes on the Theory of the Synchronous Motor," Transactions AIEE 19, 547-567 (1902), discusses excitation of and loads in synchronous motors.

Electric fan produced at the Ft. Wayne Electric Works.

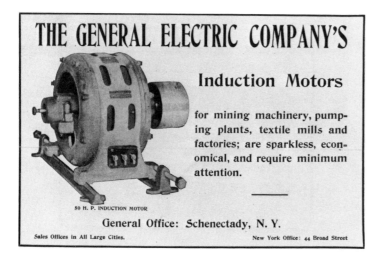

The Meridian Lamp.

William B. Potter
1863-1934

The life of an engineer in electrical manufacturing's pioneer days had its hazards. When *William B. Potter* was on his first assignment, installing a Thomson-Houston dynamo at the Greensboro, North Carolina, electric plant in 1887, an irate utility customer demanded to see the "damn yankee" engineer. Brandishing a revolver, he threatened to "shoot the daylights" out of the machine. "Shoot as much as you like," Potter is said to have replied. "But you will surely be killed by the lightning that will come out of the dynamo."

This resourcefulness saved the situation. Potter's ingenuity was to score many other triumphs during a long career. The son of a Thomaston, Connecticut, farmer, he got his introduction to machinery as a summer worker at the Seth Thomas clock factory. It so attracted him that he passed up a chance to go to MIT in 1883, in order to apprentice to the Sawtell and Judd marine engineering firm. After four years of training there, he moved on to Thomson-Houston's Lynn plant, where he decided to specialize in electric railway engineering.

From practical engineering problems as supervisor of installation of city railway systems — for example, putting in San Antonio's Alamo Electric Railway in the remarkably short time of 40 days — he moved on to advanced development work. At the suggestion of the Railway Department's chief engineer, W.H. Knight, Potter took up the problem of applying the magnetic arc-blowout method to electric railway motor control. His key concept, "using a blanket instead of a hammer to put out a fire" (that is, using a large, powerful magnetic field to blow out an electric arc), became the key to a practical control method. Solution of the control problem, in turn, greatly expanded the usefulness of electric railways in America's cities.

In 1895 he succeeded Knight as engineer of the GE Electric Railway Department. He molded a highly motivated engineering team. Subordinate engineers were given major responsibilities, and got full credit for individual accomplishments. A highlight achievement of the Potter team was electrification of New York's Grand Central Terminal.

Potter was a cheerful and pleasant man. But he had high standards, and insisted on enforcing them, particularly when it came to product reliability This is perhaps best evidenced in a story told by another great GE engineer, Philip L. Alger:

> *It is said that once Potter asked one of his young engineers to develop a new controller for trolley cars. The young man took the assignment seriously and built a model without showing it to anyone until it was done. Then he asked Potter to come and see it. Potter walked all around it, then gave it a hearty kick, when it flew to pieces, almost breaking the young engineer's heart.*

Such practices may have made life difficult for young engineers. But in the long run, insistence on excellence enabled Potter and his contemporaries to create GE's outstanding tradition in transportation engineering.

1903

Charles G. Curtis

Lighting

C.A.B. Halvorson of the Lynn River Works makes a number of improvements to the magnetite lamp making it commercially feasible.

Transportation

Ernst F.W. Alexanderson builds the first successful single-phase railway motor.

Generation and Transmission

Two 500-kw Curtis-Emmet vertical shaft turbines are operated at a newly built generating station in Newport, Rhode Island.

The largest steam turbine yet developed, a 5000-kw vertical shaft unit, is installed at the Fisk Street Station of the Chicago Edison Co. It occupies one tenth the space and is one third the cost of the reciprocating engine originally planned for the power house, but its capacity is equal to that of any steam engine in existence.

Henry G. Reist designer of the generators used with the Curtis-Emmet turbines, develops a cast iron skeleton frame for induction motors. This permits a 10-hp motor to be mounted in the space previously used for a 7.5-hp unit.

Communications

A 1-kw, 10,000-cycle alternator with an iron core armature is built for Professor R.A. Fessenden using a design developed by Steinmetz. Two years before, Fessenden had applied for a patent for such a device capable of transmission of the human voice.

Steinmetz Contributions

"Alternating Current Motors," International Electrical Congress, 1904 discusses various motor designs using his complex notation.

Magnetite Arc Lamp.

5000-kw vertical shaft steam
turbine for the Chicago Edison
Company.

High frequency alternator built by Steinmetz for R.A. Fessenden.

William Stanley
1858-1916

William Stanley

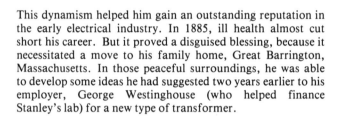

Cummings C. Chesney

Cummings C. Chesney
1863-1947

"Have had enough of this," wrote the 17-year-old Yale freshman in 1879. "Am going to New York."

With these words, *William Stanley* abandoned the career pattern that his father had laid out for him — college, law school, and membership in the family law firm — and set out instead on the more risky and exciting path of electrical invention. The decision marked the beginning of a productive career, whose highlights included the invention of the modern type of transformer, and the creation of the business enterprise that was to become General Electric's Pittsfield Works.

Stanley gave early evidence of his ability and enthusiasm. As his first employer, inventor Hiram S. Maxim described him:

> *Mr. Stanley was very young. He was also very tall and thin, but what he lacked in bulk, he made up for in activity. He was boiling over with enthusiasm. Nothing went fast enough for him.*

This dynamism helped him gain an outstanding reputation in the early electrical industry. In 1885, ill health almost cut short his career. But it proved a disguised blessing, because it necessitated a move to his family home, Great Barrington, Massachusetts. In those peaceful surroundings, he was able to develop some ideas he had suggested two years earlier to his employer, George Westinghouse (who helped finance Stanley's lab) for a new type of transformer.

This work resulted, on March 20, 1886, in the demonstration of a prototype system of high-voltage transmission employing Stanley's parallel-connected transformer. It proved the feasibility of concepts that are now employed in transmission systems throughout the world.

In 1890, he incorporated the Stanley Manufacturing Company to build and install high-voltage transmission systems. To organize it, he joined forces with two talented associates: John J. Kelley, an outstanding designer of motors; and a former Stanley laboratory worker, *Cummings C. Chesney.*

Chesney, a native of Selinsgrove, Pennsylvania, had graduated from Penn State, and had begun his career as a teacher of mathematics and chemistry. Attracted by the prospects of electricity, he came to work for Stanley. He went on to spend two years with the U.S. Electric Lighting Co. in Newark, N.J., before becoming one of the incorporators of Stanley's new enterprise. His skill in engineering and manufacturing complemented the inventive talents of Kelley, and the overall inspiration and creativity provided by Stanley.

The product of their efforts, the "SKC" system, won several early transmission contracts. When the developers of the Blue Falls project in California proposed a 200-mile, 60,000 volt transmission line, they were told by no less an authority than Charles Proteus Steinmetz that the idea was impractical. But the SKC team took on the job — and successfully completed it.

General Electric came to realize that it was better to join than fight this dynamic enterprise. In 1903, Stanley's company merged with GE; in 1906, its facilities were renamed the GE Pittsfield Works. Cummings C. Chesney became the first works manager, and went on to do major work in the areas of AC motors, lightning arrestors, and transformers, leading to his being awarded the Edison Medal in 1921. The effort which Stanley began, and Chesney helped consolidate, forms a basis for GE's present position in the field of power transmission.

1904

Lighting

The first commercial installation of magnetite arc lamps is made at Jackson, Michigan. Later, 4000 of these lamps are installed in the streets of Boston.

Willis R. Whitney develops the "GEM" carbon filament lamp. By heating the filament to 3000°C in an electric resistance furnace which he had invented, Whitney eliminated impurities in the carbon and made its resistance characteristic more metallic in behavior. Operating temperature of the lamp is increased from 1700° to 1900°C and light output efficiency is improved by 25%.

Alexander Just and Franz Hanaman of Austria claim the development of a sintered tungsten filament lamp. Almost simultaneous claims are made by Hans Kuzel of Austria and Werner von Bolton of Germany. Patent rights to all of these developments are purchased by General Electric.

Generation

Sanford A. Moss joins the Steam Turbine Dept. at Lynn and starts work aimed at the commercial development of the gas turbine. Earlier, Moss had investigated turbines at Cornell University. Although the gas turbines which are built at this time are not commercially feasible, the centrifugal compressor shows great potential for industrial applications.

A second generating station at Niagara Falls is built, with a capacity of 25,000 kilowatts.

Communications

Ambrose Fleming, scientific adviser to the Edison Electric Light Co., of London invents a two-element vacuum tube rectifier. He conceives the idea of using the "Edison Effect" lamp (observed and described by Edison in 1883) as a detector for wireless signals, and modifies the tube so that it operates in the aerial circuit of a wireless receiver.

Willis R. Whitney

Motors find use in the home sewing machine.

1905

Appliances

Commercial electric refrigerators are placed on the market by the Federal Automated Refrigeration Co. of New York. Compressor motors and controls are supplied by GE

A lightweight electric flat iron with detachable cord is introduced by the Electric Heating Dept. The large reduction in the weight of the iron makes it more attractive for household and commercial use and decreases the amount of electricity required to operate it.

GE's first electric toaster, the model X2, is placed on the market.

Transportation

The first order is placed for complete terminus-to-terminus railroad electrification — Camden, N.J. to Atlantic City, N.J.

Organization

William D. Coolidge joins the Research Laboratory from MIT.

The Electric Bond and Share Co. is organized to aid small utilities.

William D. Coolidge

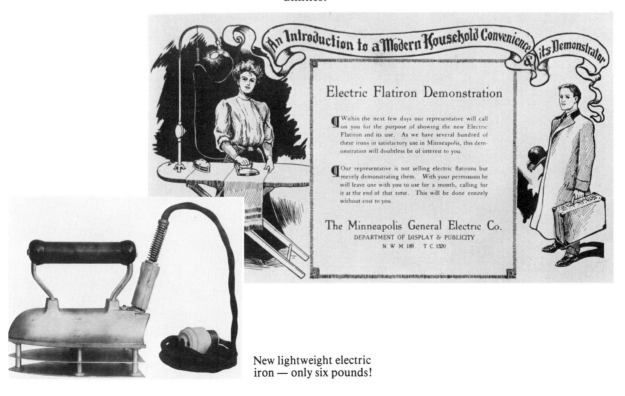

New lightweight electric iron — only six pounds!

William LeRoy Emmet
1859-1941

Some people find their vocations early. Others, like the great engineer *William LeRoy Emmet,* do so only after a struggle. In Emmet's case, the struggle was worthwhile. It helped endow him with the tenacity and originality that make for an outstanding innovator.

Both as a midshipman at the U.S. Naval Academy, and as a cadet on board the U.S.S. "Essex," Emmet's impatience with discipline and convention suggested that a career as a naval officer was not his intended niche. Accepting an honorable discharge in 1883, he tried his hand at a series of other trades — architect, clerk, accountant — with a similar lack of success. He landed in the post of laborer, at a salary of $7 per week, on the night shift of the United States Illuminating Company.

It proved the opportunity he had needed. Through on-the-job experience and self-directed study, he supplemented the knowledge of electricity he had gained in his Naval Academy courses. Applying that knowledge to some problems that cropped up at the factory, he gained the self-confidence that he had up to that point lacked. In 1887, he talked his way onto the staff of Frank Sprague, a contemporary of his at the Naval Academy who was building a career as the outstanding American pioneer in applying electricity to street railways.

Emmet moved onward through a succession of posts which gained him the status of full-fledged electrical engineer. Joining Edison General Electric not long before the merger that created GE, he came to Schenectady in 1892. There he was to spend the rest of his career, and score his greatest engineering triumphs.

His first major project for GE was the design of hydroelectric generators for the Niagara Falls project. His success at this task established his technical reputation. After consulting engineer Charles G. Curtis brought GE his steam turbine concepts in 1897, serious development difficulties were encountered. Emmet took up the project after his return from a temporary stint of naval duty in the Spanish American War. He contributed materially to the success of some of the early Curtis turbines. But his major role in turbine development was to recognize that making a practical turbine with the tools and materials available in the first decade of the twentieth century, and scaling that turbine up to a useful rating of 5000 kilowatts, required a radical design change. Accordingly, he proposed mounting the turbine shaft vertically, allowing the turbine to spin like a top. This design proved the key to GE's early domination of the turbine field.

A genial, generous bachelor — "Uncle Bill" to his many friends — Emmet had many interests beside his work: curling, skiing, fishing, and astronomy, for example. But his main role in life was that of a tireless technical entrepreneur, constantly pushing forward advanced ideas. His perseverance could irritate more conservative colleagues. "No one would have called him a patient man," his contemporary Willis R. Whitney wrote of him

> but persistence was almost personified in him. He continually battled against himself and against deficiency in other men and materials. He would weepingly condemn himself forever, because of some slip of a golf stick; but he would loan money to almost anyone without critical feelings...he never hesitated to 'stick his neck out,' whether it was about the structure of the moon, the social theories of President Wilson, his own handicap at golf, the economy of steam generation, or some vagary of ice-curling, or salmon fishing, or moose hunting.

Emmet's many successes testified to the soundness of the judgment that he so stubbornly defended. He pioneered the concept of electric drive for ships, and led the development project which proved it out. He initiated valuable work on gearing for turbines. And, even where not successful, he showed an admirable combination of resourcefulness and daring. This comes through most clearly in his advocacy of the mercury vapor turbine. This idea for increasing the efficiency of electric power generation was never destined to become sufficiently economical to displace the steam turbine. But the technical virtuosity shown in Emmet's attack on the problem, and the energy he showed in pursuing it even when, in his eighties, he could have rested on his well-earned laurels, are characteristic of his impatient advocacy of unorthodox technical advance.

1906

Lighting

The tantalum filament lamp, developed by von Bolton, is commercially introduced in the United States by the Lighting Department. The light output efficiency of the lamp is 20% higher than that of the "GEM" lamp.

Coolidge produces an improved extruded tungsten filament. By substituting an amalgam of mercury, cadmium and bismuth for the organic binder previously used, he extrudes filaments which are converted to tungsten of improved purity and strength.

Transportation

Electrification of Grand Central Terminal in New York City is begun after city authorities adopt an ordinance banning the operation of steam powered trains within the city limits.

A gasoline-electric railroad car is successfully tested on the Delaware & Hudson Railroad between Schenectady and Saratoga. Two 200-hp motors are supplied by a 120-kw generator of 6000 volts, driven by a gasoline engine which is the most powerful built for this application.

Communications

A high frequency alternator is built by Alexanderson and delivered to Fessenden's Brant Rock, Massachusetts station. On Christmas Eve, signals from the 1-kw, 50,000 cycle machine are modulated by a water cooled microphone with voice and music, and received as far away as Norfolk, Virginia.

A 2-kw, 100-kilocycle Alexanderson alternator with special iron core is delivered to the laboratory of John Hayes Hammond at Gloucester, Mass. The armature of this machine rotates at 20,000 rpm with the speed at its rim reaching 720 mph.

Ernst F.W. Alexanderson
Radio pioneer

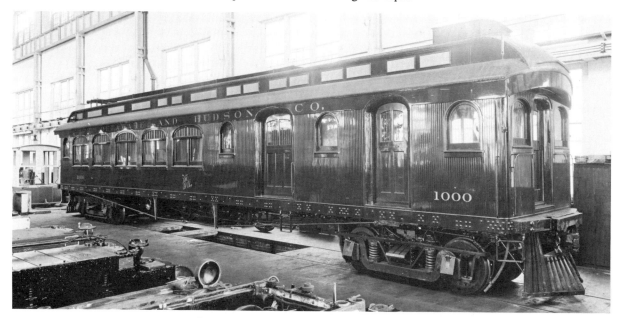

Gasoline-electric railroad car for the Delaware & Hudson.

The transformation of Manhattan — before electrification of Grand Central Terminal (top 1906) and after (1926).

1907

Edward M. Hewlett with samples of suspension line insulators.

Lighting

The sintered tungsten filament lamp is introduced in the United States. The light output efficiency of the new lamp is more than twice that of the tantalum lamp.

W. D'Arcy Ryan supervises the illumination of Niagara Falls by arc searchlights having a combined illumination of 1.15 billion candlepower.

Transportation

The city of Chicago fireboats "Graeme Stewart" and "Joseph Medill" are the first vessels in America to be successfully propelled using electrical energy. The ships' motors are supplied by generators coupled to 600-hp Curtis-Emmet steam turbines.

Generation and Transmission

Edward M. Hewlett, switchboard engineer and Harold W. Buck electrical engineer of the Niagara Falls Power Co. obtain a joint patent on a suspension and strain type of insulator. The development permits an increase in the voltage carrying ability of transmission lines from 60,000 volts to over 100,000 volts.

First electrically propelled vessel in America-City of Chicago fireboat.

The efficiency of transformers is significantly increased through the use of a silicon steel alloy discovered by Sir Robert Hadfield of England. W.S. Moody, Chief Transformer Engineer, develops processes for rolling the steel in commercial quantities.

Organization

The Stanley Electric Manufacturing Co. of Pittsfield, Mass. becomes the Pittsfield Works of General Electric. Chief Engineer and manager of the Works is Cummings C. Chesney, one of the founders of Stanley Electric and, with William Stanley, a pioneer in high voltage, alternating current, transmission.

Steinmetz Contributions

"Inductance of a Straight Conductor," with K. Ogura, Physical Review 25, 184-199 (1907) develops the physics of long-line AC transmission of power.

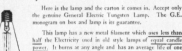

General Electric's complete heating device line.

STEINMETZ...*SCIENTIST AND EDUCATOR*

Union College secured Steinmetz's services as Professor of Electrical Engineering in 1902. Steinmetz taught courses, reorganized and modernized the department, and even joined one of the campus fraternities, Phi Gamma Delta. By 1913, when he turned the Department over to his friend Ernst J. Berg, he had enormously strengthened Union's engineering curriculum.

Above: Steinmetz assists Union College students with electrical engineering problems. Right: in honor of his contributions, the college named its electrical engineering building Steinmetz Hall.

In his Wendell Avenue conservatory Steinmetz experimented with the effects of lighting and synthetic fertilizers on the growth of plants. He also used his greenhouse for raising orchids (above) and cacti.

In his scientific laboratory, built and stocked by GE adjacent to his Wendell Avenue home, Steinmetz studied such problems as the chemistry of electrical insulating materials and arc lights. This included experiments with the magnetite arc lamp, and in 1902, he arranged a demonstration on Wendell Avenue. It was a huge success and soon cities across the country were adopting his new lighting system.

Steinmetz's physical laboratory, with an early model of his mercury arc rectifier mounted on the wall.

Another of Steinmetz's distinguished visitors was Albert Einstein who came to Schenectady in 1921. It was in that year Einstein received the Nobel Prize in physics.

1908

Lighting

Coolidge develops ductile tungsten. A disadvantage of the use of sintered tungsten filaments had been their extreme brittleness. By subjecting the tungsten to successive heating and hot working stages and drawing it through heated dies of decreasing diameter, Coolidge was able to produce material which was ductile and higher in strength.

Transportation

The Transportation Dept. supplies thirty, 94-ton gearless locomotives to the New York Central R.R. for use into Grand Central Station. Using Sprague's multiple unit system, two 2800-hp locomotives, coupled together, are able to haul the heaviest loads yet handled.

Industrial Electrification

The largest induction motors ever built (6000-hp) are supplied to a steel rail mill of the Indiana Steel Co. at Gary, Indiana. The 30,000 hp total installation produces rails at the fastest rate in the world, 166 tons per hour.

Appliances

An electric vacuum cleaner, the "Invincible Electric Renovator" is placed on the market by the Electric Renovator Manufacturing Co. of Pittsburgh, Pa. Its motor and electrical equipment are supplied by General Electric.

Steinmetz Contributions

Lectures on the operation of a steam turbine in "The Steam Path of a Turbine", Proceedings of the American Society of Mechanical Engineers, No. 90801C, March (1908), points out that the ideal gas equations will not suffice for a steam turbine.

The largest induction motor built to date (6000-hp)-installed at Indiana Steel Co., Gary, Indiana.

Coolidge demonstrates the ductile tungsten process to Thomas Edison.

Ninety-four-ton gearless electric locomotives for the New York Central Railroad.

1909

Lighting

MAZDA is adopted as the trade-mark for certain lamps produced by General Electric. The name, "Mazda", taken from Ahura Mazda, the Persian god of light, was chosen to denote superior quality and service.

John T. Marshall develops a phosphorous "getter" for application on lamp filaments. Flashing of the phosphorous coated filaments in the already sealed bulb results in an improved vacuum and longer lamp life.

Transportation

The Cascade Tunnel of the Great Northern Railway is electrified. A hydroelectric station with two 4000-hp waterwheel generators is built especially for the installation and its output is carried to the substation by a 30-mile, 30,000-volt transmission line. The stepped down voltage of 6600 volts at 25 cycles is transferred to the locomotive by two overhead wires and a running rail. On-board transformers reduce this voltage to the 500 volts required to operate the 1500-hp motors.

Generation

The original 5000-kw Curtis-Emmet turbines at Chicago Edison's Fisk St. generating station are replaced by 12,000-kw units. As a result of improvements in turbine design virtually no use of additional floor space is required.

Communications

A 2-kw, 100,000-cycle Alexanderson alternator is used by the U.S. Signal Corps in experimenting with high frequency telephony over wire lines.

Appliances

New heating elements in GE's appliances use longer lasting nickel-chromium alloy wire in place of iron wire.

A portable electric drill is introduced on the market by the Small Motor Dept.

Steinmetz Contributions

"Prime Movers," in AIEE Transactions 28, 63-69 (1909). Steinmetz looks at the economics of power, space and investment while observing operating efficiency, maintenance, reliability and depreciation. Steinmetz publishes a plea for American technologies to convert to the metric system.

Electric cars at battery charging station.

MAZDA, the new trademark for GE lamps.

Willis R. Whitney
1868-1957

William D. Coolidge
1873-1975

Irving Langmuir
1881-1957

Only an attentive stockholder would have spotted the item, buried near the bottom of GE's 1902 Annual Report. "Although our engineers have always been liberally supplied with every facility for the development of new and original designs," wrote Third Vice President Edwin W. Rice,

It has been deemed wise during the past year to establish a laboratory devoted exclusively to original research. It is hoped by this means that many profitable fields may be discovered.

From left to right, Irving Langmuir, Willis R. Whitney, and William D. Coolidge.

With this, the company announced to the world an experiment that had begun in December, 1900, when a 32-year-old chemistry professor from MIT named Willis R. Whitney had set up his experimental apparatus in a barn behind the Schenectady home of Charles Proteus Steinmetz. His original doubts about the permanence of the post are reflected in Whitney's insistence on retaining his MIT position, and accepting on a two-days-a-week basis the challenge of proving the value of science to the electrical industry. But within a year, the challenges of industry had become the main focus of his activity, and within four years he had formally committed himself to industrial research.

By then he had proved his value. His invention of the GEM lamp made the biggest advance in the efficiency of incandescent lighting since the work of Edison. But it was challenged by a number of promising lighting innovations: the "glower" invented by the great German chemist Walther Nernst; the mercury vapor arc; and a group of metal-filament lamps. To meet the lighting challenge, Whitney sought an outstanding researcher to head his laboratory's effort at perfecting the application of the most promising metal — tungsten — for lighting purposes.

He found the man he needed in the MIT chemistry laboratory. William D. Coolidge had, like Whitney, earned the Ph.D. degree at the University of Leipzig (Germany). Like Whitney, he had done his first major scientific work under the outstanding MIT chemist Arthur A. Noyes. But there the resemblance ended. Where Whitney was charming, charismatic and outgoing, Coolidge was quiet, careful and modest. His determination and experimental skill made him ideally suited to head the tungsten project, and carry it to a successful conclusion. By 1910, he had invented a process for making tungsten wire that has remained ever since the key to the manufacture of incandescent lamp filaments.

The presence of ductile tungsten and outstanding high vacuum techniques made the GE Research Lab a place of great opportunity for a capable scientific researcher. Irving Langmuir, a Brooklyn-born chemist trained at the University of Gottingen, trapped in an unsatisfying teaching post, seized on the opportunity in the summer of 1909. Finding that, as a summer employee under Whitney, he was allowed far more research freedom than he had enjoyed in a university, he gladly accepted a full-time post. He quickly blossomed both as an inventor and as a scientist. His research in 1912 and 1913 produced the gas-filled lamp, a fundamental advance in lighting, and improvements in the vacuum tube which helped make possible modern electronics and radio. Even more important were his contributions to surface chemistry, recognized by the award of the 1932 Nobel Prize. A proud, independent man, he appeared the picture of the aloof, absent-minded scientist to outsiders but inspired colleagues with his enthusiasm and scientific instinct. Langmuir did more than any other individual to prove the value of industrial research to both industry and science.

Behind the scientific triumphs of Langmuir, and the inventive genius of Coolidge (who, in 1913, added to his laurels the invention of the modern X-ray tube) stood the inspiration provided by Whitney. "Are you having fun?" he would ask on his daily tours of the laboratory. But at the same time, he knew that behind the fun lay a responsibility. "I know that I was put here for a purpose," he wrote in 1901:

The company is not primarily a philanthropic asylum for indigent chemists and I must not let it become one even secondarily.

The work of Whitney, Coolidge, and Langmuir proved that the support of science, far from being charity, was the soundest of business decisions.

1910-1911

Lighting

Ductile tungsten filament lamps are introduced on the market. During the period from 1908-1910, Coolidge had made further improvements in his filament making process and in filament life.

The National Electric Lamp Association (formerly National Electric Lamp Company) becomes the National Quality Lamp Works of General Electric after the company purchases the remaining 25% of its common stock. A new site, Nela Park, is established as the center for GE's lighting activities.

Transportation

GE's Pennsylvania site becomes the Erie Works for the production of transportation equipment.

Electrification is completed of the newly built Detroit River Tunnel between Detroit and Windsor, Ontario, Canada. Six locomotives jointly built by GE and the American Locomotive Co., are supplied for operation through the twin tube tunnel.

Appliances

The "Audiffren" a sealed unit, sulfur dioxide compressor refrigerator is manufactured by GE at the Fort Wayne Works after its initial development in France.

An electric range is manufactured by George A. Hughes, whose company would later join with Hotpoint to form the Edison Electric Appliance Company.

Materials

Coolidge develops tungsten ignition contacts for automobiles, replacing platinum and silver which were costly and caused sticking problems.

Tycho Van Allen patents a "calorizing" process for producing an aluminum alloy-coated steel which is highly oxidation resistant at elevated temperatures.

Organization

A Consulting Department is organized at the suggestion of Steinmetz. C.F. Stone is placed in charge of administration and Steinmetz is responsible for technical leadership. Its main function is to assist company engineers and to advise on major company projects.

Steinmetz Contributions

"Electric Illuminants", a lecture given at Johns Hopkins University, discusses the prospects and application of filament lamps (carbon, metal and metallized carbon), arc lamps and the vacuum arc.

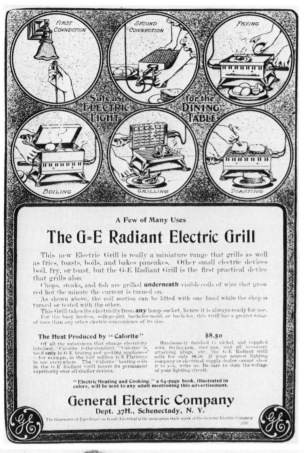

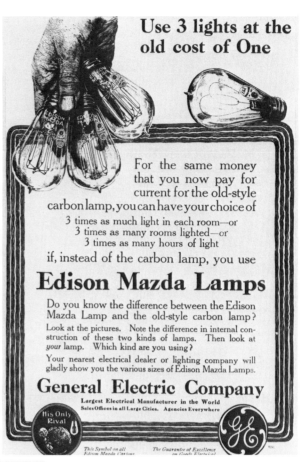

An early Hotpoint Hughes electric range.

The "Audiffren" refrigerator manufactured at the Fort Wayne Works.

STEINMETZ ... *THE CITIZEN*

When most of us think of Steinmetz, we usually picture the man who made lightning, a mathematical genius, an electrical wizard, a brilliant philosopher. Seldom do we think of him as a man with an intense interest in civic affairs. As Philip Alger wrote in the book, *Steinmetz the Philosopher,* "Charles Proteus Steinmetz was one of those rare American engineers and scientists who have combined leadership in their professions with effective participation in public affairs."

When Steinmetz was elected President of the Board of Education, there simply were not enough schools for the children. As a result of his efforts, eight new schools were built including Central Park (below), and extensive additions were made to four others.

It was during Dr. George Lunn's administrations that Steinmetz ventured into politics. Of Steinmetz, Mayor Lunn said, "—There was never any movement looking toward the improvement of the City of Schenectady for which you could not count upon his enthusiastic support. In addition to his great work educationally, he was a constant help to me with his advice on many problems that came before me as Mayor. In all matters, he was ever a tower of strength by his helpfulness."

Under Steinmetz's leadership, the Commission of Parks and City Planning called for a public park system in the City of Schenectady. Speaking of the system, he said, "I believe it is not merely a question of civic pride, recreation or physical welfare, but for our City it is a matter of self preservation." As a result, $300,000 was authorized for the purpose of purchasing land for two large parks.

Lighting

Colin G. Fink develops "Dumet" wire, a copper clad nickel-iron core wire whose thermal expansion properties make it suitable as a replacement for the costly platinum lead-in wires used in manufacturing incandescent lamps.

Transportation

Construction is completed of the first electrically propelled U.S. Navy vessel, the 20,000-ton collier, U.S.S. "Jupiter". Installation of its 7000-hp turbine-generator is supervised by W.L.R. Emmet.

Communications

Irving Langmuir develops techniques for the production and measurement of higher vacuum than had ever been achieved. This work, used in conjunction with his study of the "Edison Effect" provides a better understanding of the operation of vacuum tubes and of possible means to improve them for use in radio and X-rays. Expanding on the work of the British scientists, Sir Joseph Thomson (1897) and Owen D. Richardson (1903), Langmuir demonstrated that the flow of electrons in a vacuum could be controlled by the temperature of the tungsten source and that it could be limited by a space charge effect which was dependent on the amount of residual gas and the electrode spacing.

Materials

Coolidge perfects a tungsten target for X-ray tubes, replacing platinum which has a lower melting point, lower heat conductivity and higher rates of evaporation when heated.

Molding of plastic parts is begun using phenolic resins.

Generation

Emmet and Junggren design a 10,000-kw, 1500 rpm horizontal shaft turbine for the Lehigh Coal and Navigation Co.

Organization

The General Electric Pension Plan is established.

Owen D. Young is hired by Charles Coffin to be general counsel. Young had made an excellent impression during his legal representation of the Stone and Webster Co. in a case involving General Electric.

The first electrically propelled naval vessel-20,000 ton collier, U.S.S. "Jupiter".

1913

Irving Langmuir

First "trackless trolley" operating in Laurel Canyon, California.

Communications

Langmuir, working with Saul Dushman, and W.C. White, develops a three element high vacuum tube — the pliotron. This amplifier tube is more stable in operation and has a far greater power handling capacity than the first three element tube, the "audion", devised in 1907 by independent inventor Lee De Forest.

Dushman develops a two-element, high vacuum rectifier, the kenotron. It is capable of rectifying up to 40,000 volts and providing high voltage, direct current for radio and other uses.

Langmuir and Alexanderson jointly demonstrate the ability of the pliotron to amplify signals received from an Alexanderson alternator.

Medical Equipment

Coolidge develops the hot-cathode, high vacuum X-ray tube. By replacing the cold aluminum cathode with the hot tungsten filament in a high vacuum, Coolidge could provide tubes with better control and greater output than had ever been achieved. The development greatly facilitates the use of X-rays for diagnosis and treatment.

Appliances

Pursuing an idea suggested by Whitney, "sheath wire" heating units for electric stoves are developed by C.N. Moore and C. Dantsizen. By placing the heating wire in a metal tube which is then filled with magnesium or calcium oxide insulation and heat treated, they create an element which eliminates the danger of shock and is resistant to mechanical damage.

Lighting

Langmuir applies for a patent on a gas filled incandescent lamp. During three years of study of the effects of tungsten evaporation and gaseous impurities on lamp darkening and failure, Langmuir determined that filling the bulb with an inert gas rather than a vacuum could result in improved filament life. He also found that by coiling the tungsten filament, it was possible to improve lamp efficiency by as much as 100% over the rated life of high wattage lamps.

Nitrogen-filled incandescent lamps using Langmuir's concepts are introduced commercially in 750 and 1000-watt sizes and compete directly in much of the market held by arc-lamps.

Generation and Transmission

The capacity of oil filled transformers is increased to 15,000 kva at 150,000 volts. Outdoor units of 7500 kva and 120,000 volts are installed.

Construction is begun at Keokuk, Iowa on what is to be the largest hydro-electric station in the world, having an aggregate capacity of 300,000 hp. Each of its thirty vertical shaft turbogenerators has a record output of 17,500 kva and is driven by waterwheels which are the largest impulse type turbines ever built.

Organization

E.W. Rice, Jr., becomes the second President of General Electric. Charles A. Coffin is elected Chairman of the Board.

I. LANGMUIR.
INCANDESCENT ELECTRIC LAMP.
APPLICATION FILED APR. 19, 1913.

1,180,159.

Patented Apr. 18, 1916.
2 SHEETS—SHEET 1.

Fig. 1   Fig. 2.

Witnesses:

Inventor:
Irving Langmuir,
by
His Attorney

William D. Coolidge examining his hot-cathode, high-vacuum X-ray tube.

Edwin W. Rice, Jr.
1862-1935

In the twentieth century, many technology-based corporations began as "spin-offs" of great research universities. But one of the 19th century's seminal technology-based companies, Thomson-Houston, was a high-school spinoff. Its founder was a professor at Philadelphia's Central High School, Elihu Thomson. Its first engineer was Thomson's star pupil, *Edwin W. Rice, Jr.*

Coming from a well-to-do family, Rice could have gone on to college in 1880. But the prospect of continuing his collaboration with Thomson attracted him more. "He has been 'my professor' ever since I met him away back in the year 1876," Rice later wrote. "What a mine of knowledge ready to be explored, as willing to give as I was to receive its richness!"

Together, the two young men developed an entire range of electrical equipment, from generators to meters. Their enterprise survived early financial difficulties, and grew to compete on even terms with Edison's. Rice contributed valuable inventions — his voltage regulator was used for years on Thomson-Houston dynamos. But his real talents were in the management of manufacturing. At the age of 22, he became the factory manager of Thomson-Houston's Lynn, Massachusetts, plant.

With the formation of General Electric in 1892, Rice got the chance to exercise his administrative talents on a larger stage. He was GE's first technical director, and, from 1896, vice-president in charge of manufacturing and engineering.

In this post, he recognized the need to supplant the empirical techniques of the Edison-Thomson era with modern science and mathematics. In 1892, he was favorably impressed by a brilliant paper delivered at a meeting of the American Institute of Electrical Engineers by a young German immigrant named Charles Proteus Steinmetz. He tried to lure Steinmetz away from his employer, Rudolph Eickemeyer, to work for GE. That failing, he convinced GE's president Charles A. Coffin that the combination of Eickemeyer's patents and the genius of Steinmetz ought to be purchased. Under Rice's aegis, Steinmetz rose to the post of Consulting Engineer. And, at the urging of Steinmetz, Rice founded the GE Research Laboratory and hired Willis R. Whitney as its first director.

In contrast to some of the outgoing, dynamic leaders of the early electrical industry, Rice was reserved and judicial in temperament. In 1913 he succeeded Charles A. Coffin as president of GE; Coffin, however, recognized Rice's limitations as a businessman, and continued to hold the Company reins as Chairman of the Board. But throughout the electrical industry, Rice was widely respected as both an electrical pioneer and an industrial statesman.

Transportation

The Panama Canal opens and is the largest electrical installation in the world, with 500 motors operating the locks and 500 more installed in other parts of the canal system. The total horsepower is almost 30,000. The intricate selsyn controls for each of the locks are designed by Edward M. Hewlett of the Switchboard Engineering Depatment. Electric towing locomotives used at the canal are built at the Erie Works.

The first fully automatic electrical railway substation is equipped and placed in operation at Union, Illinois, for the Elgin & Belvidere Electric Railway.

Generation

Horizontal shaft turbines of 30,000 and 35,000 kw output, the largest ever to be constructed, are ordered by the Philadelphia Electric Company.

Communications

The Union College Radio Club, using the recently developed pliotrons, builds a radio receiver and a paper tape Morse Code recorder. In July, the station picks up a German message announcing the start of World War I.

Medical Equipment

Wheeler P. Davey demonstrates the use of X-rays for inspecting industrial objects and examining metal parts for defects. He also performs experiments on the effect of X-ray dosage on biological activity.

Organization

The General Electric Quarter Century Club is formed.

Steinmetz Contributions

"Electric Discharges, Waves and Impulses" (McGraw-Hill Book Co., Inc., 1914).

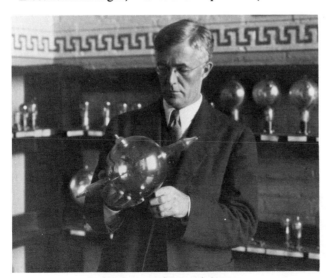

Irving Langmuir examining an early version of the pliotron.

U.S.S. "Wisconsin" passing through the Panama Canal.

1915

Lighting

The San Francisco Panama Pacific Exposition is illuminated at night by 48 searchlights having a total capacity of 2.6-billion candlepower. The display is considered the greatest spectacle of illumination in the world.

Transportation

As part of the most extensive steam railway electrification in the world, GE installs the country's first 3000 V. DC line for the Chicago, Milwaukee, and St. Paul Railroad. Forty-two locomotives of 280 tons each are delivered to the railroad. The use of regenerative braking reduces braking problems on the steep grades and improves safety and operating costs.

GE installs its first geared turbines for ship propulsion on the "Pacific".

The first "all electric" ship, the 32,000-ton battleship "New Mexico" is launched by the U.S. Navy. Its two turbine driven generators weigh 600 tons each and are rated at 15,000 hp. All vital ship's services are powered by electricity.

Communications

Gasoline-electric generator sets rated at 5-kw are installed on large steamships to provide power for auxiliary wireless service.

Steinmetz Contributions

"A New Electric Vehicle: The Dey Electric" New York Times Magazine, 1915. Steinmetz was excited by the prospects of the electric car and consulted with Harry Dey. Unfortunately, the novel design did not survive in the marketplace.

Geared turbine installed on board merchant vessel.

The "all electric" battleship U.S.S. "New Mexico".

The "greatest spectacle of illumination in the world" — at the San Francisco - Panama Exposition.

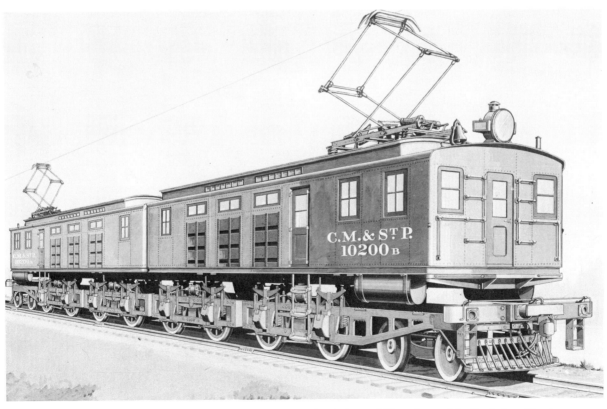

Drawing of GE 260-ton, 3,000-volt electric locomotive for Chicago, Milwaukee and St. Paul electrification.

1916

Communications

W.C. White builds circuits in which the pliotron is used as an oscillator, generating frequencies as low as 0.5 cycles per second and as high as 50 megacycles per second.

A demonstration of two-way radio telephone is made between Schenectady and Pittsfield using Alexanderson's alternator and pliotron amplifiers.

Alexanderson demonstrates his multiple tuned antenna at Schenectady and shows that it has a transmitting capability at 200 kw which is as effective as that of previous antennas with an output of 1200 kw. The development points the way to a worldwide communications nework.

Industrial Equipment

H.G. Reist and H. Maxwell patent a cast rotor made by pouring molten metal into a mold surrounding the induction motor core, and rotating it until it cools and solidifies.

G.S. Meikle develops the "Tungar" hot cathode, argon rectifier tube. Its main commercial use is for charging storage batteries.

Steinmetz Contributions

"Outline of Theory of Impulse Currents" Transactions AIEE, 35, 1-20, (1916).

"Theory and Calculations of Alternating Current Phenomena" (McGraw-Hill Book Co., Inc., 1916).

Electric Truck.

Electric Crane.

Franklin S. Terry
1862-1926

Burton G. Tremaine
1863-1948

Enthusiasm and organizational skill are two key ingredients of business success. Rarely are they combined in one individual. The story of *Franklin S. Terry* and *Burton G. Tremaine* represents another approach: the complementary qualities were embodied in a brilliant team of two men who thought and acted as one.

Organizing talents were supplied by Terry. Born in Ansonia, Connecticut, in 1862, he began his career at 18 with the Electrical Supply Company of Ansonia. In 1884 he was sent to Chicago to establish a branch office. In that city, in 1889, he formed the Sunbeam Incandescent Lamp Company. Regarded by his peers as a "keen analytical mind," and "an apostle of system, efficiency and harmony among men," he became a leader of the early lamp industry.

At a turn-of-the-century meeting of lamp manufacturers, Terry met Burton G. Tremaine, a founder of the Fostoria (Ohio) Incandescent Lamp Company. Tremaine, born in Ann Arbor, Michigan, in 1863, was an enthusiastic, outgoing salesman who had begun his career in insurance and real estate. His optimism and opportunism had earned him the nickname "Lucky B.G."

Putting together their complementary talents, Terry and Tremaine joined their two companies in 1901 to form the National Electric Lamp Association. Other lamp manufacturers were brought into the combination, which set up its headquarters at Cleveland, Ohio. The "National," was in fact (although not in name) a principal lamp manufacturing arm of the General Electric Company, which held 75% of its stock.

As co-managers of the firm, the two men acted together on virtually every important matter. Nearly every letter or memo emerging from their offices was signed "Terry and Tremaine;" nearly every business decision was made by them jointly.

Franklin S. Terry

Burton G. Tremaine

The two were concerned with the welfare and development of their employees, as well as with profits. They created Nela Park, now headquarters of the GE Lamp Division, an attractive campus-like setting for business operations. Their interest in encouraging new talent led to their setting aside annually a Company-paid week-long outing for younger staff members — "a week of jollity, sports, interspersed with comparing of notes," as they put it, for the purpose of "Strengthening the esprit de corps Nationale." From this custom grew GE's later tradition of camps at Association Island.

For their services to General Electric, the two men were named Vice-Presidents in 1922-23. Terry died three years later; Tremaine remained active in civic affairs in the city of Cleveland until his death in 1948.

1917

Lighting

Aladar Pacz of the Nela Park Development Laboratory devises a process for the production of nonsag tungsten filament wire, resulting in greatly improved lamp life.

Generation and Transmission

The U.S. government begins construction of a mile-long dam and hydro-electric generating station on the Tennessee River at Muscle Shoals, Alabama. The project will be completed in 1926 and later turned over to the Tennessee Valley Authority.

The first fully automatic hydroelectric station is installed for the Iowa Power Co. at Cedar Rapids, Iowa.

The largest capacity transformer ever, 50,000 kva, is built by GE

Communications

At the request of the Army and Navy, the Harrison Lamp Works is mobilized for the mass production (1000 per day) of pliotron tubes. W.C. White is in charge of design efforts and G.R. Fonda has responsibility for establishing the manufacturing facility. Peak wartime production reaches 10,800 per week.

Alexanderson completes a 50 kw alternator for use at the American Marconi station at New Brunswick, New Jersey. Two years earlier, Alexanderson had impressed Marconi, "father of wireless telegraphy", during his visit to Schenectady.

Appliances

Limited production of the first household refrigerator begins at GE's Ft. Wayne Works.

Steinmetz Contributions

"Theory and Calculations of Electric Circuits". (McGraw-Hill Book Co., Inc., 1917).

"Engineering Mathematics". (McGraw-Hill Book Co., Inc., 1917).

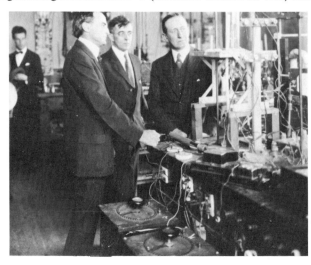

Guglielmo Marconi "Father of the Wireless" (right) visits the Research Laboratory - with Whitney (left), Langmuir (center).

STEINMETZ...*THE FAMILY MAN*

Although unmarried and childless, Steinmetz longed desperately for a family of his own. Therefore, it was not surprising that Steinmetz's relationship with his laboratory assistant, Joseph LeRoy Hayden, soon grew into that of father and son. As a result, he invited Hayden and his wife Corinne to live with him in his Wendell Avenue home. Shortly after their first child Joe was born, Steinmetz legally adopted Hayden as his son. Midge and Billy were his two other grandchildren.

Steinmetz's relationship with his grandchildren and their friends was beautiful. His own curiosity and enthusiasm were such that he met theirs as if there were no dividing line. He participated in the children's life as if he were one of them. He always stopped his work to answer each question, to consider each problem. He never considered these as interruptions. When tired, time with them relaxed him. To him, their needs were paramount.

The Hayden-Steinmetz family in the parlor of their Wendell Avenue home. At the left is Corinne (Mrs. Hayden). To Steinmetz, however, she was Mother. On her lap is William (Billy), then Steinmetz (Daddy), followed by Joe. Next is Joseph LeRoy Hayden (Father) with Marjory (Midge) on his lap.

The Elizabethan style building was home for Steinmetz and his adopted family.

Steinmetz in his 1914 Detroit Electric, along with the grandchildren Midge, Billy and Joe, and his adopted son, Joseph Hayden.

1918

Lighting

To meet war-time needs, C.A.B. Halvorson develops an open-type military searchlight and horizontal spread projector for lighting shipyards and other large areas.

Transportation

A 350-hp Liberty airplane engine, equipped with a GE exhaust driven supercharger designed by Sanford Moss is ground tested at Dayton, Ohio. To test its high altitude performance, the engine mounted on a truck body is driven to the summit of Pike's Peak and performs without loss of power at 14,109 ft.

The first diesel engines for railroad use are built at the Erie Works and installed on three experimental diesel electric locomotives for the city of Baltimore, the New York City Jay St. Connecting Railroad and the U.S. Army.

Communications

The first submarine hunt in history is carried out on a British ship using detectors developed by Coolidge, Langmuir and A.W. Hull. The underwater stethoscopes result in the detection and sinking of a German submarine.

Alexanderson designs a 200-kw, 25,000-cycle alternator for the Marconi New Brunswick wireless station. It is the foundation of the first trans-oceanic radio system and enables the United States to communicate with its Allies and with the American Expeditionary Force in France.

Alexanderson develops the "Barrage Receiver" to cancel the effects of German jamming of Allied wireless messages.

The first all-vacuum-tube radio transmitter is installed by GE aboard the U.S.S. "George Washington" for use by President Wilson.

Generation

A 45,000-kw turbine generator is built for the Connors Creek Station of the Detroit Edison Company.

The largest water wheel generator ever to be built, 32,000 kv-a, 12,000 volts, is ordered by Niagara Power for its second power house.

Steinmetz Contributions

"Radiation, Light and Illumination" (McGraw-Hill Book Co., Inc., 1918).

"The Oxide Film Lightning Arrester", Transactions AIEE 37, 891-896, (1918).

Test of the Moss airplane engine supercharger on the summit of Pike's Peak.

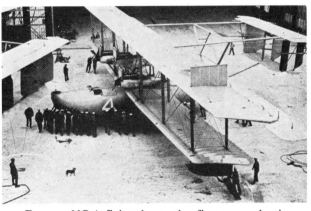

Famous NC-4 flying boat, the first transatlantic plane, used GE vacuum tubes to communicate with the "George Washington."

High intensity open-type searchlight mounted on Cadillac truck.

Alexanderson high frequency alternator at New Brunswick, New Jersey wireless station.

1919

Lighting

A machine which produces tipless lamp bulbs is perfected by L.E. Mitchell and A.J. White of Nela Park. The majority of lamps produced previously were left with a sharp tip at the large end of the bulb. This was a hazard, caused breakage and affected the distribution of light.

Transportation

A LePere biplane powered by a Liberty engine equipped with a GE turbine driven supercharger sets a record of 137 mph at 18,400 ft. altitude compared with 90 mph without supercharger.

Industrial Equipment

J.H. Payne develops an induction heating furnace which uses vacuum tubes as the source of high frequency oscillations. A year earlier, E.F. Northrup of Princeton had used spark oscillators to power a furnace.

The first sectional drive for the manufacture of paper is supplied to the Crown Willamette Paper Co.

Organization

The International General Electric Company is formed from what was previously the Foreign Department. Gerard W. Swope is appointed its first president.

The General Engineering Laboratory is formed by the merger of the Standardizing Laboratory and the Consulting Engineering Laboratory. Its head is L.T. Robinson.

Under the encouragement of the U.S. government, which was interested in maintaining its status in worldwide communications, GE organizes the Radio Corporation of America and purchases the British holdings in the Marconi Wireless Telegraph Co. of America. Alexanderson is named first Chief Engineer of the new company, while continuing to work part time at GE.

The Business Training Course is organized for college graduates.

L.T. Robinson

LePere biplane powered by Liberty engine equipped with Moss turbine driven supercharger.

Generator room of Power House No. 2 on the American side of Niagara Falls.

Mazda lamps are used in a new model runabout.

Portable radio transmitter built for U.S. Signal Corps.

1920

Transportation

The turbo-electric propelled U.S.S. "Jupiter" (see 1912) is converted to an aircraft carrier and renamed the "Langley".

Industrial Equipment

A 250-kw, 4000 pound capacity induction furnace is developed and placed in operation for the reclamation of steel scrap.

H. Maxwell and W.B. Hill develop a process for the centrifugal casting of squirrel cages for induction motors. By forming the bars and motor end rings with fans in one piece, problems in motor assembly and costs are greatly reduced. The motor frame which could house a 7.5 hp motor in 1900 can now house a 20-hp unit.

Charles C. Abbot invents the Calrod unit. First applied for industrial heating, it subsequently replaces sheath wire in appliances.

Medical Equipment

Coolidge develops an oil immersed X-ray tube and transformer assembly, weighing only 20 pounds, and suitable for dental and portable X-ray use.

Communications

Langmuir completes the development of the thoriated tungsten filament which has much higher electron emission than tungsten for the same heat input. These new emitters make it possible to produce high power vacuum tubes for radio broadcasting. A 20-kw transmitting pliotron using this filament is developed by Langmuir and White.

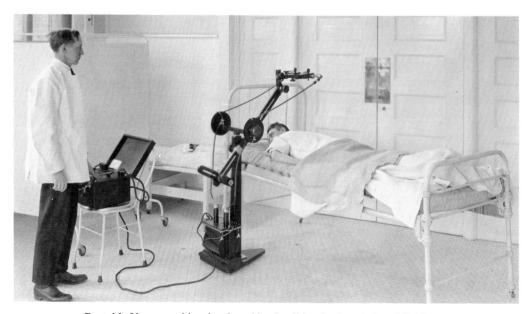

Portable X-ray machine developed by Coolidge for hospital and field use.

Alexanderson inspecting his high frequency alternator at "Radio Central", Rocky Point, Long Island.

Radio transmitter for use aboard submarines

Alexanderson multiple tuning coils and antennas at "Radio Central", Rocky Point, Long Island.

1921

Transportation

The first turbine electric cargo ship, the 15,000-ton S.S. "Eclipse" returns to New York after a successful initial voyage of 26,500 miles. The N.Y.-Gibraltar running time is reduced by two days.

One of the most powerful fighting vessels in the world, the U.S.S. "Maryland" undergoes official sea trials. It's two Curtis-Emmet turbine generators rated at 11,000-kw each, supply four 7000-hp motors, and are capable of producing enough energy for a city of 100,000.

The M.S. "Fordonian", the first diesel engine-electric drive U.S. cargo ship is completed.

A new altitude record of 40,800 ft. is set over McCook Field, Dayton, Ohio, by a LePere biplane equipped with a GE supercharger. Superchargers are now produced on a commercial basis.

Industrial Equipment

The largest electric furnaces in the world, with 40-ton capacity, are put in operation at the U.S. Naval Ordnance Plant, South Charleston, W.Va. They are used for the melting and refining of steel.

Electric motors (75 and 100-hp) are adapted for rotary rig oil well drilling.

Communications

A.W. Hull invents the magnetron tube.

"Carrier current" communications from a moving railcar is successfully demonstrated over electric railway power lines.

Transmission and Generation

Four 8333 kv-a, 220,000-volt single phase, water cooled transformers are built for the Southern California Edison Co. These are the first built for service at this high a voltage.

Steinmetz Contributions

"Einstein's Theory of Relativity". Steinmetz gives four lectures interpreting the theory of relativity.

Sanford Moss (second from left) with record setting, supercharger equipped LePere biplane.

Jesse R. Lovejoy
1863-1945

A technically trained college graduate entering the electrical industry in the 1880's received a small starting salary — but a big opportunity for career advancement. *Jesse R. Lovejoy,* the builder of GE's sales organization, joined the Thomson-Houston Company upon his graduation from Ohio State with a degree in physics in 1886. For a starting salary of 10 cents an hour he performed the standard test man's chores: chipping castings, winding armatures, and assembling and testing incandescent lamps at the West Lynn, Massachusetts, plant.

The real reward was a firsthand acquaintance with the leaders of the emerging electrical industry: Elihu Thomson, Edwin W. Rice, Jr., and, most important for Lovejoy, the brilliant shoe salesman turned electric company executive, Charles A. Coffin. Called upon by Coffin to report on an early technical project, Lovejoy made such a favorable impression that he was admitted into Coffin's inner circle of associates, and was called on to perform a series of important business and personal missions.

At the same time, he was gaining broad experience in the technologies of electrical manufacturing. He helped develop incandescent lighting systems, and became aware of their superiority over arc lamps for indoor illumination. He installed some of the early central stations, and correctly surmised that the future of the electrical business lay in these large-scale generating plants, rather than in home power plants. But his major strengths were in organization and supervision, rather than in engineering. In 1889 he was made Construction Superintendent, and established policies that were later to become embodied in General Electric's famous "Test Program".

When Thomson-Houston merged with the Edison General Electric Company in 1892, the Corporation's first president, Charles Coffin, called on his chief lieutenants for an organization meeting. After assigning the major business areas — lighting, motors, electric railways and the rest — Coffin turned to Lovejoy and said:

> *Whatever is left over in our business, after these departments have taken what belongs to them, you can have, Lovejoy, and make into the Supply Department.*

It may have seemed at first like an unrewarding assignment. But Lovejoy soon found that the odds and ends left over to his department — switches, connectors, and the rest — were in great demand from the customers in the explosively growing electrical businesses. He proved adept at meeting and anticipating the demand. At the weekly meetings where the staff reported on departmental sales, his department's steadily growing contribution often exceeded that reported by the more technically glamorous branches.

As a result, when the time came in 1907 to select a General Sales Manager of the company, Lovejoy was the natural choice. In this capacity he made his greatest contribution to the growth of General Electric. His drive and optimism were well fitted to the most rapid growth period the industry was to experience. He carefully selected a sales force, trained it to cope with the tremendous problems faced by the application of electricity to new industrial and domestic roles, and helped GE expand into the international arena.

His success at this crucial task was recognized by his being named to the company board of directors in 1922, and to an honorary vice-presidency in 1928. The company's top spot eluded him: Charles A. Coffin decided in 1922 that the company needed an administrator, not a salesman, in the presidency. Lovejoy went on to perform a number of important services both within the Company — serving, for example, as president of the GE Employees Security Corporation, a forerunner of today's pension plan — and in the community. But his main place in GE history is that of the creator of a sales force second to no other in American industry.

1922

Transmission

Steinmetz develops a lightning generator for testing the effects of simulated lightning on electrical transmission equipment. It is capable of producing flashes of 10,000 amperes at 120,000 volts. At Pittsfield, Mass., Giuseppe Faccioli and Frank Peek Jr. transmit current at 1,000,000 volts.

Communications

General Electric radio station WGY, Schenectady, one of the first in the country, begins regularly scheduled broadcasting using its 1500-watt transmitter. It presents the first U.S. radio drama, "The Wolf". The WGY transmitter uses a 20 kw vacuum tube fabricated with a newly developed copper-to-glass seal.

J.H. Payne develops an electronic switch tube rated at 250 kv, 40 amps and 70% efficiency.

An experimental tube transmitter containing six pliotrons rated at 20 kw each, generates high frequency power equivalent to that of the 200-kw alternator.

Medical Equipment

A 200-kv Coolidge X-ray tube is produced. As a medical tool, it allows deep therapy to be performed. For industrial applications, it permits inspection of thick metal parts for flaws.

Organization

Chairman Charles A. Coffin, at the age of 78, and President E.W. Rice, Jr., retire from active leadership of the Company. Gerard Swope and Owen D. Young succeed them as President and Chairman, respectively.

The Thomson Research Laboratory is established at Lynn.

Giuseppe Faccioli

Coolidge high voltage X- ray tube .

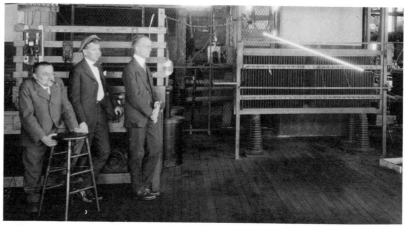

Artificial lightning generator being tested by Steinmetz. At his right is Joseph LeRoy Hayden, his adopted son, and N.A. Lougee, an assisting engineer.

Radio Station WGY, Schenectady,
one of the first in the country.

Charles Steinmetz
broadcasts from WGY
Studio in Schenectady.

Edison and Langmuir examine
high-power transmitting tube
in GE Research Laboratory
while George Morrison,
Manager of the Harrison
Works looks on.

1923

Communications

Transcontinental airmail service begins with the airplanes using GE designed radio transmitters and receivers — and the night route marked with GE searchlights.

Radio tubes of decreased size are produced, permitting the construction of "portable" receivers.

Generation and Transmission

The largest waterwheel generator yet produced is shipped from the Schenectady Works - 65,000 kva, 12,000 volts.

The rated output of turbine generators reaches a record 50,000 kw.

W.L.R. Emmet develops a mercury vapor turbine. The first commercial installation planned is a 10,000-kw unit for the Hartford Electric Light Company.

Industrial Equipment

An induction motor of a record 8000 hp is built for the Ford Motor Company.

Langmuir develops the process of atomic hydrogen welding. The flame, hotter than that of any prior welding torch, and capable of reducing surface oxides, permits the joining of many metals that had been difficult to weld.

5000-hp, 1200 volt motor for the Bethlehem Steel Co.

Type "H" transformer of record size — 24,500 kva, 6600 volts to 101,200 volts.

THE STEINMETZ HERITAGE

Charles Proteus Steinmetz died suddenly in Schenectady on October 16, 1923. Tributes offered by leaders from government, industry, engineering, academia, and science reflect the esteem in which he was held.

Herbert Hoover, Secretary of Commerce:

His mathematical reasoning broke the path for many of the advances in electrical engineering in recent years and solved problems that were vital to the progress of the industry. In his writings he has left engineers a heritage of mathematics that will endure, and as a man he has set us all an example of physical courage and of devotion to our life work.

E.W. Rice, Jr., Honorary Chairman of the Board of Directors of the General Electric Company:

Steinmetz was a prolific inventor, a skilled mathematician , a trained engineer and an inspiring teacher. He possessed a marvelous insight into scientific phenomena and had unequaled ability to explain in simple language the most difficult and abstruse problems. During his short life, he rendered services of a most conspicuous character and inestimable value.

Prof. Harris J. Ryan, President of the American Institute of Electrical Engineers:

Through a decade he led the advance of electrical engineers to the modern understanding of the electric circuit, the transformer, induction motor, alternator and high-voltage phenomena. Dr. Steinmetz assisted his brother engineers to an untold degree by his books, papers and discussions, by his profoundly intelligent vision and by his example of persistent, ably directed enthusiasm.

S.W. Stratton, President of the Massachusetts Institute of Technology:

Dr. Steinmetz was perhaps the ablest man in America in theoretical electricity. His great mathematical talents were combined with an insight into engineering that enabled him always to keep his feet upon the ground. He contributed richly to research, especially in the field of high-voltage phenomena.

R.A. Millikan, Director of Physics at the California Institute of Technology, and recipient of the Nobel prize for Physics in 1923:

The passing of Dr. Steinmetz is a great loss to the electrical industry of the world. He was one of the few electrical engineers who understood the importance of the application of modern mathematics and physics to engineering problems. He has performed a great service in impressing these values, through his books and his lectures, upon the younger generation of American electrical engineers. In addition, Dr. Steinmetz was extraordinary in his breadth of human sympathy, his devotion to ideals and in his continual effort to improve human society. America and the world lose irreparably by his death.

The New York Times summed it all up as follows:

To describe the freedom given to Steinmetz by the General Electric Company, his friend, Prof. Vladimir Karapetoff, of the Cornell School of Electrical Engineering, has evolved a happy phrase — 'he was allowed to try to generate electricity out of the square root of minus one.' That, doubtless, was what the man often seemed to be doing to those to whom mathematics as he knew it was equally incomprehensible and useless. Fortunately his employers — no genius ever had better and few as good — took a different view.

*A small sampling of General Electric people
and their workplaces during the early 1920s.*

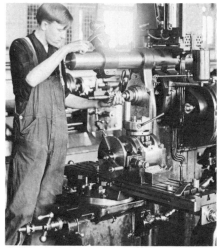

West Lynn Works,
Lynn, Mass.

Pittsfield Works
Pittsfield, Mass.

Lamp Works,
Harrison, N.J.

Gray Iron
Foundry,
Erie, Pa.

Nela Park, Cleveland, Ohio.

Fort Wayne Works, Fort Wayne, Indiana.

127

During a 1922 visit to the Schenectady facility by Edison, he and Steinmetz look at the transplanted 1903 Chicago Edison Co., Curtis steam turbine generator, now a monument to turbine engineering. At the far left, is Edwin W. Rice, Jr., president of General Electric. Looking on, at the far right, is Nicholas Mangano, a GE messenger boy.

CHAPTER THREE

TURNING INNOVATION INTO INDUSTRY
1924-1946

In 1923, Gerard Swope and Owen D. Young presided over a company whose work force had grown from 4000 employees in 1892 to over 74,000; and whose factory floor space had grown from 400,000 square feet in a handful of cities to 25,000,000 square feet in 40 cities. Annual sales had increased from about $12,000,000 in 1892 to $243,000,000 in 1923. This growth was being fueled by the endless flow of innovations from its laboratories and factories and by the development of "an Electrical Consciousness" which helped increase the demand for a great variety of electrical products to meet the needs of consumers, transportation systems, farms, factories and utilities. To meet this demand, government agencies across America and around the world would launch massive "electrification" projects as a means of improving the lives of their citizens. The horizons seemed endless – until the arrival of the Great Depression in the late 20s which challenged the existence of many companies. After a relatively brief period of economic recovery, America was to be thrust into World War II, and most of the innovative and industrial resources of General Electric would be turned toward helping the country fight for its survival. Once again, the creative genius and the industriousness of General Electric's people would be up to the challenge.

The world's most powerful searchlight is at Idora Park, Oakland, California.

An Artificial Moon

This giant searchlight throws a beam so strong that you can stand ten miles away and read a newspaper by its light.

Such searchlights aid navigation on sea and in the air. Their splendid beams are a dramatic reminder of how much electricity has added to the comfort of life by conquering the night.

The General Electric Company which built this huge searchlight also produces MAZDA lamps which light your home. MAZDA is not the name of a product. It is the "mark of a research service" centered in laboratories where scientists search constantly for better and less costly light.

GENERAL ELECTRIC

One of a series of G-E Advertisements now appearing in General Magazines

Waterfalls, transformed into electricity, carry the trains of the C. M. & St. P. 660 miles over the Rockies.

And you know what coal costs!

Fifty-one G-E electric locomotives are now doing the same work which 130 coal and oil-burning engines used to do on the 650 mile electrified sections of the Chicago, Milwaukee and St. Paul.

Engineers estimate that the complete electrification of our railroads would save over 100 million tons of coal a year.

Saving coal is important, but saving human energy is much more important. General Electric Company designs and produces the equipment by which electricity does *both*.

GENERAL ELECTRIC

Millions of American women voted for President in 1920 and are finding time to take active interest in civic affairs

The suffrage and the switch

Woman suffrage made the American woman the political equal of her man. The little switch which commands the great servant Electricity is making her workshop the equal of her man's.

No woman should be required to perform by hand domestic tasks which can be done by small electric motors which operate household devices.

The General Electric Company is working side by side with your local electric light and power company to help lift drudgery from the shoulders of women as well as of men.

GENERAL ELECTRIC

One of a series of G-E Advertisements now appearing in General Magazines

Installing General Electric incandescent street lighting system in Nagoya, Japan.

Everywhere, this monogram

You may travel through a tropical jungle on a train which a G-E locomotive pulls; in an Oriental city you may drink water which a G-E motor pumps.

The sun never sets on this monogram; and wherever you find it, it is a symbol of service — an evidence that electricity is doing one more heavy task which men and women used to do.

The International General Electric Company carries products of American industry to every land, and brings back developments which foreign scientists have worked out. Thus, by a league of minds, peoples know one another better, and humanity moves forward with a swifter stride.

GENERAL ELECTRIC

One of a series of G-E Advertisements now appearing in General Magazines

130

Your Boy

He will have more leisure than you had. And yet, with the aid of electricity, he will do more than you did.

Radio, the electric locomotive and the electric ship will have shortened his distances. Electric motors will have taken upon their shoulders life's burdensome tasks.

A different world it's going to be—and a better one!

GENERAL ELECTRIC

The world's biggest coal saver

This is the largest hydro-electric generator in the world; one of three new giants installed by the Niagara Falls Power Company. Two million people share in the increased electric light and power supplied by these great generators.

Each of these machines will save the equivalent of 700,000 tons of coal a year.

GENERAL ELECTRIC

If father did the washing just once!

If every father did the family washing next Monday there would be an electric washing machine in every home before next Saturday night.

For fathers are used to figuring costs. They'd say: "The electricity for a week's washing costs less than a cake of soap. Human time and strength are too precious for work which a machine can do so cheaply and well."

GENERAL ELECTRIC

And 5,000 farmers came to his door

On a farm near Harrisburg, Pa., in connection with the 1925 State Farm Products Show, a hundred electrical conveniences were installed to show the varied uses of electricity in agriculture.

These harbingers of a better farm life included everything from a little G-E fan to heavy-duty motors, as well as appliances for the household, laundry, barns, chicken house, dairy and workshop.

A rural service line works a magic transformation over the countryside.

GENERAL ELECTRIC

1924

Reading a newspaper by light transmitted through a fused quartz rod.

Stage directions for this scene from William Vaughn Moody's play, "The Great Divide," call for a woman's muffled scream, a pistol shot, and the crash of breaking furniture. The microphone on the right sends them all to your home.

An Exciting Evening

WGY and KGO are the broadcasting stations of the General Electric Company at Schenectady and Oakland. Each, at times, is a concert hall, a lecture room, a news bureau, a theatre, or a place of worship.

Here are four of the WGY Players (the world's first radio dramatic company) at a thrilling climax which almost turns sound into sight.

Tune in, some evening, on one of their productions. You will be surprised to find how readily your imagination will supply stage and setting.

GENERAL ELECTRIC

LIGHTING

The depressible beam automobile headlight is invented. It contains two filaments for "driving" and "passing" beams.

MATERIALS

A process for fusing quartz in pure form is developed by the Thomson Laboratory at Lynn. When bent, a fused quartz rod can allow light to turn corners, thus providing a useful tool for scientific and medical application.

MEDICAL EQUIPMENT

A portable electrocardiograph for studying the heart's electric currents is developed by H.B. Marvin of the General Engineering Laboratory.

COMMUNICATIONS

General Electric radio station KGO, located at Oakland, California, and sister station of WGY — Schenectady, is placed in regular operation, thus "bringing every corner of the Union within earshot of their messages and music."

The first rectifier tubes (UX-213) are developed for radio receivers to eliminate the need for high-voltage B batteries and thus supply this requirement from the AC line.

INDUSTRIAL EQUIPMENT

The largest hoist motor built to date is placed in operation. Rated at 2150 hp, 51 rpm, it is capable of lifting 5,000 tons of ore per 8-hour shoft from a depth of about 1/4 mile.

TRANSPORTATION

The first practical diesel-electric locomotive is demonstrated in New York City. It is a 60-ton, 300-hp unit, built by the American Locomotive Company using an Ingersoll-Rand diesel engine and General Electric generators and motors.

POWER GENERATION AND DISTRIBUTION

The Pittsfield Works High Voltage Engineering Laboratory headed by Frank W. Peek, Jr., uses a record 2,000,000 volt lightning generator to test apparatus designed for protection against lightning.

Two 65,000-kva, 12,000-volt waterwheel generators are installed for the Niagara Falls Power Company. They represent the maximum development in capacity and physical dimensions for this type of machine.

Frank W. Peek, Jr.

Nation's first diesel-electric locomotive, an Alco-GE unit.

65,500-kva generator for the Niagara Falls Power Company.

1925

Marvin Pipkin with inside-frost lamp.

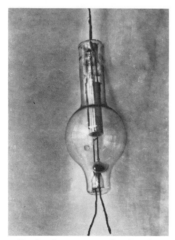

Early thyratron tube developed by A.W. Hull.

LIGHTING

Inside frosting is adopted as a means of reducing glare and improving light distribution in standard light bulbs. An improved method of etching the bulb interiors, invented by Marvin Pipkin of the Nela Park Lamp Development Laboratory, produces lamps which are stronger and easier to keep clean than exterior frosted types.

COMMUNICATIONS AND ELECTRONICS

Albert W. Hull dramatically improves the stability of vacuum tubes by the introduction of a screen grid tube, the tetrode. A similar tube was independently invented by Walter Schottky.

The Thyratron, a grid controlled mercury vapor rectifier, is developed by Hull and Irving Langmuir. The tube shows great promise of finding application in electronic control of medium power devices.

INDUSTRIAL EQUIPMENT

The world's largest steel mill motor is built. It is an 8000-hp, 240-rpm unit with higher continuous rating and operating voltage than any other induction motor in steel mill service.

World's largest motor, 22,500 hp, 220,000 lbs, for the "Saratoga"; World's smallest (Arrow), 1/4,000,000 hp, 4 oz.

Aircraft carrier U.S.S. "Saratoga."

TRANSPORTATION

Aircraft carriers U.S.S. "Saratoga" and U.S.S. "Lexington" are launched, each to be propelled by four 35,200-kw steam engine generators supplying power to eight 22,500-hp motor-driven propeller shafts. These 180,000-horsepower carriers are the largest naval vessels afloat.

A Canadian National Railway diesel-electric locomotive makes the longest non-stop run ever made by any engine — 2967 miles from Montreal to Vancouver in slightly under 67 hours, with a top speed of 60 mph. The controls and motors are supplied by Canadian General Electric, Ltd.

The Indianapolis 500 race is won by Peter DePaolo driving a Duesenberg Special with GE supercharger designed by Sanford A. Moss of Lynn's Thomson Laboratory.

MATERIALS

Thoriated tungsten filaments are developed for use in electron tubes. Work by Irving Langmuir at the Research Laboratory resulted in filaments from 8 to 50 times more efficient as producers of electrons than pure tungsten filaments.

"Glyptal" alkyd resins are introduced for paints, bonding laminates, lacquers, sealants and electrical insulation. Expanding on work started in 1912, Roy H. Kienle, J.G.E. Wright and others originated a number of reactions that could be used to produce Glyptals having properties specially tailored to the desired applications.

The first large-scale use of plastics for appliances is introduced when molded phenolic is used for the handle and thumb rest of flatirons. Pittsfield's John DeBell pioneers the large-scale application of phenolic for vacuum-tube bases.

APPLIANCES

GE announces the first hermetically sealed domestic refrigerator. The development of this compact, quiet, low maintenance unit is the result of the combination of many technologies.

Indianapolis 500 winner with GE supercharger. (from left) Sanford Moss, August Duesenberg, R.W. Mercer, F.S. Duesenberg, James Kemp, and Peter DePaolo at the wheel.

1926

LIGHTING

The GE monogram and wattage and voltage ratings are etched on the ends of light bulbs, replacing paper stickers.

POWER GENERATION AND DISTRIBUTION

The world's largest single phase transformers, four 28,866-kva units, are built at the Pittsfield Works for the Pennsylvania Power and Light Company.

The highest voltage yet produced by man, 2,100,000 volts, is generated at Leland Stanford University with a six-unit GE transformer test set. This equipment, more powerful than any previously available, will permit the stringing and testing of full-sized transmission lines.

Three 50,000-kva synchronous condensers, the largest of their kind, are designed by GE engineers to regulate the voltage of the 220,000-volt transmission lines that carry power from the Big Creek hydroelectric development to the city of Los Angeles and vicinity.

TRANSPORTATION

A combination storage battery, gasoline-electric locomotive hauls a passenger coach 450 miles from the Erie Works to Chicago. Capable of using either energy source or a combination of the two, the electric locomotive can operate without an overhead trolley or third rail.

The most powerful single-unit motor-generator locomotives yet, 3300-hp, 270-ton units, are being built for use in the Great Northern Railroad's new 8-mile-long tunnel through the Cascade Mountains.

Single-unit, motor-generator locomotive for the Great Northern.

Record size 28,866-kva transformer being built at Pittsfield. In foreground (r. to l.) transformer pioneers, C.C. Chesney, G. Faccioli and W.S. Moody.

INDUSTRIAL EQUIPMENT

The first all-electric car dumper for loading coal into ships goes into operation at Toledo, Ohio, with General Electric equipment. Great Lakes coal transportation can now be significantly faster as these units replace older steam-driven dumpers.

COMMUNICATIONS AND ELECTRONICS

Charles A. Hoxie of the General Engineering Laboratory receives a patent for a method of recording sound on photographic film. The equipment for talking movies, which he called the "Pallo-Photophone," was first demonstrated in 1921.

Chester W. Rice and Edward W. Kellogg develop the dynamic loudspeaker to replace the horn arrangement currently used for group listening to radio broadcasts. The sound reproduction is excellent and virtually devoid of distortion. A magnetic phonograph pickup is also developed to improve the fidelity of recorded sound.

E.W. Kellogg working with new dynamic loudspeaker.

1927

The Monitor Top refrigerator.

INDUSTRIAL EQUIPMENT

A mercury vapor detector for improved plant safety is developed by B.W. Nordlander.

APPLIANCES

The Electric Refrigeration Department is established and begins production of the "Monitor Top" hermetically sealed refrigerator. Its all-steel cabinet is another GE innovation.

POWER DISTRIBUTION

Underground single-conductor oil-filled cables capable of carrying 132,000 volts are successfully put in service in a six-mile line by the Commonwealth Edison Company of Chicago and a twelve-mile line by the New York Edison-United Companies.

Underground cable installation

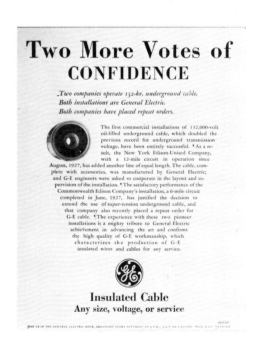

138

COMMUNICATIONS AND ELECTRONICS

Transmitting equipment rated at 100 kw is successfully used by GE Station WGY — Schenectady. Only a few years past, station powers were half-kilowatt power. Now several stations are transmitting with 50 kw.

The first home television reception takes place at the Schenectady, N.Y., residence of E.F.W. Alexanderson.

E.E. Burger develops the first General Electric Cathode Ray Oscilloscope.

TRANSPORTATION

The S.S. "California" is launched — the first large passenger ship with turbo-electric drive. With a cruising radius of 15,400 miles and speed of 18 knots, she is the largest electrically driven ship of her class in the world. The Marine and Aircraft Department is established.

ORGANIZATION

The Gerard Swope Load Fund is established to provide educational opportunities for employees and their children, and the Educational Loan Fund is established to supplement it.

First home television reception at Schenectady residence of Ernst F.W. Alexanderson.

100 kw transmitting equipment at station WGY.

Christian Steenstrup
"Father" of the Monitor Top Refrigerator

Chris Steenstrup
1873-1955

An American home today without an electric refrigerator is a rarity, but in the early 1920's only a few thousand homes in this country had refrigerators, and nearly one half did not have an icebox. Christian "Chris" Steenstrup changed all that when he took an idea conceived by a French monk, Marcel Audiffren, and championed by Ft. Wayne's James T. Wood, and adapted it for mass production and consumer acceptance. Prior to Steenstrup's invention, refrigerators produced by General Electric at Ft. Wayne under contract to the American Audiffren Co. of N.Y. sold for as much as $1,000, twice the cost of an automobile.

Before accepting an offer from General Motors to obtain the rights to this technology, the Company conducted a study under the leadership of Alexander Stevenson. It concluded that a significant market for refrigerators existed, and that they could be produced at a lower cost with high reliability. Designers throughout the Company were requested to submit their ideas. The most promising concepts came from Clark Orr of the Fort Wayne Works and from Chris Steenstrup of the Schenectady Works. Late in 1925, Steenstrup's design was selected for development. It was not long before the success of that design was to earn for him the title, "father of the 'Monitor Top' " refrigerator, one of GE's most successful products.

Born in Aarhas, Denmark, Steenstrup migrated to America in 1894, joining a friend in Bridgeport, Connecticut, to work for a large company manufacturing artillery and ammunition. He had been trained as an apprentice in a machine shop for three years and as a journeyman for two years. While working, he attended night school to acquire a technical education.

In 1901, following a strike at the ammunition company, he sought employment elsewhere to support his family. He came to Schenectady General Electric one day with some friends and found a crowd of men waiting at the gate for employment. A man with a bullhorn asked if there were any mechanics in the crowd and Chris presented himself. He was hired immediately as a mechanic's helper. It was not long before his inventive genius became apparent. He developed a method of hydrogen brazing which became a manufacturing process widely used in the production of reliable, leak-free connections. The invention won him the Company's prestigious Charles A. Coffin Award.

He served as Supervisor of Mechanical Research and was responsible for the design and development of a variety of equipment used throughout the Schenectady Plant. He became involved in several large turbine construction projects and made contributions that added to the efficiency of these units.

Chris rose to the position of Chief Engineer of the Electric Refrigeration Department which was organized in 1927, after his work led to the design of the first successful hermetically sealed refrigerator. The original patent on the refrigerating machine was filed on November 13, 1926 and granted on April 15, 1930. Thirty-nine additional patents in refrigeration followed that initial work. In 1936, at the Centennial celebration of the American patent system, he was identified as one of the 20 living Americans awarded 100 patents since the founding of the system.

Under Steenstrup's guidance, a relatively small but highly trained group of Factory Contact Engineers and a quality conscious factory organization steadily raised the quality level of electric refrigerators until a degree of perfection was attained that had probably never been experienced with a manufactured article of such complexity.

From the very first day of his employment at GE, Steenstrup never hesitated to interject an idea when he thought it could help a colleague or the Company. In 1949, he was honored by the National Association of Suggestion Systems for his pioneer work in 1906 leading to the development of a suggestion system that has since brought many benefits to the Company and its employees, and has served as a prototype for industry.

The Birth of the Monitor Top Refrigerator

Clark Orr
Ft. Wayne designer
of some of GE's
earliest refrigerators

Abbe Marcel Audiffren, inventor of the first electric refrigerator. Second from left is A. Singrun, French manufacturer. A. Myers, left, and James J. Wood, right, who arranged for GE to build the Audiffren machine at Ft. Wayne, Ind.

Alexander Stevenson whose recommendations placed GE firmly in the refrigeration business.

Lowering icing unit into refrigerator cabinet.

Wilbur L. Merrill, head of the Schenectady Works Laboratory, developed the double wall steel cabinet for the Monitor Top Refrigerator.

Steenstrup inspecting refrigerating machine mechanism set up in lathe.

1928

World's largest electric shovel, 15 cu. yd.

Samuel Hoyt with Carboloy tools and machined samples.

LIGHTING

The most powerful lamps to date, rated at 50 kw, are introduced for airport and other high intensity lighting applications.

INDUSTRIAL EQUIPMENT

The world's largest electric shovel, a 15-cu.-yd. unit, goes into operation in the coal mining industry, using GE motors and controls.

POWER GENERATION AND DISTRIBUTION

The first hydrogen-cooled machine to be placed in commercial service is a 12,500-kva synchronous condenser, manufactured by GE and installed at the New England Power Company's Pawtucket, Rhode Island, station. Experiments leading to its construction were performed by Chester Rice in response to a suggestion by Willis R. Whitney, head of the Research Laboratory. The use of hydrogen in place of air reduces friction and heat losses, thus permitting increased capacity for a machine of given size.

Hydrogen cooled synchronous condenser at Pawtucket substation of New England Power Association.

Metal-clad switchgear for the City of Los Angeles.

"Metal clad" switchgear is introduced by GE for outdoor switching stations. The total enclosure of every current-carrying part not only gives protection to operators and maintenance men but prevents secondary breakdowns that may occur in open-type switching equipment. The Switchboard Department is changed to the Switchgear Department.

MATERIALS

"Carboloy," a GE registered trade name given to extra hard alloys made of tungsten carbide and cobalt, is perfected at the Research Laboratory by a team including Samuel L. Hoyt, Floyd Kelley and Emory G. Gilson. The new material is harder and tougher than the best high speed steels, making it excellent for use in cutting tools, drill bits and dies. The Carboloy Company is organized to produce and market the new material.

TRANSPORTATION

The first single unit diesel-electric freight locomotive, rated at 750 hp, is in service on the New York Central, providing economical as well as clean service.

COMMUNICATIONS

WGY initiates the broadcasting of television programs twice weekly. One of these is the first play ever presented on television, "The Queen's Messenger." On August 22 Governor Al Smith is televised as he accepts the nomination as presidential candidate of the Democratic Party. This marks the first use of a portable television transmitter as an outside pick-up for a news event.

E.F.W. Alexanderson devises a method of calculating the altitude of a plane by directing a radio beam downward and picking up its reflection. A radio altimeter based on this principle is under development and will enable pilots to determine their altitude in all kinds of weather, making air travel safer.

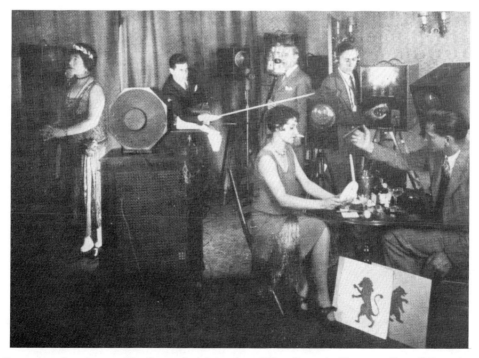

Preparing for the world's first television play, "The Queen's Messenger" at GE station WGY.

AROUND THE WORLD WITH GENERAL ELECTRIC

Japan

When Tokyo recently opened its new subway, the very first subway in the Orient, the gates were crowded from 6 o'clock in the morning until 12:30 the next morning, when they were closed. Many people stayed around just for the thrill of riding underground for the first time. The turnstiles were furnished through the Tokyo office of the I.G.E. and the cars were run by G-E motors.

Bolivia

Above the clouds in the mountains of South America, at an elevation of 14,000 feet, the Ratio Mines and Enterprises Co. of Bolivia will install 23 switchboard panels. This board which is being built at the Philadelphia Works, will control 10,000-volt incoming line and transformer banks, 3000-volt synchronous motors and 220-volt lighting, small motor, and generator circuits.

India

The selling field of wire and cable is highly competitive. Many firms manufacture it. It is difficult to create an outstanding product. However, the Mysore Government has ordered G-E cable for ten miles of underground service. This is probably a reflection of its confidence in the material and workmanship of G-E products, as similar cable has been furnished by us to this native government before.

1928

INTERNATIONAL GENERAL ELECTRIC COMPANY INC.

Electricity has a mission—to bring more comforts into the daily lives of more people

Russia

The International General Electric Company and the Amtorg Trading Corporation, of New York, announced recently that they had signed, under date of October 9th, a contract covering the supply of electric apparatus for export to the Union of Soviet Socialist Republics (Russia).

The contract provides for the purchase on the part of the Amtorg Corporation of not less than $5,000,000 or more than $10,000,-000 worth of apparatus and material during the first two years.

England

Following the successful application of turbine-electric drive to approximately 40 American ships, the British have taken up the cue. A 19,000-ton passenger liner, using this means of propulsion, is being built in England for the Peninsula and Oriental Navigation Company, one of the oldest ship-operating companies in the world. This ship, 600 feet long, will be the first large electrically-driven vessel built in Europe. It will operate between ports in England, India and Australia.

Brazil

An order for $100,000 worth of light was received from Brazil recently. This includes 774 General Electric novalux lighting units, and about 500 standards on which they will be mounted. In addition, the necessary cable, insulators, and other G-E material needed for this installation will be supplied. This is one of the largest orders ever received by the International General Electric. This order not only brings us more work, but shows that G-E products, because of their high quality and the excellent service they give, are gaining steadily in popularity.

Chile

The Chile Exploration Company bought six 70-ton G-E electric locomotives about a year ago, and recently turned in a repeat order for three more. This has made necessary an extension of substation capacity. So the order includes a G-E mercury arc rectifier together with the necessary transformers, switching equipment and an ample supply of spare parts. This apparatus will be installed at an elevation of 9500 feet above sea level.

Canada

In order to transmit power from the new Gatineau Power Company's generating station at Paugan Falls to Toronto, a distance of 250 miles, it has been necessary to use the highest transmission voltage ever used in Canada, 110,000 volts. Twelve transformers for operation at 220,000 volts were supplied by the Canadian General Electric Co., Ltd. Nine of these will step the generator voltage up from 6600 to 220,000 volts, and the remaining three will be used to supply power to the 110,000-volt transmission system.

France

In spite of high import duties and shipping costs, G-E equipped products are being shipped in ever greater quantities abroad. This alone is a high compliment to the quality of our products and would seem to indicate that they are more highly efficient and economical than those of our European competitors. A whole carload of washing machines and ironers, all fitted with G-E equipment, was recently shipped from Chicago to the French Thomson-Houston Co.

EXTRACTS FROM FT. WAYNE WORKS NEWS — 1928

RELIVING THE EDISON ERA

Henry Ford's intense admiration for the genius of Thomas Edison made him one of the chief supporters of Light's Golden Jubilee, the 50th anniversary of the invention of the incandescent lamp.

"Light's Golden Jubilee," said Mr. Ford, "is conceived and planned as a celebration of electrical progress in the last 50 years as it is typified by the improvement and universal acceptance of the incandescent lamp from its invention in 1879. But it is not that alone. I believe Mr. Edison would agree with me that the celebration should be taken, not as glorifying what has been done in the past 50 years, but as indicating what will be done in the next ten. I say ten years, because in that period we shall see an advance as great as that made in the past 50 years. The world is just getting its momentum. Ideas accomplish themselves much more rapidly than they did even 25 years ago.

The use of electricity is yet little to what it will be in the next ten years. Power is the center of industry. It is assuming an indispensable place in agricultural and domestic life. We have not yet fully realized that the function of the workman is to direct power, not to exert it. We are closer to that realization in industry than in agriculture or in housekeeping. Having the energy of electricity to do our bidding, there is no reason for human backs to strain, for arms to lift nor legs to stagger under heavy loads."

Electrical World, 1929

Celebrating the Golden Jubilee of the Incandescent Lamp

Thomas Edison recreates his invention of the incandescent lamp as Henry Ford (center) and former Edison assistant Francis Jehl look on.

Location: a replica of Edison's Menlo Park laboratory, built at the Henry Ford Museum, Dearborn, Mich.

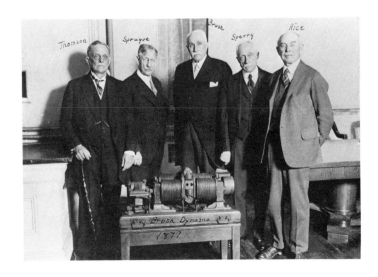

Meeting of Electrical Pioneers at Franklin Institute, celebrating the Golden Jubilee of the Brush Dynamo. From left to right: Elihu Thomson, Frank Sprague, Charles F. Brush, E. Sperry, and Edwin W. Rice, Jr.

1929

"Palm Beach in Brooklyn" with the aid of GE sunlamps at the swimming pool of the Hotel St. George.

Drum Cartridge facsimile transmitted from Station KGO, Oakland, to Schenectady's General Engineering Laboratory.

LIGHTING

The S-1 mercury vapor sunlamp is introduced. It is the first lamp bulb generating ultraviolet rays for the purpose of suntanning without danger of damage to the eyes.

APPLIANCES

The "Handy" hand-held electric vacuum cleaner is announced. A new iron is marketed with a "button nook" to facilitate ironing around buttons.

TRANSPORTATION

The aircraft carrier U.S.S. "Lexington" breaks all existing records for a capital naval ship in its California-to-Honolulu run, averaging 30.7 knots for 72 hours. She produces 31% more power than the largest naval vessel heretofore built.

COMMUNICATIONS AND ELECTRONICS

Radio-photos are received regularly by the General Engineering Laboratory at Schenectady from Radio Station KGO, Oakland, California. Drum cartridge facsimile photographs of Colleen Moore, Norma Talmadge, Douglas Fairbanks and Mary Pickford are favorites for transmission. A time of 2-1/2 minutes is required to broadcast a single photograph.

ORGANIZATION

The General Electric Supply Corporation is formed with headquarters at Bridgeport, Conn. C.E. Patterson is selected as president and director.

POWER GENERATION AND DISTRIBUTION

The largest electrical generation unit in the world is installed by General Electric engineers at the Commonwealth Edison Company's State Line Power Station in Hammond, Indiana. The 208,000-kw, three-unit steam turbine-generator has a capacity four times that of most units in service.

Four 77,500-kva vertical shaft waterwheel generators are under construction for the Dnieper River Development in Russia. With an overall diameter of approximately 40 feet, they exceed in physical dimensions as well as electrical capacity any waterwheel generators previously constructed.

The world's largest single shaft steam turbine-generator, 160,000 kw, is installed at the East River Station of the New York Edison Co.

The Pittsfield High Voltage Laboratory announces the production of 5,000,000-volt artificial lightning, and GE radio station WGY broadcasts the event.

Charles E. Eveleth

Waterwheel generator room of Dnieper River Station, Russia.

Three-unit, 208,000-kw turbine generator at State Line Power Station, Hammond, Indiana.

PIONEERING BIGGER AND BETTER

Oscar Junggren
1865-1935

When built in 1902-1903, the Curtis-Emmet turbine ordered by Samuel Insull for the Chicago Edison Co. was the largest of its kind in the world, and, with a rating of 5000 kilowatts, was just ten times more powerful than any of its predecessors. During design work on this previously unheard-of titan of power generation, there were many who said "It cannot be done." Oscar Junggren helped prove them wrong.

He collaborated with Chief Engineer W.L.R. Emmet in the design and construction of a machine that clearly demonstrated the superiority of the steam turbine and set the stage for its widespread use. That historic machine is now displayed in the Schenectady Works as a "Monument to Courage."

Born in Landskrono, Sweden, Junggren attended the engineering college of Malmo in that country, graduating in 1885 from the mechanical engineering course.

After coming to the United States, he was first employed by the Edison General Electric Company in New York City in 1889 and later transferred to Schenectady where he became involved in the design of steam power equipment. In 1902, he was appointed design engineer of the Turbine Department, continuing in this capacity until 1922, when, in recognition of his outstanding design ability, he was made consulting engineer of that department.

From then until he became ill in 1934, he worked with Glenn Warren and others in the conception of a number of unique designs that resulted in ever increasing operating efficiency and reliability. In 1931 he received a Charles A. Coffin Award, having been cited for his work as "a creator and designer of large turbine units and particularly for his invention of the steeple-compound turbine." That was indeed a conservative description of a man who was one of the giants of the turbine industry.

Oscar Junggren

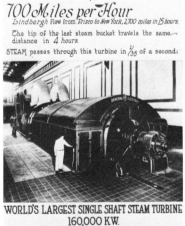

700 Miles per Hour
Lindbergh flew from Frisco to New York, 2,700 miles in 15 hours.
The tip of the last steam bucket travels the same distance in 4 hours.
STEAM passes through this turbine in $\frac{1}{35}$ of a second.

WORLD'S LARGEST SINGLE SHAFT STEAM TURBINE 160,000 K.W.
In Operation Since October 1929
GENERAL ⓖⓔ **ELECTRIC**

Generator installation at East River Station of the New York Edison Company.

A Tribute

If it was Archimedes who said "Give me a place to rest my lever and I will move the world," that pioneer physicist and mathematician would have been astounded to hear that, in Schenectady, New York, in a land outside his ken, 2147 years after his death, there would be a man whose genius would be credited with energizing one-half the world, not in theory, but in fact.

For it is said by even the unimaginative engineers that fully one-half the electric power developed in the world today is produced by means of turbines designed by the fertile brain of Oscar Junggren, so modest a man that few of us even recognized him as he went back and forth through our streets for four and forty years.

The production of kilowatt-hours has been said to be the big industry of Schenectady. It is such a tremendous undertaking to devise machines which will produce economically the harnessed thunderbolts of Jove that move half the world that, when the designing brain that put forth these machines is stilled in its earthly activities, it is an event which is of importance far beyond the ordinary range of human affairs.

None but technical people can grasp the immensity of this genius' labors who, in the eight years from 1924 to 1932, produced 30 turbines, each of an entirely new design; but the most nontechnical of us can recognize the amazing productive power of that prolific mind, and the man's unremitting industry in giving form to these new ideas which move half the world.

This is the substance from which the fame of Schenectady is built. The city has every reason to honor such genius.

—*Schenectady Union-Star, 1935*

STEAM TURBINES

Glenn B. Warren
1898-1979

Engineer and distinguished businessman, Glenn Warren was associated with the General Electric turbine business during a period when approximately 96 million kilowatts of steam turbine-generators for electrical power generation were produced in Schenectady and Lynn for electrical utility and industrial applications around the world. Much of this output and the growth of an entirely new industry for the application of gas turbines to electrical production were due, in no small measure, to his contributions.

Glenn B. Warren holds smallest GE turbine wheel (6-in. diameter, 34,000 rpm, for supercharger). In background is portion of largest (14 ft. diameter, 1800 rpm, for steam turbine) wheel.

Born in Western Missouri in 1898, Warren grew up in neighboring eastern Kansas and was graduated from the University of Wisconsin with a B.S. degree in 1919 and an M.E. in 1924. His thesis on gas turbines was supported by extensive experiments.

Warren joined General Electric in 1919 as a member of the Test Engineering Program. Shortly thereafter he received a letter indicating that he had been nominated for a Rhodes Scholarship. As a result, he talked with Charles Eveleth, Executive Engineer of the Turbine Department, who asked Warren what he really wanted to do. Warren replied, "I guess I want your job eventually." "O.K., we'll take you on in the Turbine Department for three months. If you don't like it after that, you can quit," was Eveleth's response. Warren accepted and stayed on to receive worldwide recognition as a skilled turbine engineer and eventually became Vice-President and General Manager of the Turbine Division.

After joining the Turbine Department, he proposed that work be started on gas turbines in Schenectady. This was delayed for a number of years as Warren said, "We didn't have the materials technology at that point in time." Instead he undertook an extensive research program to improve the efficiency of steam turbines which had over a period of five years exhibited less than expected efficiencies. Experiments with W.E. Blowney and H.L. Wirt on wood and metal models of the steam passages enabled fundamental laws of turbine design to be established which are the basis of present day GE turbine designs.

General Electric's 208,000-kw unit at the Commonwealth Edison Company's State Line Power Station, now an ASME National Historic Mechanical Engineering Landmark, was a major development in turbine technology under Warren's direction. Placed in service in 1929, this unit's capacity was four times greater than most units then in service and remained the largest generating unit in the world for 25 years. It was still in daily operation in 1978.

Warren directed the design activities in the mid-thirties that led to the now worldwide standard type of turbine design employing a double shell construction.

During World War II, he and Alan Howard led a Schenectady-based Turbine Department team involved in the development of GE gas turbines for aircraft jet and propeller propulsion.

Warren's honors during his career were numerous. For his excellence in engineering and advancement of turbine-generator technology, he was awarded an honorary Doctor of Science degree by Union College. Other career honors included the ASME Gold Medal and Honorary Life Membership; the John Fritz Gold Medal, presented by four engineering societies; the David W. Taylor Gold Medal, SNAME; and the Newcomen Gold Medal for Steam Power.

1930

First photoflash lamp.

Karl B. McEachron

GE electric clothes washer.

LIGHTING

A new era in photography is begun in the United States as Photoflash lamps are introduced to replace the cumbersome and dangerous, open pan, flash powder ignition light sources. The sealed bulbs produce a brilliant flash of white light timed to a fraction of a second and able to be synchronized with the camera shutter.

MATERIALS

The Plastics Department is formed to implement developments in plastics beyond the company's needs for insulation materials.

The "Thyrite" lightning arrester is developed by Karl B. McEachron of the Pittsfield High Voltage Laboratory. Thyrite, a densely fired material made principally of silicon carbide bonded with a class of clay, has the unique property of being an insulator for ordinary high voltages, but becomes a conductor to ground for extra-high voltages and surges produced by lightning, thus protecting transmission lines.

APPLIANCES

The first commercial line of electric clocks is introduced by GE affiliate, Warren Telechron Co. In 1917, Henry E. Warren invented an electric clock which would operate on household alternating current. Telechron clocks were first used as master clocks for frequency regulation in electric utilities.

The Calrod® high speed heating unit is incorporated in home electric ranges by the Hotpoint Company. An electric clothes washer for home use is placed on the market.

INDUSTRIAL EQUIPMENT

A new line of totally enclosed, fan-cooled induction motors, rated at 3/4 hp to 30 hp, is introduced. The units have the same mounting dimensions as the open-type motors but are fully protected for operation in dust and other potentially damaging environments.

MEDICAL EQUIPMENT

The General Electric X-Ray Corporation is the new name given to GE's affiliate, the Victor X-Ray Corporation. Ten years earlier, Victor had begun distribution of GE X-ray equipment stemming from developments pioneered by William D. Coolidge.

Willis R. Whitney invents the "artificial fever" machine for use of high frequency waves in the treatment of certain illnesses. The machine, known as the "inductotherm" or "radiotherm," is manufactured by the X-Ray Corporation. Experiments also indicate its potential for the cooking of food and industrial heating.

Willis R. Whitney and "artificial fever" machine.

COMMUNICATIONS AND ELECTRONICS

E.F.W. Alexanderson demonstrates projection television in Proctor's Theatre, Schenectady, with images on a 7-foot screen. GE radio station WGY increases its radiated power to 200 kw.

TRANSPORTATION

The motor-driven magneto compass turn compensator is designed, correcting the turning errors previously experienced on compasses. Accurate indication of direction, even in steeply banked airplane turns, is now possible.

GE welding equipment is utilized in the construction of the "Carolinian," the first all-welded steel cargo vessel built in America, reducing both manufacturing time and maintenance requirements. Similar welding equipment is being manufactured for airplane fabrication.

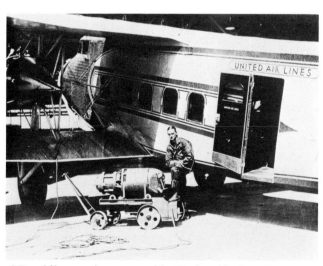

GE welding equipment used by Boeing Airplane Company to build transports for United Air Lines.

The Age of Arc Welding

THE MORE YOU ARC WELD THE MORE YOU SAVE

PIONEERING IN COMMUNICATIONS

Ernst F.W. Alexanderson
1878-1975

Young Alexanderson on GE "Test".

On Christmas Eve, 1906, the world's first voice radio broadcast passed into history. Behind that event stood a young General Electric engineer, Ernst Frederick Werner Alexanderson, who had spent the previous two years designing and constructing the high-frequency alternator that made the broadcast possible. That achievement, which gave the U.S. its start in the field of radio communication, was to prove but one of many during Alexanderson's career. During his 46 years with GE, he was to receive 322 patents.

Ernst F.W. Alexanderson was born on January 25, 1878, at Uppsala, Sweden. The young man developed an early interest in electrical engineering that was stimulated by a year of technical work at the University of Lund in 1896. He then spent three years at the Royal Institute of Technology in Stockholm, from which he was graduated in 1900 as an electrical-mechanical engineer. Upon reading a copy of "Alternating Current Phenomena," by Charles P. Steinmetz — GE's mathematical giant, he was so impressed that he decided to move to America to seek work with the author.

In 1901, Alexanderson visited Steinmetz in Schenectady and in 1902, on the latter's recommendation, GE gave him a drafting job. The following year, he took GE's Test Engineering Course, and in 1904 he became a member of the engineeing staff designing generators under the direction of Steinmetz.

When Steinmetz organized a Consulting Engineering Department in 1910, Alexanderson became a member of the group. In 1915, Guglielmo Marconi arranged to have a 50-kilowatt Alexanderson alternator installed in his transatlantic Marconi Company station in New Brunswick, N.J.

During World War I, Alexanderson perfected a 200-kilowatt alternator which was installed at the same station. It was used by President Woodrow Wilson in transmitting messages to the war theatres of Europe and, on October 20, 1918, transmitted Wilson's ultimatum to Germany, which brought the war to a close.

In 1918, Alexanderson became head of GE's newly organized Radio Engineering Department. The next year, when Marconi bid for exclusive rights to the alternator, President Wilson appealed to GE not to sell and instead to help organize an American company that would use it. This led to the formation of the Radio Corporation of America, with Alexanderson becoming its chief engineer in 1919.

Meanwhile, Alexanderson's inventive genius had been hard at work. Among his notable radio developments were the magnetic amplifier, the electronic amplifier, the multiple tuned antenna, the antistatic receiving antenna, and the directional transmitting antenna. He also devised radio altimeters, and his studies in the polarization of radio waves made possible effective radio direction finders.

Alexanderson himself made the magnetic amplifier obsolete with his invention of the electronic amplifier. This was essentially the application to radio telephony of the vacuum tube improvements worked out by Irving Langmuir of the GE Research Laboratory. These tubes became the basis for all present-day radio broadcasting.

From 1919 to 1924, he divided his time between General Electric and the Radio Corporation of America, maintaining his residence and laboratory in Schenectady but personally superintending construction of powerful radio stations around the world.

In the next few years, Alexanderson performed pioneering work in television and the transmission of pictures by radio. With equipment employing a perforated scanning disk and high-frequency neon lamps, he staged the first home and theater demonstrations in 1927 and in 1930, in Schenectady.

AND ELECTRONICS

Television projector designed by E.F.W. Alexanderson and demonstrated at Schenectady's Proctor's Theatre.

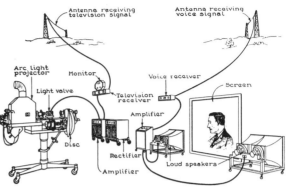

A Diagram of the Entire Television Receiving Apparatus

Alexanderson's experiments with picture transmission from San Francisco to Schenectady forecast the regular radio transmission of pictures and facsimile broadcasting. On June 5, 1924, he had sent over the Radio Corporation of America's stations the first transatlantic facsimile. It was a handwritten greeting to his father in Sweden.

With GE's withdrawal from the affairs of the Radio Corporation of America in 1933, Alexanderson devoted himself at GE to the power applications of electronics, such as power transmission with direct current. In 1935, GE installed a direct-current power-transmission system using the mercury arc inverter which he had invented more than a decade earlier.

The GE inventor's laboratory also produced the amplidyne, an extremely sensitive and powerful system for amplification and automatic control that was successfully applied in steel mills and other places requiring delicate control of continuous operations. The principle of the mercury arc inverter used in DC power transmission found another application in the development of a variable-speed AC motor known as the thyratron motor.

Alexanderson never wavered in his interest in shortwave phenomena and in television. In 1939, GE engineers in the Helderberg Hills near Schenectady regularly began to receive high-definition television from New York, 129 miles away. In 1940, the first television relay station operating at such a distance began to rebroadcast New York programs.

With the broadening scope of its activities, Alexanderson's Radio Consulting Department had become the Consulting Engineering Department in 1928 and finally the Consulting Engineering Laboratory in 1933. In 1945, this organization was merged with GE's General Engineering Laboratory to form the General Engineering and Consulting Laboratory. Alexanderson served as a consulting engineer on the staff of the new organization until his retirement in 1948, then continued as a consultant for another year.

The awards and honors that came to Ernst F.W. Alexanderson are too numerous to list here, but one need not look too far to see the working monuments which embody the results of his pioneering efforts in communications and electronics.

Alexanderson and A.H. Mittag with part of thyratron motor control equipment.

1931

Louis Navias, "Mr. Ceramics" of General Electric.

Vertical-mount motor for rayon spinning.

Everett S. Lee

LIGHTING

Albert W. Hull of the Research Laboratory receives a patent on a low pressure mercury-vapor lamp.

MATERIALS

High-melting-temperature oxide ceramic supports for tungsten filaments needed in vacuum tubes developed for the radio industry are produced in the Research Laboratory under the direction of Louis Navias.

APPLIANCES

Demonstrating the rapid consumer acceptance of a product introduced only four years earlier, the one millionth GE electric refrigerator is presented to the Henry Ford Museum.

INDUSTRIAL EQUIPMENT

Specially designed high speed vertical-mount motors for spinning rayon are introduced. These motors meet the special demands of a new industry.

TRANSPORTATION

Increased capacity AC-DC locomotives from the Erie Works will handle fifteen 80-ton Pullmans at an average 65 mph express speed, for the New York, New Haven and Hartford Railroad. The locomotives also have double-ended operation to ease switching.

ORGANIZATION

Everett S. Lee succeeds Lewis T. Robinson as head of the General Engineering Laboratory.

POWER GENERATION

Improvements in the efficiency of steam turbines reach a point where it requires about 1.5 lbs of coal to produce 1 kilowatt-hour of electricity, compared to more than 3 lbs needed ten years earlier for the same output.

COMMUNICATIONS AND ELECTRONICS

Photo-electric control equipment has now been developed to a point where its position in the industrial field is definitely established.

MEDICAL EQUIPMENT

The most powerful X-ray machine developed, a 900,000-volt unit, is installed at Memorial Hospital, New York City. Its record high voltage is made possible through use of the "cascade" principle developed by William D. Coolidge and Ernest E. Charlton.

Automatic photoelectric control of a GE water cooler. Similar controls are gaining widespread use in industrial control processes.

Ernest E. Charlton (l.) and William D. Coolidge with 900,000 volt X-ray tube.

OWEN D. YOUNG AND GERARD SWOPE

Gerard Swope
1872-1957

The story of Owen D. Young (the "D" signifying no particular name) is the American story of the farm boy who made good. He became an industrial statesman whose heart remained with his home community and who gave his time unstintingly in public service to his state, the nation, and the world.

The path he trod from the farm led to the threshold of the White House. From 1924 through 1932, his name figured prominently as a possible Democratic nominee for President, but he refused to encourage the hat-flingers.

Young was born in Van Hornesville, N.Y., on October 27, 1874. He was 16 years old when his parents mortgaged the farm to send him to St. Lawrence University at Canton, N.Y. Upon his graduation in 1894, he sought permission to work his way through Harvard University's Law School but was turned down. He turned instead to Boston University where he completed the three-year law course in two years, at the same time supporting himself by tutoring and library work.

After his graduation from law school in 1896, Young joined the Boston Law office of Charles H. Tyler and within a few years was a partner. He handled much litigation for the electrical engineering firm of Stone & Webster and eventually came to the attention of Charles A. Coffin, the first president of General Electric.

Owen D. Young
1874-1962

One morning in 1913, Coffin asked to see him. Young told his wife he expected to be "spanked" because he recently had inflicted a legal defeat upon General Electric.

Instead, Coffin invited him to become the Company's Chief Counsel and Vice President in Charge of Policy. When Young accepted promptly, Coffin observed that salary had not been mentioned. Young replied:

"I would like to have you pay me less rather than more than those holding similarly responsible positions. I wish to be sure of earning what I get. I would much rather have the organization feel that I am underpaid than overpaid."

Owen D. Young posing as "Keystone Cop" during lighter moment at Association Island.

LEADERS OF GENERAL ELECTRIC

In 1922 he succeeded Coffin as chairman of the board of General Electric, while Gerard Swope was appointed president of the Company

Young appeared on the international scene, in which he was destined to play a major role, as a member of the German reparations commission in 1924. Out of this international conference came the Dawes plan. When the American delegation returned, General Charles G. Dawes referred reporters seeking details to Young. General Dawes told them, "Young knows more about it than anyone."

In 1929, Young was called upon to head another committee of experts to unify further German payments. This group drafted the Young Plan for handling reparation payments on the basis of a new total sum.

His talents as a conciliator and mediator and his abilities to achieve agreement among men of divergent views came into full play in 1919 when, at the request of the government, he created the Radio Corporation of America to combat threatened foreign control of America's struggling radio industry. He served as RCA's board chairman until 1929.

Long active in education, he was a trustee of St. Lawrence University from 1912 to 1934, serving as president of the board the last 10 years. He was a member of the New York State Board of Regents, governing body of New York's educational system, until 1946.

Governor Thomas E. Dewey called upon him in 1946 to head the state commission which laid the groundwork for a state university system in New York. Although the commission represented a wide range of views and opinions, Young achieved a surprising unanimity which resulted in a report containing recommendations adopted by the legislature.

Gerard Swope, who started out with the General Electric Company in 1893 as a helper at $1 a day, became president of GE in 1922, and served in that post for nearly 20 years.

His career and his personality were once summarized by an associate: "Probably no man in his generation has been more ardently devoted to his country and its interests and more willing to devote his great energies and abilities unsparingly to this work than Gerard Swope. These qualities have manifested themselves in everything with which he has come into contact. And in all his activities, whether as business executive or economic leader, his thinking is of a fundamental and analytic quality undoubtedly influenced by his engineering training."

He was born in St. Louis, Mo., on December 1, 1872. As the result of a desire to see the Chicago World's Fair in 1893, he went to that city while still an undergraduate at Massachusetts Institute of Technology and became a helper at the GE Chicago Service Shop.

American Members of the Dawes Committee. From left to right: Owen D. Young, Charles G. Dawes, Henry M. Robinson.

Swope was graduated from M.I.T. in 1895, with a Bachelor of Science degree in electrical engineering and returned to Chicago, this time in the shops of the Western Electric Company. Four years later, he went to St. Louis as manager of the Western Electric office, and in 1906 was transferred to Chicago. He went to New York as general sales manager two years later.

In 1913, Swope was named a vice president and director. Four years later, he visited the Orient, organizing a Chinese Western Electric Company and promoting trade interests and telephone service in the East.

During the first World War, Swope served on the War Department General Staff in connection with the Army's procurement and supply program. For his outstanding achievements, he was awarded the Distinguished Service Medal by the President of the United States and was named a Chevalier of the Legion of Honor by the French government.

He was brought to General Electric in 1919, by Charles A. Coffin, then president. When the foreign department of GE was enlarged that year into a new organization, the International General Electric Company, Swope became its first president. He was elected president of General Electric in May, 1922.

Young and Swope worked out a division of responsibilities that was to continue as long as they held office. As Young described it, "one of us shall act as captain of the ship, the other as navigator". He would concern himself with policy, while Swope would oversee production, research, engineering, and sales. Yet, in the words of Philip Alger, in *The Human Side of Engineering*, "They were so much in accord that it is hard to say whether any given policy was due to one or to the other."

Under Young's and Swope's direction, General Electric began the extensive manufacture of electric appliances for home use. Before 1922, the only product sold directly to the public, on the basis of mass production and wide distribution, was the incandescent electric lamp. The Company had until then concentrated its efforts on producing equipment for generating, transmitting, and controlling electricity.

The introduction of a host of electrical consumer goods required extensive enlargement of GE's advertising, marketing, distribution, and service organizations — not to mention its engineering and manufacturing facilities. But the commitment of resources was successful. It helped revolutionize the American household, speeded the electrification of farms, factories and transportation systems and increased the demand for the Company's utility-related equipment.

The onset of the Depression did not spare General Electric, but the diversification measures which Young and Swope had instituted protected it from the fate of countless other industrial concerns. At the same time, their plans for improving the economic security and general welfare of General Electric workers helped cushion the blows of the Depression and other personal misfortunes. Though at first considered radical by some, these served as prototypes for other segments of American industry.

Plans which they introduced or expanded included the General Electric Mutual Benefit Association, providing sickness and death benefits; free and contributing group insurance; educational scholarships and loan funds; and a savings plan made possible by organization of the General Electric Employees Securities Corporation providing bonds as a medium for investment of employee savings.

Secretary of Labor Frances Perkins and GE president Gerard Swope during broadcast of symposium on government and business cooperation.

The most outstanding example of Young's and Swope's distinctive contributions in the area of employee benefits, however, was an unemployment insurance plan, which greatly influenced thinking on this subject throughout the United States, both in industry and in government. It preceded the Social Security Act by more than five years.

One of the more publicized demonstrations of Gerard Swope's genius for evolving solutions to the problems of industry was reached in 1931, during the Depression, when he proposed the "Swope Plan" for stabilization of industry. For this and other social services, he was awarded the gold medal of the National Academy of Social Sciences in 1932.

On November 17, 1939, the team of Young and Swope, in a manner reminiscent of many of their previous actions, jointly announced, "We took up these offices together, and we wish to lay them down together." — January 1, 1940.

They were succeeded by Philip D. Reed and Charles E. Wilson, chairman and president, respectively. In 1942 the needs of the War effort caused Reed and Wilson to resign their posts and to enter government service. Reed left for London to become deputy to W. Averell Harriman who headed the Lend Lease Mission to England; and Wilson assumed the post of vice chairman of the War Production Board.

Young and Swope took up the General Electric reins again. "I like this resurrection so well that I'm less apprehensive about the next one," Young smilingly told a reporter.

He and Swope stepped aside once more, late in 1944, to make way for the return to the Company of Reed and Wilson.

Thus ended more than twenty years of their leadership which had produced one of the greatest periods of expansion in the history of the Company, sustained it through one of the country's greatest economic declines and mobilized it to supply the resources that helped America and its allies to be victorious in World War II.

Owen D. Young (l.) and Gerard Swope after presentation of gold medal
award of National Academy of Social Sciences to Swope.

NOBEL PRIZE FOR CHEMISTRY IS AWARDED TO IRVING LANGMUIR

December, 1932

A THRILL of pride ran through all the General Electric organization when the news dispatcher announced that Dr. Irving Langmuir, associate director of the Research Laboratory at Schenectady, had been accorded the highest honor that any scientist can receive — a Nobel Award. It was given to Dr. Langmuir for outstanding research work in chemistry.

In the 31 years during which the awards, created by provisions of the will of the late Alfred B. Nobel, Swedish scientist, and administered by the Swedish Academy of Science, have been given, only one other American chemist has received this award — Dr. T.W. Richards, in 1914.

Other Americans who have attained to the distinction of a Nobel Award include: Physics, A.A. Michelson, R.A. Millikan, and Arthur Compton (divided with C.T.R. Wilson, of England); medicine, Dr. A. Carrel and Dr. Karl Landsteiner; literature, Sinclair Lewis; the promotion of international peace, Theodore Roosevelt, Elihu Root, Woodrow Wilson, Charles G. Dawes, and F.B. Kellogg.

Honors given in recognition of his scientific work are by no means new to Dr. Langmuir. Among the awards he has received are:

The Nichols Medal, awarded to him on two different occasions by the New York Section of the American Chemical Society, once in 1915 for his work on chemical reaction at low pressure, and in 1920 for his work on atomic structure; the Hughes Medal from the Royal Society of London for his researches in molecular physics; the Rumford Medal, awarded by the American Academy of Arts and Sciences for his thermionic researches and his work on the gas-filled incandescent lamp; the Cannizaro Prize, awarded him by the Royal Academy of Lincei, Rome; the Perkins Medal; and the Chandler Medal; and this year *Popular Science Monthly* awarded him its annual medal and honorarium of $10,000 as an American who has done outstanding scientific work.

His outstanding achievements from a practical viewpoint are the development of the high-intensity incandescent lamp, an improvement which, it is estimated, saves the American public a million dollars a night; his work on vacuum tubes, with all the effect it has had on radio broadcasting, on electrical control operations, and in other fields; his work on electric welding by the atomic hydrogen method. In addition to this, scientists attach a very high value to his many published papers.

With a simple film balance and trough, Langmuir explored complex phenomena at liquid surfaces. He explained such varied occurrences as the formation of oil films on water and the diffusion of material through the walls of living cells in terms of a novel conception of short-range forces acting on surface molecules. The originality and fundamental importance of the work led to the Nobel Award.

King Gustavus V of Sweden presents Nobel medal to Irving Langmuir on December 10, 1932.

1932

World's largest lamp, 50,000 watts, and smallest, "grain of wheat" lamp used in surgical instruments.

Cutaway view of typical GE gear-motor.

LIGHTING

The mogul "bi-post base " lamp is devised by Daniel K. Wright of the Lamp Development Lab. By using two heavy metal prongs as the lamp's base and as its electrical connections, stronger units can be constructed for high power lighting applications in the 10,000, 20,000 and 30,000-watt range.

Photoflood lamps are developed by Gwilym Prideaux and others at Nela Park. The low-cost bulbs produce high light intensities for 3-10 hours and are designed for photography and other short duration uses.

INDUSTRIAL EQUIPMENT

Gear motors for slow-speed drives from 600 to 13 rpm are introduced in 3/4 hp to 75 hp sizes to provide industry with compact, easily installed drives.

APPLIANCES

The GE oil burning furnace is placed in production. Burner units are manufactured in Schenectady, boilers in Pittsfield, and the complete heating package is assembled in the customer's home.

The Air Conditioning Department is established to handle electric devices for home heating, humidifying and temperature control.

New year-round room air conditioner.   GE oil-burning furnace.

The first GE dishwashers are marketed. Consumer financing by the General Electric Contracts Corporation is made available to meet the widespread demand for the great variety of new electric appliances.

T. S. Fuller, Roy Moore and Louis Navias of the Research Laboratory develop a motor-driven razor sharpener.

MATERIALS

The Pittsfield Works announces the use of "Pyranol," a family of organic liquids having superior dielectric insulating properties, which make them particularly suitable for capacitors of large size. Frank M. Clark of the Works laboratory was principally responsible for their development.

TRANSPORTATION

The French superliner "Normandie" is launched, propelled by four of the most powerful motors ever built — 40,000 hp each, manufactured by GE Associate, Als-Thom, in France. This 1029-foot ship is the largest commercial vessel in the world and is destined to usher in a new era of superliners.

ORGANIZATION

Willis R. Whitney retires from his position as Director of the Research Laboratory and is replaced by William D. Coolidge.

The liner "Normandie" — propelled by four of the most powerful electric motors ever built.

Dr. Whitney Retires? Pooh!

Under the above heading, the *New York Sun* of November 1, 1932 said, editorially:

"The General Electric Company announces that Dr. Willis R. Whitney has 'retired.' It means that he has been relieved of the obligations that devolve on the head of its research laboratory. In one of his numerous enlightening asides Dr. Whitney, speaking for humanity at large, has said that 'we are lamentably bound by words.' The corporation bulletin illustrates the truth of his incidental declaration.

"Dr. Whitney in seclusion, Dr. Whitney in retreat, Dr. Whitney withdrawn from circulation — these are unthinkable. The Whitney intellect has served knowledge too long to be suspended in its operations by a mere rearrangement of opportunities. The Whitney curiosity has so persistently projected into the abyss of man's ignorance that no shifting of titles can restrain it from future excursions into that fascinating, unplumbed gulf. The Whitney utilitarianism is too robust to be manacled by assignment to non-routine duties. The Whitney spirituality is too pervading to be definitely engrossed on a scroll and filed away in a cabinet, no matter how artistically the engrossing be done or how elegantly the cabinet be fashioned.

"And, ultimately, Dr. Whitney possesses a sense of humor and a quality of wit which veto the notion that a useful man should or can retire."

THE GENERAL ELECTRIC SALES FORCE...HELPING TO BEAT THE DEPRESSION...

OUR JOB

E.O. Shreve, Chairman —
General Sales Committee

THE SPIRIT with which these difficult times have been met is wonderful, and I can say to each man in the field that his cooperation, loyalty, and continued evidence of determination to get all the business possible are recognized and very deeply appreciated by the officials of our Company.

I believe brighter times are not far away. We must recognize, however, that our business lags behind general business and, therefore, we still have some serious problems to solve.

While a good job has been done, I am satisfied that we *can* and *must* do even better. If each one could walk down the streets of our factories, he would picture more vividly the tremendous responsibility the Commercial Department has in providing work, and with that vision would grow a greater determination to get more of the business being offered and to do more *creative* selling. Think it over and realize that not only the Company and our own economic lives, but the economic lives of many other workers depend upon *our* success.

Call on more customers (always with an optimistic message), study our lines, analyze successful methods of sales technique, seek ideas from others on important transactions, and, above all, build a determination to get more business by real, *creative* selling. We at the General Office will back you on any reasonable sales proposition.

We are proud of you all! These trying years have been, above all else, a test of men. We know *our* sales organization has stood the test, and we have confidence that that kind of men will go on to greater sales results through thoughtful planning and a determination which *must* bring success. With such a spirit, I am sure you will have the satisfaction of seeing a large number of men back at work this year because of a larger volume of sales than that obtained in 1932.

E.O. SHREVE
ASSISTANT VICE-PRESIDENT

. . . and Creative selling they did!

SOME NEW PRODUCTS FOR THE HOME

Portable electric sewing machine.

Lowboy radio, Model H-31.

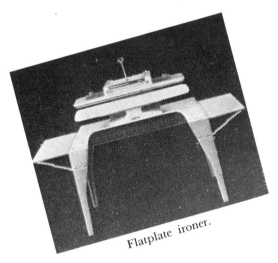

Flatplate ironer.

Clothes washer with spin basket.

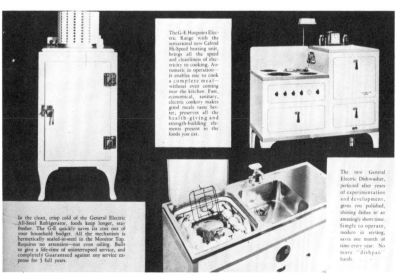

The G-E Hotpoint Electric Range with the sensational new Calrod Hi-Speed heating unit, brings all the speed and cleanliness of electricity to cooking. Automatic in operation—it enables one to cook a complete meal—without even coming near the kitchen. Fast, economical, sanitary, electric cookery makes good meals taste better, preserves all the health-giving and strength-building elements present in the foods you eat.

In the clean, crisp cold of the General Electric All-Steel Refrigerator, foods keep longer, stay fresher. The G-E quickly saves its cost out of your household budget. All the mechanism is hermetically sealed-in-steel in the Monitor Top. Requires no attention—not even oiling. Built to give a life-time of uninterrupted service, and completely Guaranteed against any service expense for 3 full years.

The new General Electric Dishwasher, perfected after years of experimentation and development, gives you polished, shining dishes in an amazingly short time. Simple to operate, modern in styling, saves one month of time every year. No more "dishpan" hands.

1933

570 Lexington Avenue
New GE Headquarters

POWER GENERATION

Two waterwheel generators are under construction at GE — Schenectady for Boulder Dam. Each unit is greater in electrical capacity (82,500 kva) and physical dimensions than any previously constructed. With a height of 32 feet above floor level, each unit will weigh more than 2 million pounds.

TRANSPORTATION

E.F.W. Alexanderson demonstrates caboose-to-engine radio communication in Schenectady. Inductor coils are suspended from the train to transmit and pick up signals to and from the rails and direct them to transmitting and receiving equipment. This communication system contributes immeasurably to fast, safe railway service.

LIGHTING

The three-way lamp is developed for multi-level illumination. Each of its two filaments can be turned on independently with a multiple switch or used together to increase the lighting level.

The Lamp Department introduces the high efficiency sodium-vapor lamp for street and open area lighting. Although such lamps had been in existence for some years, their lifetimes were limited by deterioration of the glass. Louis Navias and others at the Research Laboratory and at Nela Park produced glass coatings that resist the damaging effects of the sodium vapor.

A 400-watt, mercury-vapor lamp is also introduced for "whiteway" street lighting and floodlighting.

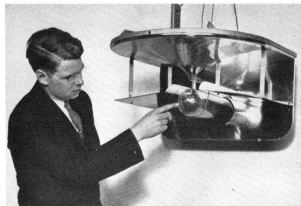

Sodium-vapor lamp for highway illumination.

Lighting pioneer C.A.B. Halvorson examining new mercury-vapor lighting unit.

INDUSTRIAL EQUIPMENT

A variable speed AC motor using thyratron tube control is developed. Rated at 400 hp, 4500 volts, 3-phase, zero to 925 rpm, this motor offers industry continuously variable speed with a control system having essentially no moving parts.

A specially designed motor, rated 200 hp, 3600 rpm, is built for testing airplane propellers at Langley Field.

The world's largest supersynchronous motor, rated at 800 hp, is applied to flour mill drive. This motor, with a stator that revolves at start, is able to accelerate heavy equipment to synchronous speed.

"Zeppelin"-shaped induction motor for Langley Field propeller testing.

Operating molding presses for plastics.

GE plastics exhibit for 1933 "Century of Progress" world's fair.

1934

George Inman (l.) and Richard Thayer (r.) examining fluorescent lamp.

The final link in the home laundry arrives — the GE cabinet dryer.

LIGHTING

The lumiline tubular incandescent lamp, with contacts at both ends, is placed on the market for decorative and specialized lighting applications.

A fluorescent lamp 10-in. long and 3/4-in. diameter is constructed by a group from Nela Park, including Richard Thayer, Eugene Lemmers, Willard A. Roberts and George E. Inman.

Miniature lamps with built-in lenses are introduced for "fountain pen" flashlight and other small lighting devices.

APPLIANCES

General Electric announces a line of domestic gas-burning furnaces. A new household electric clothes dryer is introduced. It will handle as many as eight sheets or the contents of an 8-pound washer at one time.

COMMUNICATIONS AND ELECTRONICS

Mobile two-way radio is developed and installed in various police agencies throughout the country. The system also permits mobile radio tie with telephone lines for long distance or local phone calls.

Police radio test car.

Communicating with police automobiles by radio from police headquarters.

INDUSTRIAL EQUIPMENT

GE engineers design a new line of explosion proof, fractional horsepower motors especially designed for gasoline vending pumps.

POWER GENERATION AND DISTRIBUTION

In building apparatus for installation at Boulder Dam, GE continues to set new records: 287,600-volt water-cooled transformers, and high voltage impulse oil circuit breakers operate at the highest commercial voltage ever.

TRANSPORTATION

The "Zephyr," the first streamlined diesel-electric train, equipped by GE, makes a "dawn to dusk" run from Denver to Chicago, 1017 miles, on the Chicago, Burlington, and Quincy Railroad. Speeds up to 112-1/2 mph and an average of 77-1/2 mph are achieved.

A trolley bus uses trolley lines to climb a 6% half-mile grade in Weehawken, N.J., to the top of the Palisades, and then disengages from the lines to run on gas. This flexibility is made possible by a dual controller and GE motors designed for operation in series with trolley power, and in parallel with bus generator power.

287,000-volt transformer for Boulder Dam.

Record-size oil circuit breaker for Boulder Dam.

Pullman trolley coach equipped with GE two-motor drive.

1935

Night baseball at Crosley Field, illuminated by GE Novalux lamps.

The new "Disposall" garbage disposer.

LIGHTING

A two-foot-long fluorescent lamp is displayed at the annual convention of the Illuminating Engineering Society. A display card reads, "The fluorescent lumiline lamp — a laboratory development of great promise." The new lamps provide more light per watt of energy consumed than filament lamps and throw off less radiant heat.

The first major league night baseball game is played at Crosley Field, Cincinnati, Ohio under GE Novalux lamps. The Cincinnati Reds defeat the Philadelphia Phillies by a score of 2-1.

APPLIANCES

The first household electric food waste disposer, the "Disposall", is introduced by General Electric. In recognition of its inventor, the new product is designated, within the Company, as "Bill Merrill's electric pig."

TRANSPORTATION

The most powerful single cab locomotive, the streamlined GG-l, is built by the Erie Works for the Pennsylvania Railroad's extensive electrification program. This 460,000-lb, 79-ft unit has an all-welded cab and is capable of safe running speeds up to 90 mph.

MATERIALS

The Research Laboratory improves upon the properties of Alnico, making it the most powerful magnetic material available, and capable of supporting more than 60 times its own weight.

POWER GENERATION AND DISTRIBUTION

GE demonstrates a new method of high voltage DC transmission over the Mechanicville to Schenectady lines of the New York Power and Light Corporation using thyratron and phanatron tubes to convert alternating current to direct current and back again.

Research by C.G. Suits on high pressure arcs results in greatly improved high current switchgear. His work also produces basic knowledge of the behavior of arcs in gases under various pressure and temperature conditions.

COMMUNICATIONS AND ELECTRONICS

Metal-enclosed vacuum tubes — better shielded, smaller and more rugged than their glass counterparts — are developed by W.C. White and others at the Research Laboratory. The metal construction is made possible by new alloys and improved lead-in seals.

Alnico magnet (nine ounces) lifting Underwood typewriter.

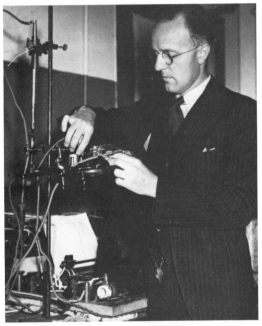

C. Guy Suits.

Rear Admiral Richard E. Byrd with his all-wave radio in the cabin of the "Jacob Ruppert" in which he set sail for the Antarctic.

PIONEERING IN MOTOR TECHNOLOGY
Howard Maxwell
1879-1967

Howard Maxwell

Engineer, innovator and business leader with courage and understanding of men, these are the qualities that gave Howard Maxwell his place in the archives of motor achievements. As Managing Engineer and then Manager of General Electric's Schenectady Induction Motor Department, he earned the love and respect of all who were engaged in the manufacture of these new workhorses of industry.

A 1900 graduate from the University of Kansas, Howard Maxwell joined the General Electric test program and became an engineer in motor design at Schenectady. Among his early successes with induction motors were the first large steel mill motors. These giant machines, installed in 1909, drove the main rolls of a new Gary Steel Mill plant. They were assembled at the site without previous test, a courageous undertaking for all concerned, and their success was a major achievement. Some years later, Maxwell designed the motors for the aircraft carriers "Lexington" and "Saratoga". This time, following his motto "try it first," he built and tested a 500-horsepower model. Even so, the extrapolation to 35,000 horsepower to drive these huge ships required courage and determination.

As induction motors began to take their place in industry, they soon began to be needed in great numbers, but design and manufacture of suitable rotors were beset with many problems. Following earlier attempts with cast aluminum windings, Maxwell invented and developed centrifugally cast aluminum windings. This method of manufacture produced motors with such successful performance that the entire motor industry soon adopted this construction.

When the motor business grew to large proportions, the Induction Motor Department was formed with Maxwell head of both engineering and manufacturing. He had a most friendly and altogether charming manner and took a great interest in all who worked for him, always keeping in mind their ambitions and abilities and, together with his associates, arranging their education, transfer or promotion in a farseeing way. During the great depression of the 1930's, with his characteristic courage, in the face of orders to reduce his staff, he kept his organization intact with greatly reduced time but nevertheless with everyone on the payroll.

In the late 1930s, Maxwell became convinced that American manufacturers were getting far less output from a frame size than was possible by more effective design. He backed this with test data and provided leadership and drive to convince the National Electrical Manufacturers Association, responsible for the standards, that American motor companies should redesign their motors to reduce costs without decreasing quality.

Maxwell had long planned to retire in 1941, but after Pearl Harbor, he felt that motors would have to be produced in large quantities and that he could do more as manager of the Motor Department than anywhere else. He stayed on until after the war was over and conditions had returned to near normal. During his time and mostly under his direction, he had seen the output of a fixed-size motor frame go from 7-1/2 horsepower to 40 horsepower. His Department had designed and manufactured the standard and special lines of motors needed by its sales and application engineers to make GE the outstanding leader in the induction motor field. While doing all of this, Howard Maxwell earned for himself the highest regard of his employees and his associates, world-wide.

H.G. Reist

C.J. Koch

M.H. Wells

Philip L. Alger

The philosophy, "Rules are made to be broken — in a nice way," characterizes the man whose courage, foresight, and engineering ability brought many important innovations to electric power during the first half of this century. In 1894, the year this man was born, Steinmetz, Pupin and others engaged in extensive discussions of the merits of the induction motor that Tesla had given to the world a few years previously. It became the role of Philip Alger, engineer and mathematician, to further unravel its mysteries and to make the many technical contributions which would earn for him the name, "Mr. Induction Motor."

Philip L. Alger

Alger's General Electric career began in 1919 after he had served as a lieutenant in the Ordnance Department, U.S. Army. His early work on motor reactance produced first induction motors, and then synchronous motors capable of direct, across-the-line starting, greatly simplifying motor controls. His 1928 AIEE paper, "The Calculation of Armature Reactance of Synchronous Machines," remains a classic in the annals of rotating electric machinery.

In 1929 Alger was appointed to the staff of the vice president of engineering to sponsor and coordinate developments in electric apparatus throughout the General Electric Company. He became a leader in professional engineering societies, in industry-wide standardization in education, and in local government, as well as in technology. He was impressed by the observation that men are creatures of habit, and he realized that one must first have the wisdom to recognize what is sound and then have the courage to propose it, even when this means breaking with tradition.

Alger saw clearly that for the greater expansion of electrification in industry, motors must be made smaller and lighter in weight for the same output. This task required the critical examination of many traditions in design engineering and among motor users. His many published papers give only a glimpse of the extent of his contributions as a worker and leader of the committee and working groups of AIEE and ASA which led ultimately to the adoption of a succession of new NEMA standards for motors in the 1940s. Motors built to those standards weighed less than a third as much as their predecessors of the late 1920s. They were quieter and did their jobs as well or better.

Alger also was a leader in bringing about acceptance standards for new synthetic insulations introduced in the 1950s, resulting in further reductions in motor size and improved insulation performance.

Following his retirement from General Electric in 1959, he continued his interest in motors as Adjunct Professor of Electrical Engineering at Rensselaer Polytechnic Institute. His knowledge and enthusiasm — together with his published books and numerous technical papers — continued to bring a following of many students to the power field.

Throughout his career, Philip Alger has paralleled his technical work with equally vigorous pursuits in other areas. He says with pride that he has tried never to refuse an invitation, an advice of Benjamin Franklin. This has brought him to the fields of professional and ethical standards for engineers, engineering education and recruiting practices, and local government, all of which have enriched the lives of others as well as his own. His career truly epitomizes the complete professional engineer.

K.A. Pauly

P.O. Noble

L.E. Hildebrand

1936

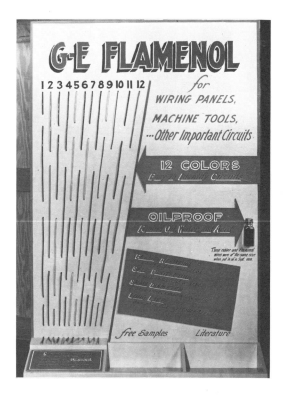

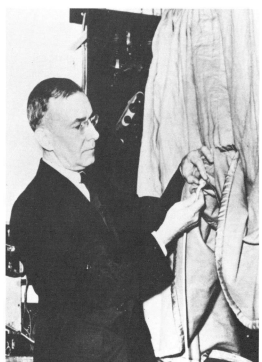

W.K. Kearsley and electric blanket.

LIGHTING

The coiled-coil filament lamp is introduced in standard lamps. First patented in 1917 by B.L. Benbow, the double coiling of the tungsten filament increases the efficiency of a 60-watt lamp by more than ten percent.

The San Francisco-Oakland Bay Bridge is opened in California, lighted by more than 1000 GE sodium luminaires.

MATERIALS

Flamenol®, a non-combustible, oil- and moisture-resistant insulation is developed for copper conductors used in home and industrial wiring. The new polymer, made by plasticizing polyvinyl chloride, was perfected by J.G.E. Wright, Moyer M. Safford and others under the direction of A. Lincoln Marshall, head of the Chemistry Section at the Research Laboratory.

Molding of wiring devices is begun at its Providence, R.I., plant by GE affiliate Monowatt Electric Co. The corporation was formed primarily to meet the rapidly growing chain store market for consumer wiring materials.

John H. Payne invents the "silent" mercury switch for home use. The mercury makes contact between metal caps through an opening in a ceramic barrier invented by Louis Navias.

APPLIANCES

W.K. Kearsley of the Research Laboratory invents the electric blanket. The first model consists of two sheets sewed together with flexible insulated copper wire between them. Kearsley had also invented a vascular exercise machine designed to help improve blood circulation in the legs of arteriosclerosis patients.

TRANSPORTATION

The Erie Works is building another "world's first" for the Union Pacific Railroad. It is a locomotive with a closed high pressure steam boiler-condenser-steam turbine system, whose steam is condensed to water for recirculation, eliminating the need to stop en route to replenish water.

COMMUNICATIONS AND ELECTRONICS

The General Engineering Laboratory announces the commercial availability of a recording spectrophotometer. This instrument, invented by Professor A.C. Hardy of MIT, measures the spectral reflectance or transmittance of materials and will be used to match colors accurately.

Sealed-ignitron tubes are used commercially for the first time for power control and conversion purposes.

ORGANIZATION

President Swope announces an income adjustment plan for the stabilization of earnings in accordance with the Department of Labor cost-of-living figures.

Walt Disney with GE recording spectrophotometer.

Juice-o-Mat (r.); Hotpoint automatic roaster (top center); Toaster, "A-la-carte" table cooker and Dorchester coffee maker (bottom center); Portable mixer (l.).

New Small Appliances for the Kitchen

1937

POWER GENERATION AND DISTRIBUTION

The first hydrogen-cooled turbogenerator built for commercial service is constructed for the Dayton Power and Light Company. This 3600-rpm generator is rated at 31,250 kva.

New "Spirakore" distribution transformers are designed with machine-wound steel ribbon replacing hand assembled laminations.

"Spirakore" distribution transformer, internal structure.

APPLIANCES

A new assembly line for the large scale production of electric washing machines is placed in operation at Bridgeport, Connecticut.

A high-sensitivity photo exposure meter is marketed by GE. Combined with photoflash bulbs introduced a few years earlier, it makes possible significant improvements in home and professional photography.

TRANSPORTATION

Over a mile of continuous rail track is formed by flash welding the ends of rails. This joint development of the Delaware and Hudson Railway, Sperry Products, Inc. and GE portends smoother, safer riding and fewer maintenance problems.

Howard Hughes sets a transcontinental air record of 7 hours, 28 minutes, 25 seconds. The GE supercharger helps make this historic flight possible.

ELECTRONICS

The first AC network analyzer is built to simulate electric utility power systems and will provide a speedy measurement method of power flow analysis in place of the old longhand calculations.

The GG-I for the record-breaking Pennsylvania Railroad electrification.

MATERIALS

A.W. Hull and others at the Research Laboratory develop Fernichrome and Fernico alloys for glass to metal seals used in vacuum tube constructions. Because the coefficients of expansions of the alloys are close to those of the glasses used, strains at the points of sealing are eliminated, and the dangers of seal failure are greatly reduced.

INDUSTRIAL EQUIPMENT

A GE-powered "lift and turnover" car dumper placed in service on Lake Superior can pick up a 95-ton car and empty its contents into the hold of an ore carrier in a minute.

95-ton electric car dumper on the Great Lakes.

Chicago, Burlington and Quincy "Zephyr" diesel-electric locomotive.

The Union Pacific "City of Los Angeles" diesel-electric locomotive.

THE STREAMLINERS ARE HERE!

1938

TRANSPORTATION

A record 20,000 feet is reached by a U.S. Army Air Corps stratosphere plane which has the first supercharged cabin in the United States. GE superchargers make it possible to maintain cabin pressure and temperature at high altitudes. New controls for fully feathering plane propellers in seconds are introduced by GE.

POWER GENERATION AND DISTRIBUTION

The Pittsfield High Voltage Laboratory produces record 10,000,000 volt artificial lighting at the New York World's Fair.

LIGHTING

General Electric announces the commercial availability of fluorescent lamps. The production lines for the 15-watt, 20-watt and 30-watt units were developed by a group led by P.J. Pritchard. New phosphors for brightness and daylight color are developed by Willard Roberts of Nela Park and by Gorton Fonda and others at the Research Laboratory.

Hot-cathode mercury-vapor germicidal lamps are marketed by the Lamp Department. Because of their ability to produce ultraviolet radiation effective in destroying air-borne bacteria, the lamps are used in hospitals, nurseries and other public areas.

Ten-million-volt man-made lightning at the New York World's Fair.

Fluorescent lighting on display at the New York World's Fair.

INDUSTRIAL EQUIPMENT

The Company's 19,000,000th meter is completed at the West Lynn Works as the 85th birthday of the late Elihu Thomson was being observed.

COMMUNICATIONS

WGY moves into a new home that contains the latest in studio and control-room equipment. The new building boasts five studios, including one two stories in height and equipped with a balcony for spectators.

A new television studio is opened in Building 36, Schenectady, to house GE experimental TV Station W2XB, (later to become WRGB).

MATERIALS

Formex wire enamel developed by Winton I. Patnode, A.L. Marshall and others in the Chemistry Section of the Research Laboratory is introduced for use in electric motors. The ability of the enamel to form an exceptionally tough and adherent wire coating with superior electrical properties and resistance to solvents and high temperatures makes possible significant reductions in motor size and further improvements in motor performance.

New GE television studio in Schenectady.

Formex wire enameling equipment at GE's Lynn River Works.

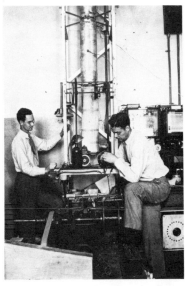

Winton I. Patnode of the Research Laboratory and Edward J. Flynn of the General Engineering Laboratory working with an experimental tower used in Formex wire enamel studies.

1939

Charles E. Wilson

LIGHTING

The all-glass, sealed-beam headlight is developed for the automotive industry. Each hermetically sealed lamp is a complete headlight unit with lens and aluminized reflector.

ORGANIZATION

Board Chairman Owen D. Young and President Gerard Swope asked for retirement; Philip D. Reed and Charles E. Wilson are elected to succeed them, respectively, as of January 1, 1940.

The GE Vapor Lamp Company merges with the Incandescent Lamp Department to form the Lamp Deprtment of the General Electric Company.

Philip D. Reed

COMMUNICATIONS AND ELECTRONICS

General Electric broadcasts television programs from the New York World's Fair. The Radio and Television Department is formed; and the first lines of TV and FM receivers are announced.

New GE console television receiver, HM-225.   New AM-FM radio.

Katharine B. Blodgett in her laboratory in 1929.

MATERIALS

Katharine B. Blodgett of the Research Laboratory develops "glareless glass" using a process of depositing single layers of molecules on the surface of the glass, rendering it non-reflective.

TRANSPORTATION

A GE turbo-charged P-38 makes an unofficial cross country record of 7 hours, 20 minutes. Over Pittsburgh, the pilot radios his 22,000 ft. altitude and 420 mph speed.

The highest cog railway in the world, up Pike's peak and its partial 25 degree grade, switches from steam to diesel-electric. GE builds its first rack-rail diesel-electric locomotive which pushes, rather than hauls, a 50-passenger sight-seeing car 14,109 feet to the peak.

Katharine B. Blodgett

Known widely as a woman who invented "invisible glass," Katharine Burr Blodgett was the first woman scientist to join the General Electric Research Laboratory. This she did in 1918 after receiving a B.A. degree in physics from Bryn Mawr and an M.S. from the University of Chicago.

Assigned to Irving Langmuir's staff, she assisted him in his experimental research and collaborated with him in writing technical papers reviewing their work. Early in his long, productive association with her, Langmuir observed, "Katharine is a gifted mathematician, who has that rare combination of theoretical knowledge and practical ability."

In 1924 she took a leave of absence to become one of the few women students at the Cavendish Laboratory of Cambridge University in England. Two years later, she received the first Ph.D. degree in physics ever awarded to a woman by the university. Her worktable in Langmuir's laboratory was waiting for her when she returned, and she became the first woman Ph.D. on the staff.

In 1938 her invention of nonreflecting, "invisible" glass received widespread public recognition, and it became the prototype of coatings used today on virtually all camera lenses and optical devices. However, this was only a by-product of her long-time research in surface phenomena and her development of methods of depositing films of minuscule and precisely controlled thickness.

During World War II the efficiency of submarine periscopes and aerial cameras was increased immeasurably by the use of coatings that she developed. She also tackled the problem of ridding airplane wings of ice and helped devise a faster, denser smoke screen than that provided by the simple smudge pots in use at the time.

Katharine Blodgett's attitude toward her career was best described in her own words during an interview over GE radio station WGY. She declared, "Each year I learn some new ways to make life in the laboratory more fun, and wonder why I never learned them before. They consist mostly in tackling the problems to which I used to say, 'I can't,' and I usually find that they are not so difficult as I thought they would be."

PIONEERING IN ELECTRONICS

Albert Wallace Hull
1880-1966

Albert W. Hull

A genuine Connecticut Yankee, Albert Wallace Hull was born in Southington, Conn., on April 19, 1880. He was the second oldest of eight boys. Science seems to have held an appeal for the family, for five chose technical careers: physics, bacteriology, metallurgy, forestry and engineering. All five went to Yale.

He chose physics for a profession and never regretted it. Perhaps this experience accounts for the advice which he invariably gave young men, that it is more important to find the right job than to get a high salary. Receiving a Ph.D. from Yale in 1909, he taught at Worcester Polytechnic Institute before Langmuir and Coolidge discovered him and invited him to the General Electric Research Laboratory for the summer of 1913. This taste of industrial research proved infectious; after finishing out the year of teaching, he returned to Schenectady, never to leave. In 1928, he became assistant director of the Research Laboratory.

Alert, scholarly, incisive, Hull was the creator of a greater number of new types of electron tubes than any other man, and an important contributor to the fundamentals of physical science as well.

His first work at the laboratory was on electron tubes, X-ray crystallography and piezoelectricity. After World War I, he published a classic paper on the effect of uniform magnetic fields on the motion of electrons between coaxial cylinders. During the 1920s, he studied noise in diodes and triodes, which led to the development of the tetrode, or screen grid tube, thus eliminating the ion bombardment of the cathodes. During this same period, he invented the thyratron, a gas-filled electron tube that found application in the control of medium powered devices and led the way to a new branch of technology, industrial electronics.

During the 1930s, he directed his research to metallurgy and glass science, which led to the development of new alloys such as Fernico.

Albert Hull's industrial scientific work with General Electric has had tremendous scientific and practical consequences. Together with Coolidge's work on tungsten and Langmuir's work on high vacuum electronic phenomena, he was one of the pioneers who provided the foundation for the electronics businesses of General Electric.

He retired from GE in 1950 but remained professionally active for many years after. His last publication, in 1966, came fifty-seven years after his first.

Many honors came to Hull: the Howard N. Potts Medal of the Franklin Institute, given in 1923 for work on X-ray crystal analysis; the Morris Liebmann prize of the Institute of Radio Engineers in 1930 for his work on vacuum tubes; membership in the National Academy of Sciences; and presidency of the American Physical Society.

It is difficult to summarize a great career like Albert Hull's, but of all his many accomplishments, two outstanding characteristics seem to have provided the essence of his success. First and foremost was his great courage and optimism, which opened doors that were closed to many people. The second characteristic was his willingness to enter a brand new field. He was constantly challenged by new problems, and he had the courage to become a neophyte in a new field where his native abilities soon brought him again to the top as an expert and an authority.

AND COMMUNICATIONS

Walter Ransom Gail Baker
1892-1961

"When the history of the first century of the electronics' age is written, the name of one man will stand preeminent on its pages. That man is Walter R.G. Baker. No other man in the field of electronics today combines so many talents and has applied them with such benefits to the profession and industry." So said Donald G. Fink, President of IRE in presenting the Institute of Radio Engineers Founders' Award to Baker in March, 1958.

W.R.G. Baker

A graduate of Union College, Schenectady, N.Y., from which he received three degrees, Baker joined the GE General Engineering Laboratory in 1917. The following year, his work with new vacuum-tube transmitters and receivers for the Army and Navy included development and testing of radio apparatus for aircraft, submarines, captive balloons, torpedo boats, destroyers, and battleships. As work in this field increased, a separate Radio Department was established, and Baker was made design engineer in charge of transmitters.

In 1924 his responsibility was enlarged to include the design of all radio products, and in 1926 he was given complete charge of development, design and production. On the formation of the RCA-Victor Corporation in 1929, he went to Camden, N.J., to head the radio engineering activities of the new organization. Within the year, he was placed in charge of production and later became general manager of the RCA-Victor plant. In 1935 GE transferred its radio receiver activities to Bridgeport, and there Baker resumed his connections with the Company. He was named managing engineer in 1936 and, in 1938, became manager of the new Radio and Television Department. His work with Major E.H. Armstrong in the further development of frequency-modulation transmission resulted in the widespread use of FM broadcasting and the production of a whole new line of radio receivers providing sound fidelity previously unattainable. In 1941, he was elected vice president by the Board of Directors.

Says Dudley Chambers, one of Baker's close associates, "Doc was an inveterate worker, traveling and working all the time. What's more, he had a knack for getting people together. An example of this was the organization and direction of two national committees which recommended engineering standards to the FCC, thus paving the way for commercial monochrome telecasting in 1941 and color TV in 1953 — a major contribution to the electronics industry."

When Baker retired from GE in 1956 he launched upon a new career. He was appointed vice president of Syracuse University, with responsibilities for the contract research program. Soon afterward, he became president of the Universities Research Corporation, a position he held until his death in 1961.

W.R.G. Baker viewing laboratory-built TV receiver.

1940

COMMUNICATIONS AND ELECTRONICS

The disk-seal tube, later known as the "lighthouse" tube, is announced. The use of plane electrodes permits closer electrode spacing and operation at 200 megacycles. It is expected that future designs will operate at 3000 megacycles.

GE's television station WRGB becomes the first to relay television broadcasts from New York City. This relay marks the formation of the first television network.

APPLIANCES

Window-mounted air conditioners are introduced for home use.

INDUSTRIAL EQUIPMENT

A gas turbine is installed to operate an air compressor at a Union Oil Company refinery at Oleum, California. It is powered by 1000°F gas obtained as one of the refinery's products of combustion. Numerous other industrial compressors are manufactured using the centrifugal flow design originated by Sanford Moss.

A new line of small, integral horsepower polyphase and single phase motors called "Tri-Clad" is introduced. These motors have improved protection and insulation as well as streamlined appearance. Very soon, all induction motors from 1 hp to 1000 hp will have similar construction and appearance.

"Lighthouse" transmitting and receiving tubes.

A pictorial review of progress in motor design over the years.

Eugene George Rochow

It was fortunate for the silicone industry (and GE) that Eugene G. Rochow began the General Electric silicone project in 1938. His personal qualities and his scientific abilities, his career at Cornell, and his early experience in the Company all made it virtually certain that he would do successful applied research on silicones if such success was in the cards.

H.A. Liebhafsky:
SILICONES UNDER THE MONOGRAM

The silicone project was an outstanding success, and what's more, it led to the founding of a major industry.

When Rochow came to the Research Laboratory in 1935, he was well schooled at Cornell University, receiving a B.A. in 1931 and a Ph.D. in 1935. His graduate work involved research in organometallic chemistry, and this was soon to stand him in good stead.

MATERIALS

Kenneth H. Kingdon and Herbert C. Pollock of the Research Laboratory, using a mass spectrometer of their own construction, isolate a very small quantity of the rare form of uranium known as "U-235."

Eugene G. Rochow of the Research Laboratory devises the "direct process" for making chlorosilanes, the compounds from which silicones can be produced. The process eliminates much of the hazardous nature and inefficiencies of alternate methods of preparation.

William F. Gilliam, Winton I. Patnode and others under the direction of A.L. Marshall collaborate with Rochow in other silicone related developments leading to a family of materials that can be produced in many forms for superior flexibility, resistance to oxidation and good dielectric properties.

POWER GENERATION AND DISTRIBUTION

The number of electrified farms in the United States reaches an estimated 2,000,000. There are about two hundred uses of electricity on the average farm.

Pittsfield builds its heaviest transformer to date, a 491,000-lb, 66,667-kva, unit for the Central New York Power Corporation.

His first assignment was with the ceramics group, under the direction of Louis Navias. His task was to improve the electrical properties of fused magnesium oxide used in all Calrod® heating units manufactured at the Pittsfield Plant and at Hotpoint in Chicago. When the program was well on its way to a successful conclusion, A.L. Marshall encouraged him to experiment with organic compounds containing silicon.

At that time, there was need for higher temperature capability resins and several laboratories were working hard to develop them. The only method known then to couple a silicon atom to a carbon atom was by means of a Grignard reagent involving magnesium. So, Rochow first tried to make the Grignard reagent approach simpler, more efficient, and less expensive. Other researchers elsewhere tried it also, with no commercial success.

Rochow's inspirational solution was to use elemental silicon with various organic compounds, and copper as a catalyst, reacting at about 300°C. This process became the forerunner of many desirable new materials. A whole group of chemists, and finally chemical engineers, entered the field. They developed a pilot plant, and then under the direction of Charles E. Reed, a large-scale production facility was put on stream at Waterford, N.Y., in 1947. Among the great variety of products now made there are silicone resins, greases, liquids, and elastomers.

For his pioneering work in this field, he received several prestigious awards and honors, including the Baekeland Medal in 1949, the Matiello Award in 1958, the Perkin Medal in 1962, the Kipping Award in 1965, and the Norris Award in 1974.

In 1948, he became associate professor of chemistry at Harvard University, and full professor from 1952 until retirement in 1970. Until well into 1974, he acted as consultant to GE's Silicone Products Department.

PIONEERING IN MAN-MADE MATERIALS

Abraham Lincoln Marshall
1896-1974

Abraham Lincoln Marshall

During his 35-year GE career, Abe Marshall led pioneering efforts resulting in a variety of man-made materials that became the basis for important new directions of the Company's growth.

Born in Victoria, British Columbia, Marshall completed his undergraduate degree in chemistry at the University of British Columbia in 1918 and received the Ph.D. degree in physical chemistry from the University of London in 1922. While serving as an instructor at Princeton, he spent two summers at the General Electric Research Laboratory, and accepted a full-time position there in 1926.

As a research associate, he continued his earlier work in photochemistry and also performed fundamental investigations that contributed to a better understanding of the "bake-out" step required in the manufacture of vacuum tubes. His brilliance and administrative potential were recognized by William D. Coolidge who, in 1932, succeeded Willis R. Whitney as Director of the Research Laboratory. In 1933, Marshall became head of the Insulation Section, a group that soon incorporated other activities as it evolved first into the Chemical Section, and later, in 1950, into the Chemistry Research Department.

In describing Marshall's contributions, Arthur M. Bueche, now Senior Vice President for Corporate Technology, said,

> "Abe was one of the true giants of chemistry during a period when chemical research revolutionized many industrial processes and made possible new products of broad benefit to mankind."

The superior properties of Formex® and Alkanex® wire enamels and Flamenol®, Irrathene® and Vulkene® cable insulations resulted in improvements in the design and performance of motors, transformers, and a variety of other equipment produced by the electrical industry.

The Laboratory's basic studies of polymers for high temperature applications led to the development of a "direct process" method by which virtually all silicones are produced today. It is the key to commercial production of a host of silicone-based products manufactured by GE's Silicone Products Department.

Lexan® polycarbonate, PPO® polyphenylene oxide and Noryl® thermoplastic resins were representative of new classes of engineering plastics that became major Company businesses.

Scientists and engineers under Marshall's direction announced, in 1955, the invention of the first reproducible process for making diamonds. This process became the basis for GE's Man-Made™ industrial diamond business, which is today one of the world's major sources of industrial diamond abrasives.

Known as the "Dean" of General Electric chemistry, Abe Marshall saw the number of chemists and chemical engineers throughout the Company grow from approximately 400 to 2700 during the years he headed chemistry research at the Research Laboratory. A member of the American Chemical Society since 1918, he was active in that organization as a member or chairman of several executive committees. He also served as a member of the management committee and the advisory board of the Gordon Research Conferences.

The stimulating intellectual environment that he fostered and the sound business judgment he exercised were key sources of support for the many talented people who worked for and were inspired by him.

The silicone research team: from left, William J. Scheiber, Eugene Rochow, Robert O. Sauer, Abe Marshall, W.F. Gilliam, Winton I. Patnode and Murray Sprung.

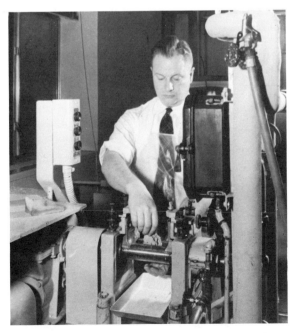

Maynard Agens processing silicone rubber compositions.

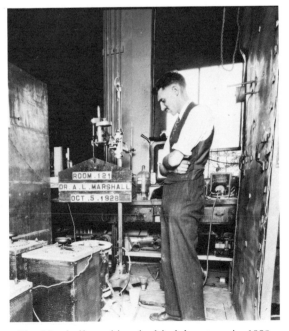

Abe Marshall working in his laboratory in 1928.

1941

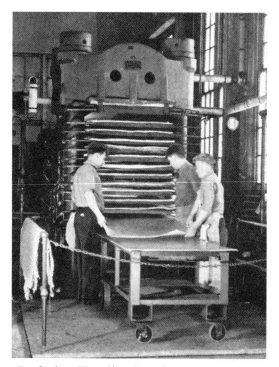

Producing Textolite sheet for a variety of industrial uses.

LIGHTING

"Black light" lamps are placed in production. The ultraviolet radiation produced by these low luminosity lamps can activate fluorescent materials, causing them to glow brightly.

George Inman is granted a U.S. patent for the basic principles of fluorescent lamp design. (see 1936)

MATERIALS

It is announced that General Electric is the largest producer of finished plastics in the United States.

TRANSPORTATION

GE-designed turbosuperchargers for aircraft engines are manufactured at its plants at Ft. Wayne, Indiana, and Everett and Lynn, Massachusetts. From 1925 through this wartime period, GE has been practically the sole supplier of impellers for all of the Wright and Pratt and Whitney engines.

The new battleship "North Carolina," the largest U.S. warship, is launched; equipped with GE propulsion, she is expected to develop 115,000 hp and have a speed of more than 27 knots.

INDUSTRIAL EQUIPMENT

GE installs a 1,400,000-volt industrial inspection X-ray machine for the U.S. Bureau of Standards. By using a gaseous insulating medium in place of oil, a sizable reduction in the physical size and weight of the unit is accomplished. Similar high-voltage X-ray machines are used for treatment of deep-seated cancers.

Mobile X-ray unit for medical use.

Million-volt X-ray unit for inspecting castings.

PIONEERING IN AVIATION

Sanford A. Moss
1872-1946

At the age of 16, while employed as a $4 per week mechanic in a shop that produced compressed air machinery, Sanford Moss had an idea: that if fuel could be burned in compressed air, the energy output would be increased tremendously. This idea, which was to make possible the altitudes, the speed and range of today's aircraft, came years before the Wright Brothers made their historic flight at Kitty Hawk.

Moss took the idea with him to the University of California. By 1900 he had earned his Bachelor's and Master's degrees, and he went on to Cornell where, in 1903, he wrote his Ph.D. thesis on the gas turbine. The thesis attracted the interest of engineers at GE and got him a job at the West Lynn plant. Working with Charles Steinmetz and Elihu Thomson, Moss first concentrated on centrifugal compressors used in blast furnaces and then on steam turbine development. The experience he gained in these fields was rec-

Sanford A. Moss

ognized during the first World War by the National Advisory Committee for Aeronautics, which asked him to find a way to give military planes more power. Moss's solution, worked out with the cooperation of the U.S. Air Corps, was the turbocharger — a unique turbine-type compressor.

On June 19, 1918, Moss and his associates ascended Pikes Peak with a 350-horsepower Liberty engine in tow in order to test his turbosupercharger. The new device attached to the reciprocating engine was designed to boost power by compressing air into the intake, allowing the engine to "breathe" normally even in the thin air at 14,019 feet. His turbosupercharger was a success. In 1921, a new world altitude record of 40,800 feet was established in a biplane equipped with the device.

Interest in it extended even to the automobile racing circuits, where at least one Indianapolis 500 winning car was fitted with a Moss turbosupercharger. During most of the period between World War I and World War II, while at GE's Lynn Works, Moss also developed the geared supercharger using design principles that have since been followed on most radial-type airplane engines.

Although over 65 years of age, he returned voluntarily to GE at the outbreak of World War II and went to work refining the turbosupercharger. When the United States entered the war, he became consultant to the Army Air Forces. Soon, the B-17 Flying Fortresses, the B-24 Liberators, the P-47 Thunderbolts, and, later, the B-29 Superfortresses, all equipped with turbosuperchargers, were flying higher, faster, and farther than planes had ever flown, including those of the enemy.

As for the industrial gas turbine, it waited until after World War II when GE engineers combined metallurgical developments with new jet engine technologies to turn Moss's dream of some 40 years earlier into reality.

Moss's technical contributions were also evident in areas outside of the hardware used in airplanes, automobiles and industrial equipment. He will be remembered for the militant enthusiasm and energy with which he advanced the standardization of symbols and terms used internationally in science and engineering. In this and in other pursuits, it was said of him that he had "a bit of the maddening quality of the devil, blended with the evangelical fanaticism of the crusader." His zeal bore fruit. As a result of his pioneering efforts, Moss received the Collier Aviation Trophy in 1941, the Sylvanus Albert Reed Award of the Institute of the Aeronautical Sciences, the A.S.M.E. Holley Medal and the Howard N. Potts Medal of the Franklin Institute.

1942

MATERIALS

To meet wartime needs, GE plants manufacture 400 different plastic parts for aircraft, demonstrating some of the most important engineering applications of plastics to date.

TRANSPORTATION

The first successful American jet aircraft undergoes its initial flight tests on October 2. The plane is the Bell XP-59 Airacomet, and is powered by two GE I-A turbojets, each rated at 1250-lb thrust. Designed at Lynn, Mass., and using a centrifugal compressor, this model is soon uprated to 1600-lb thrust and designated the I-16, becoming the first production jet engine in the United States.

ELECTRONICS AND COMMUNICATIONS

GE's first electron microscope is designed and constructed at the General Engineering Laboratory. The microscope magnifies ten times better than the best light microscopes.

TV station WRGB at Schenectady becomes the second station in the country to receive an FCC commercial license.

The first GE Ordnance gun directors, manufactured for the U.S. Navy, are shipped from the newly completed facility at Pittsfield, Mass.

ORGANIZATION

Charles E. Wilson resigns to become a member of the War Production Board; Gerard Swope comes out of retirement to serve as President of General Electric.

Philip D. Reed resigns to help administer the Lend-Lease Program and later becomes Chief of the United States Mission for Economic Affairs in London, with the rank of Minister; Owen D. Young returns as Chairman of the Board.

Owen D. Young (l.) with Philip D. Reed, then Chief of United States Mission for Economic Affairs in London

Cooling molten phenolic resin.

From Resin

to Rocket Launcher

Loading projectiles into P-47 rocket launchers, built by GE of paper and plastic composition.

From left to right: S. Ramo, W.C. White and C.H. Bachman and GE Electron Microscope.

THE WAR YEARS
1941-1945

"No single industry has made a quicker response to our appeal for equipment than General Electric."

Frank Knox, Secretary of the Navy

War has always been a grim drama of men and materials. In the early part of World War II, the allies were short of both. But when the productive capacity of American industry was mobilized, that force became irresistible.

Most important was the spirit of the men in the armed forces, but equipment was also essential.

"To the civilian workers, we are forever indebted," said General Eisenhower. "No army or navy was supported so well."

American industry reached a production level three times peacetime capacity. New plants were built and people trained to use new techniques. It was an accomplishment exceeding any similar effort of man.

Every unit of American industry participated. Upon some companies fell an exceptional burden of responsibility.

One such company was General Electric.

Speaking at the Syracuse Plant, Frank Knox said: "What has been done here could not be duplicated anywhere in the world. So lift your heads with pride because, like our fighting men, you are battling for everything for which America stands."

The partial story of how the largest electrical manufacturer mobilized all the skills and resources for America's war effort on land, at sea, and in the air is depicted here.

General Electric's accomplishment represented the work of more than 175,000 people. It is impossible to mention all to whom credit is due.

It is probable that General Electric produced a greater variety of complex war equipment, and solved a greater variety of technical problems, than any other manufacturer. It is a story of hard work, long hours, drama, excitement, and romance, a dynamic pattern woven by human hands and brains, fired by enthusiasm and tempered by organization."

From GE President Charles E. Wilson's foreword in *Men and Volts at War* by John A. Miller

In the Front Office

General Electric's War Projects Committee, which supervised all the company's far-flung war activities, shown here in 1942 reporting to President Charles E. Wilson. Left to right: J.F. Cunningham; Chester H. Lang, chairman; Wilson; J.G. Farrar; and H.A. Winne.

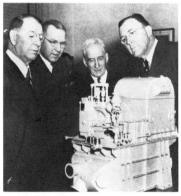

Secretary of the Navy Frank Knox (left) and Charles E. Wilson, Executive Vice Chairman of the U.S. War Production Board, inspecting model of a destroyer escort turbine at Syracuse. In background Gerard Swope, then President of General Electric, and on his right, W.E. Saupe, Superintendent of the Syracuse Plant.

Philip D. Reed (r) with Lt. Gen. Jacob L. Devers (l), Commander of U.S. Forces in Europe at dedication of airfield in England.

And REMEMBER they did . . . the 175,000 GE people who tackled the war production job that couldn't be done and *did it!*

More than 50,000 men and women of General Electric served in the Armed Forces during World War II.

GE at Sea . . .

75% of the Navy's ship propulsion and gears were designed and manufactured by General Electric.

Launching on June 7, 1941, of the GE equipped U.S.S. "South Dakota," which later became widely known as the mysterious "Battleship X."

SS "Mission Purisima" — a fast new tanker built during the war. GE supplied turbine-electric drive for 378 ships of this general type.

The compact but powerful 10,000-horsepower turbine generator set in the engine room of the SS "Mission Purisima," one of 44 high speed tankers that could travel without escort. Turbine-electric propulsion for the tanker program was built in Schenectady, Lynn, Pittsfield, Philadelphia and Erie.

Enormous but precise — gears for ship propulsion as large as 200-inch diameter had to be cut to .003-inch tolerances.

Aloft on the U.S.S. "Juneau" are a variety of types of air and sea search radar antennas and radar jammers. Before the war was over, GE participated in the design and manufacture of 50 different kinds of radar sets for the armed services.

. . . on Land . . .

One of the Army's most useful weapons, the 75-mm pack howitzer. Breech mechanisms being finished at Erie.

Making radio transmitters for U.S. Navy at Schenectady. Every type of Navy transmitter above 24 kilowatts was produced by the Company.

Portable smoke generator of Chemical Warfare Service, principle for which was developed in the GE Research Laboratory.

Checking completed 60-inch antiaircraft searchlights at Erie.

Rotor for one of many big land turbine-generators that GE built in Schenectady to supply power for the war effort.

Diesel-electric power for military railroads — locomotives under construction at the Erie Works.

. . . and in the Air

The Aeronautics Ordnance and Marine Division, the Electronics Division, the Aircraft Jet Engine Division and the Federal Marine Division led the Company effort. Engineers and scientists in the General Engineering Laboratory and the Research Laboratory solved complex system problems.

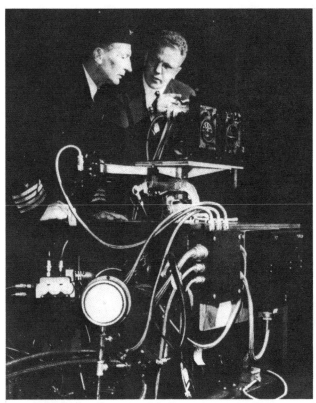

Automatic pilot — a GE first — to keep a plane continuously on predetermined course, being inspected by Capt. J.S. Evans, Inspector of Naval Material, and Charles Young, A&OS engineer.

Two-gun aircraft turret designed for power operation by remote control. The B-29 armament system used an analog-type computer.

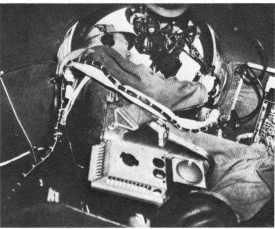

Rear sighting position for remote control of turrets.

Production line at one of GE's turbosupercharger plants.

"The Battle of Kansas"

Early 1943, a call for help from the Air Force and Boeing. "Everybody needed in Kansas to help check out the B-29 fleet leaving for the Far East."

- GE engineers and factory workers with tools and test equipment descended on Wichita, Kansas.

- Red tape is ignored, parts installed, systems checked out.

- As each B-29 soared away, a piece of GE went with it parts and efforts.

- It took months to straighten out the records and accounts, but the B-29s were in the air.

The Supreme Sacrifice

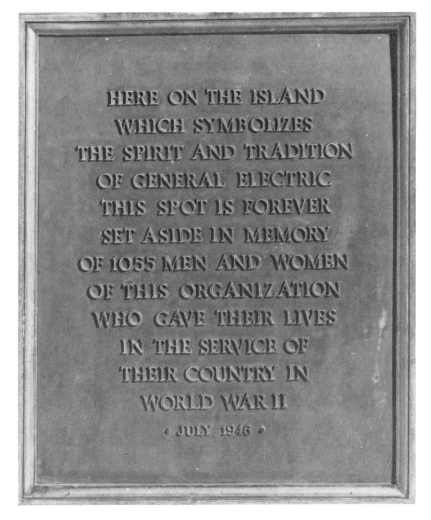

HERE ON THE ISLAND
WHICH SYMBOLIZES
THE SPIRIT AND TRADITION
OF GENERAL ELECTRIC
THIS SPOT IS FOREVER
SET ASIDE IN MEMORY
OF 1055 MEN AND WOMEN
OF THIS ORGANIZATION
WHO GAVE THEIR LIVES
IN THE SERVICE OF
THEIR COUNTRY IN
WORLD WAR II
• JULY 1946 •

50,000 General Electric men and women entered the armed forces during World War II. 1055 gave their lives in the service of their country. This bronze plaque was erected on Association Island in their memory.

1943-1944

MATERIALS

A dense smoke generator for military applications is devised by Langmuir, Vincent Schaefer and Katharine Blodgett.

A new family of varnishes requiring no volatile solvents is developed in the Chemistry section, led by A.L. Marshall.

New high strength alloys for jet propulsion aircraft are developed in the continuing effort to produce faster-flying planes.

New silicone rubber gaskets that maintain their elasticity from -60° to 575° are developed for aircraft and other applications. Maynard Agens, James Marsden and others of the Research Laboratory collaborate with Edward Flynn and Thomas J. Rasmussen of the Schenectady Works Laboratory in the development of these and other silicone-based products, including specialized lubricating and insulating oils and greases, water repellents and resins for binding inorganic insulating materials.

100 million-volt electron accelerator, with E.E. Charlton (l.) and W.F. Westendorp (r.) in foreground.

C. James Marsden with silicone rubber gaskets for operation at extreme temperatures.

INDUSTRIAL EQUIPMENT

The world's most powerful electron accelerator, a 100-million volt unit, is completed as the result of work by E.E. Charlton and W.F. Westendorp. The "betatron" and its smaller predecessors are of great value in exploring the structure of the atom. A few years earlier, the first "betatron" had been devised by Donald W. Kerst while working at GE X-Ray. He went on to build a 2.5 Mev unit at the University of Illinois with the aid of GE scientists.

General Electric announces the first commercial mass spectrometer. The spectrometers are being manufactured by the General Engineering & Consulting Laboratory and marketed through the Special Product Section of the Apparatus Sales Department.

ORGANIZATION

Charles E. Wilson is again elected president of General Electric.

The new GE Credit Corporation is announced, with G.F. Mosher as president.

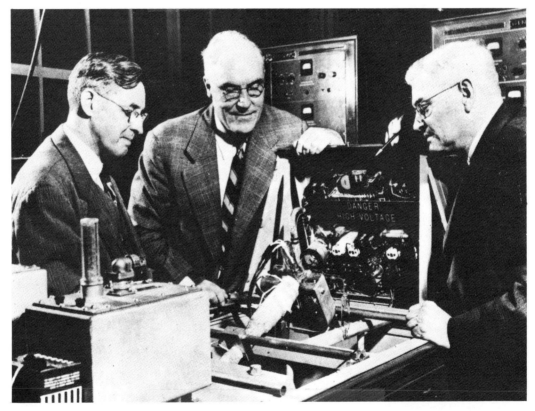

E.S. Lee (l.), D.C. Prince (c.) and C.M. Foust examine mass spectrometer.

1945

Circline fluorescent lamp.

LIGHTING

The circline fluorescent lamp is placed on the market. A 1-in. diameter tube, bent to the form of a circle 12-in. across, draws 32 watts and finds applications in portable lamps and ceiling fixtures.

COMMUNICATIONS

General Electric demonstrates the first commercial use of radar, the electronic navigator with which vessels can detect, through darkness, unseen hazards as far as 20 miles away.

TRANSPORTATION

GE's second production turbojet, the 4200-lb-thrust I-40 (designated J33 by the Air Corps) is developed to power Lockheed's P-80 Shooting Star. The plane establishes a California-to-New York speed record of 4 hrs and 13 minutes. At 584 mph, it is faster than any plane ever flown by either side during World War II.

One of the world's first turboprop engines, the TG-100, is given its initial flight test in a Consolidated Vultee XP-81 plane. Developed at the Large Steam Turbine Department by a team headed by Alan Howard, the engine combines the thrust power obtained from the geared propeller with that of the axial flow gas turbine exhaust.

TG-100 turboprop engine.

MATERIALS

All of General Electric's chemical manufacturing activities are united in the new Chemical Department headquartered at Pittsfield, Massachusetts. Zay Jeffries is its first Vice President and General Manager.

Construction of a Silicone Products plant is started at Waterford, New York. The synthesis of chlorosilanes, the precursors of silicones, was developed to an engineering scale by Charles E. Reed.

Charles E. Reed (r.) directed the operation of the first GE pilot plant for the production of chlorosilanes. He became the first General Manager of the Silicones Products Department and, in 1971, after serving in a number of key management positions, would be appointed Senior Vice President -- Corporate Technology.

ORGANIZATION

Philip D. Reed is again selected Chairman of the Board after resigning his Government position.

C. Guy Suits succeeds W.D. Coolidge as Director of the General Electric Research Laboratory. Ground is broken for a new home for the Laboratory.

The Research Laboratory's first three directors: Willis R. Whitney (l.), W.D. Coolidge, and C. Guy Suits (r.).

THE BEGINNINGS OF THE JET AGE

Bell XP-59, first American turbojet to fly, with two GE 1-A engines.

GE's flying laboratory, a U.S. Army Air Force B-29 Superfortress, with jet engine slung under fuselage for testing.

Dale D. Streid (l.) and G.R. Berg (r.) of Gas Turbine Division with a cutaway of I-40 (J-33) turbojet.

America's first operational jet fighter, the Lockheed P-80 Shooting Star, powered by I-40 (J-33) engine.

Alan Howard (l.) and Chap Walker (r.) inspecting axial flow TG-100 turboprop engine. A Consolidated Vultee XP-81 long range fighter, powered by the TG-100, was the first American plane ever flown with a turboprop engine.

The axial flow, TG-180 (J-35-GE). Its 4000-lb thrust powered a Republic F-84 Thunderjet to a record speed of 619 mph in 1946.

PIONEERING IN MAN-MADE MATERIALS

Zay Jeffries
1888-1965

Highly honored worldwide for his early contributions to the science of metals, Zay Jeffries earned the equal respect of his business associates for his unusual ability to teach, promote and direct the application of scientific principle and advanced materials technology to beneficial use. He played a major role in the establishment of the chemical and metallurgical materials businesses of General Electric.

After graduating from high school in Pierre, South Dakota, Zay entered the South Dakota School of Mines, financing his education by working in the local mines. He was graduated in 1910 with the Degree of Bachelor of Science in Mining Engineering. He later received the Degree of Metallurgical Engineer from the same school (1914) and a Doctorate of Science from Harvard University (1918).

Zay Jeffries

Following a year's employment in the gold mines, Jeffries accepted appointment as an instructor in metallurgy and ore-dressing at the Case School of Applied Science in Cleveland, Ohio. His early work there in the structure and properties of metals attracted the interest of Burnie L. Benbow, Manager of the Cleveland Wire Works who, in 1914, brought him into the General Electric Company as a consultant on problems associated with tungsten lamp filament production.

His important contributions to tungsten production and to the general research program at Nela Park led to his appointment as Chairman of the Technical Committee of the Incandescent Lamp Department in the early 1920s. His shift from active research to technical management was complete by 1928. By 1936, he had become a full-time General Electric employee with the title of Technical Director of the Lamp Department.

In 1926, he was introduced to cemented tungsten-carbide by Samuel L. Hoyt of the Research Laboratory and correctly evaluating its commercial potential, he used his by now considerable influence with Company management to promote the establishment of the Carboloy Company, a GE subsidiary, in 1928. He was a founding Director and successfully steered the fledgling company through the Great Depression, serving as President in the critical years 1932 to 1936 and as Chairman of the Board for several years thereafter.

Jeffries' wartime technical service to the nation began as Chairman of a National Research Council committee on the treatment of metals in World War I. In World War II, he was appointed Vice-Chairman of the Council's giant war metallurgy committee and served on the advisory board to the Manhattan Project. In a letter to Dr. Arthur Compton in 1944, he coined the term "nucleonics" and again demonstrated his great foresight in discussing atomic energy and its postwar applications.

In late 1944, at the request of Charles E. Wilson and Ralph J. Cordiner, Jeffries led a study of the chemical operations of the Company to determine the advisability of establishing a General Electric business based on their products. His positive recommendation was accepted, and he was appointed Vice President and General Manager of the new Chemical Department on January 1, 1945, with headquarters in Pittsfield, Massachusetts.

After electing early retirement in December 1949, he maintained his office at Chemical Department Headquarters in Pittsfield where he continued to be a source of advice and encouragement to his successors and particularly to his many young engineers and scientist friends concerned with materials and processes. Zay Jeffries died in May 1965 as he approached his 77th birthday.

During the latter half of his career, he received many medals and honors, and in his acceptances would always state his indebtedness to his teachers and mentors for their generosity, to his peers for their friendly cooperation and to his proteges for their dedicated labors. Even in his retirement years, he continued to repay this self-assumed debt in kind; and the numerous beneficiaries of this unofficial "Dean of American Metallurgists" testify to its more than full repayment.

THE ADVENT OF NUCLEAR ENERGY

"It seems therefore possible that the uranium nucleus has only small stability of form and may, after neutron capture, divide itself nto two nuclei of roughly equal size. The two nuclei will repel each other and should gain a total kinetic energy of 200 Mev, as calculated from nuclear radius and charge." — L. Meitner and O.R. Frisch, Nature, February 11, 1939.

This was the exciting interpretation of a discovery in Europe by Hahn and Strassman that when uranium is bombarded with slow neutrons, isotopes of barium, lanthanum and cerium are formed. From theoretical considerations, it appeared probable that the uranium isotope of atomic weight 235 would fission more readily than the more abundant U-238 isotope. For this reason GE Nobel laureate Irving Langmuir recommended to William D. Coolidge, Director of the Research Laboratory, "It is very important (now for the first time) to work in nuclear physics and particularly to develop methods of separating isotopes on a large scale" — May 23, 1939. The following day a GE research team was at work on schemes to separate isotopes. To assess the success of any method required the construction of a mass spectrometer capable of resolving the isotopes. In those days, the construction of such a spectrometer was still a research task. The completed instrument was used early in 1940 by Kenneth H. Kingdon and Herbert C. Pollock to provide early samples of pure U-235 and U-238 to confirm experimentally at the Columbia University cyclotron that U-235 was indeed the isotope fissioned by slow neutrons.

While attempts to perfect new separation methods were in progress, the Research Laboratory became for a time a producer of pure uranium hexafluoride for other American laboratories that were also working on isotope separation. Cooperation with university scientists came easily, for under Whitney and Coolidge, scientists such as Arthur Compton, Ernest Lawrence, Jesse Beams and Frederick Seitz were at times consultants or employees of the Research Laboratory.

After the Manhattan Project was organized by the government to develop atomic weapons with speed and in secrecy, many engineering and manufacturing components of the Company became involved in supplying technology and equipment for new atomic development cities in Tennessee, New Mexico, and Washington. The work of the Research Laboratory began to focus more on critical problems relating to antisubmarine warfare radar, and countermeasures. But, in 1944, at the request of Ernest Lawrence and General Groves, Coolidge recalled Kenneth Kingdon from a torpedo project in Florida to take an eight-man GE scientific team to California to support research on isotope separation with the "calutron," a gigantic mass spectrometer developed by Lawrence at Berkeley. By this time, multiple beams with amperes of ions were being used to separate U-235 in the calutron factories at Oak Ridge, Tennessee.

Herbert C. Pollock and Kenneth H. Kingdon with mass spectrometer used in isolating uranium (U-235) in GE Research Laboratory in 1940.

At the end of the War, when the DuPont Company withdrew from operating the plutonium producing reactors at Hanford, GE offered to take over the management of this facility and also to organize a new government-funded laboratory in Schenectady aimed at the development of nuclear power. Both plans were accepted by the United States Government and C. Guy Suits, who had succeeded Coolidge as Vice President of Research, expanded the staff of the Schenectady laboratories by hiring many able young scientists who had been active in nuclear research. Even before May 15, 1946, when the contract for the Knolls Atomic Power Laboratory was signed, scientists were beginning to arrive in Schenectady to work on new applications of nuclear energy, particularly the development of useful power. The Nucleonics Project, with Kingdon its Technical Manager, soon became the temporary Atomic Power Laboratory, on Peek Street in government-owned buildings previously used by the American Locomotive Company for army tank assembly. In the summer of 1947, ground-breaking ceremonies were held at the site of KAPL which was to become a key laboratory for the development of U.S. naval reactors. An initial KAPL project was aimed at demonstrating the engineering feasibility of a fast breeder reactor using an intermediate energy neutron spectrum. The successful operation of the "Submarine Intermediate Reactor" and the power plant of the submarine "Sea Wolf" validated the engineering concepts on which the modern liquid metal fast breeder reactor (LMFBR) is based. Henry Hurwitz, who led the theoretical section at KAPL, has written, "The successful operation of early naval reactors caused industry to give serious attention to the possibility of commercial light water reactors. The fact that the underlying technology of steam power plants was familiar and well developed gave industry the courage to aggressively undertake the commercialization of the LWR concept."

The time span assigned to this book does not include the history of General Electric's development of the commercial boiling water reactor (BWR), the feasibility of which was demonstrated in the early 1950s, and the subsequent growth of the Company's commercial nuclear power business. The efforts of many General Electric people, among them Harry A. Winne, Vice President-Engineering, who served on an important advisory committee for President Harry S. Truman, aided this country in the rapid development of the new nuclear technology.

Harry A. Winne

One of seven manufacturing plants of the Hanford Works, Richland, Washington.

1946

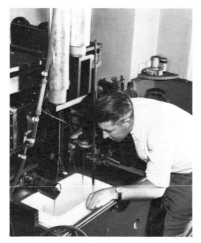

Vincent J. Schaefer studying snow-making in laboratory.

Rocket test site at White Sands, New Mexico.

MATERIALS

"Snow-making" is announced by Vincent J. Schaefer of the Research Laboratory. He found that by dropping dry ice through a supercooled cloud, it was possible to nucleate snowflake formation.

APPLIANCES

Within weeks after Japan's surrender, General Electric starts producing washing machines and other large appliances by "improved methods used in building bazookas."

TRANSPORTATION

The gas turbine project team at the Large Steam Turbine Department designs the axial flow TG-180 (designated J-35 by the Air Corps) turbojet engine for use in the Republic Aviation, Thunderjet F-84 fighter. The engine's 4000-lb thrust enables the plane to achieve a record 619 mph airspeed during its initial flight tests. Almost ten years earlier, Glenn Warren and Alan Howard had advocated the use of the axial flow compressor for high performance gas turbines.

A team of GE scientists led by Richard W. Porter works in support of the U.S. Government to help assemble and launch recovered German V-2 rockets at White Sands, New Mexico. The tests mark the beginning of the missile and space age in America.

POWER GENERATION

GE takes over operation of the U.S. Government's Hanford Works near Richland, Washington. In addition to the operation, development and enlargement of the Nuclear Works, GE's contract with the Atomic Energy Commission calls for research and development in the use of atomic energy as a source of power. Administrator of the facility is William H. Milton, Jr.

ELECTRONICS

The APS-10 light weight radar, based on the invention of the magnetron by Albert W. Hull in 1921, is the first airborne radar to be put into service by a commercial airline. Developed during World War II, the APS-10 was an invaluable navigation aid in the Berlin airlift of 1948

CONVERTING TO A PEACETIME ECONOMY

Preparing picture tubes for home television receivers at Electronics Department's Buffalo plant.

Checking radio sets to be used in private planes at Electronics Department's Syracuse plant.

The first post-war refrigerators on the assembly line at Erie.

Winding transformer coil at Pittsfield Works.

Designer creates a clay model for a washing machine at Bridgeport.

Designing locomotives to be built at Erie.

CHAPTER FOUR

PATHWAYS OF PROGRESS
1947-1980

The Jet Age, the Space Age, and the Electronics Age were the terms popularly used to describe some of the most spectacular areas of technological development following World War II. Considering the impact on society of jet air transportation, data processing, space exploration and electronics, these characterizations were appropriate. It was no coincidence that GE scientists and engineers played a crucial role in the birth and growth of these technologies and others. The post-war resurgence, led by Charles E. Wilson until his retirement in 1950, would result in a multitude of innovative products and services stemming from new developments as well as those born to meet war-time needs. The shrinking of the globe, resulting from improved transportation and communications, offered new areas for growth on an international scale. But vigorous growth also brought with it a critical challenge in the need for effective management of a far-flung and diverse organization. A succession of management teams headed by Ralph Cordiner, Fred Borch and Reginald Jones would prove equal to the task. Behind the abilities of an enterprising and enlightened management to anticipate the needs of a rapidly changing world and to chart the directions that would lead to growth was an impressive record of achievements – in science, engineering, manufacturing, finance, advertising, sales, and numerous other disciplines.

1947

ELECTRONICS AND COMMUNICATIONS

The Audio Electronics Department announces the first radio phonograph combination with variable reluctance cartridge, providing improved sound reproduction of recordings and greater convenience in a home entertainment package.

A two-to-one brightness improvement in black and white television is achieved through a patented picture tube aluminizing process.

Mobile radio communications systems for police, fire and other emergency uses reach a new level of mobility with the development of the first single-unit set, housing both the mobile transmitter and the receiver in the same package.

The first microwave relay system is put into commercial operation between New York City and Schenectady, relaying television programs to WRGB at Schenectady for rebroadcast.

INDUSTRIAL EQUIPMENT

Appliance Motor Department pioneers the use of aluminum magnet wire to replace copper wire in producing lighter weight motors used in appliances and other applications.

The first application of high-performance feedback control in the metals industry takes place on a 42-inch tandem cold rolling mill built for Jones & Laughlin Steel Company. An amplidyne regulating system coordinates the drives of each of its five stands with a precision that permits much higher speeds and greatly increased output.

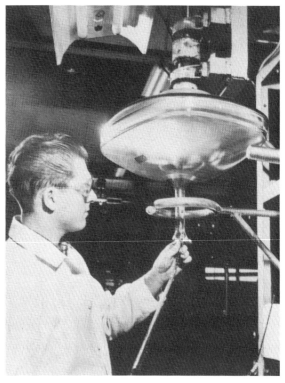

Preparing television picture tube bulbs for aluminizing.

MATERIALS

The production of plastic refrigerator inner doors is begun at a new plant is Coshocton, Ohio. These panels eliminate heavy steel inner doors and breaker strips and improve thermal insulation.

The Chemical Department produces the first all-plastic dinghy for the Beetle Boat Company. Weighing only 80 pounds, the boat is capable of holding loads of more than 1500 pounds, while its plastic foam seats and gunwales make it virtually unsinkable.

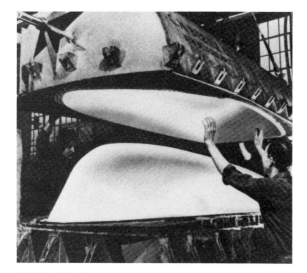

Molding the first all-plastic boat at Pittsfield.

The first two-door refrigerator-freezer.

APPLIANCES

Hotpoint introduces the first custom-matched cooking equipment for fast food service operations. An electronic oven for restaurants is developed and is being used in food heating experiments. It is designed to heat pre-cooked frozen foods to table temperature in about a minute.

The Erie Plant produces the first two-door refrigerator-freezer combination. In this 7.5 cubic foot unit, the freezer compartment keeps frozen foods protected at zero to 10°F, while the refrigerator section maintains about 38°F for normal food storage and does not have to be defrosted.

The first completely automatic clothes washer is introduced. An added advantage is the mechanical design which reduces vibration to the point that the washer no longer need be bolted to the floor.

Hotpoint cooking equipment for fast food service restaurants.

1948

Alco-GE 4500-hp gas-turbine locomotive.

TRANSPORTATION

The first American gas-turbine electric locomotive, an Alco-GE 4500-hp unit, begins track tests at the Erie plant prior to shipment to the Union Pacific Railroad.

A new "supertanker" is launched. This ocean-going giant is powered by a GE turbine operating at the highest combined steam temperature and pressure ever used in a merchant ship and capable of delivering 12,500 horsepower.

LIGHTING

A new fluorescent lamp is developed to provide the same light for only 85 watts that the former lamp gave for 100 watts. Responsible for the increased output is the use of the rare gas, krypton, in place of argon which had previously been used.

MEDICAL EQUIPMENT

Largest of its kind in the world, the William D. Coolidge Laboratory of the General Electric X-Ray Corporation is dedicated to commemorate and perpetuate the tradition of x-ray development symbolized by its namesake.

William D. Coolidge (c.) inventor of the modern type of x-ray tube, and his wife Dorothy (r.) at dedication of new Coolidge X-Ray Laboratory with Dr. A.C. Christie (l.), nationally known radiologist.

INDUSTRIAL EQUIPMENT

A new 66-inch reversing hot strip mill produces steel strip at the record speed of 3900 feet per minute using GE motors and a new magnetic side register control which automatically guides the strip along its predetermined path.

The first completely new watthour meter in 50 years, the type I-50, is introduced. Its magnetic suspension virtually eliminates the wear problems associated with conventional bearings and results in an estimated life of over 60 years, eight times the service expected of conventional meters.

POWER GENERATION

A 100,000-kilowatt turbine generator is put into service at the Sewaren, New Jersey, station of the Public Service Electric and Gas Company. Operating at 1050 °F, it is the largest of its type in the world.

The Knolls Atomic Power Laboratory (KAPL) initiates the use of digital computers for the design of naval propulsion reactors. KAPL was organized at Schenectady, New York, two years earlier for the purpose of developing nuclear reactors for the U.S. Atomic Energy Commission.

I-50 watthour meter, with disk and shaft suspended magnetically.

Rotor for 100,000-kw turbine-generator being lowered into position.

1949

Experimental model of "heat pump" unit for year-round air conditioning.

APPLIANCES

Ten experimental models of the "heat pump" are installed around the country as GE engineers test the system's capability for year-round air conditioning. The heat pump works like a refrigerator, reversible to pump either warmed or cooled air into the house at the turn of a switch.

MATERIALS

Man-made mica paper insulating tapes are introduced by the Insulating Materials Department. The precise control of thickness and porosity in the paper-making process produces an insulation with superior high voltage and high temperature capabilities.

INDUSTRIAL EQUIPMENT

The first successful molded instrument transformer, Type JKM-3, 5 kv, is introduced. A new formulation of butyl rubber molding compound and new molding techniques make possible exceptional indoor and outdoor stability.

Molded instrument transformer proves its durability in steam-chamber test.

LIGHTING

The Q-coat process, developed by Marvin Pipkin of Nela Park, results in an improved household lamp known as the "Soft White." By coating the inside of incandescent lamp bulbs with tiny particles of silica, the process provides an excellent light diffuser and reduces glare with almost no loss of light.

Marvin Pipkin of Nela Park compares the even diffusion of "Soft White" lamp, on left, with standard frosted lamp on same wattage, on right.

TRANSPORTATION

Driven by six J35 jet engines, a Boeing XB-47 Stratojet bomber averages 607 miles per hour and sets a new coast-to-coast speed record of three hours and 46 minutes. The new J47 turbojet will boost the Stratojet's total power by 25%. The J47 engine powered the North American F-86 Sabre jet to a world's record 670 miles per hour in September of 1948 and enabled the F-86 to score a 14 to 1 win ratio during the Korean conflict in the early 1950s. The J47 also powered the Boeing B-47 and North American B-45 bombers and provided boost power for the Convair B-36 bomber. More than 35,000 J47 engines were produced.

Lightning strikes the Empire State Building during high voltage tests by Pittsfield's High Voltage Laboratory.

GE J47 engine powers the North American F-86 Sabre jet.

POWER GENERATION AND TRANSMISSION

The first gas turbine for power generation, the GE MS3001, rated at 3500 kw, is shipped to the Oklahoma Gas & Electric Company's Belle Isle Station. One innovation is the use of the exhaust to preheat the boiler feed water for a 52,000-kw steam station.

Completion of the new High Voltage Laboratory in Pittsfield gives GE the world's most modern facility to understand the effects of lightning and switching voltage on power equipment.

The largest industrial building constructed after World War II is occupied by the Steam Turbine Department in Schenectady. Floor space of the new facility extends over more than twenty acres.

First gas turbine for power generation in the U.S.

CHARLES E. WILSON

Charlie Wilson's career follows a certain classic American pattern. He was born in 1886 on the lower West side of New York. His mother was English, his father Irish. At the age of twelve he left P.S. 32 while in the seventh grade to take a job as office boy with the Sprague Electrical Works, a GE subsidiary. He was soon made a factory hand and augmented his on-the-job training with night courses in accounting, engineering, and mathematics. By the time he was twenty-one he was assistant superintendent of the plant and married to Elizabeth Marsh on a $20-a-week salary.

In 1923 he was transferred to Bridgeport, with the title of managing engineer. As Bridgeport became heavily involved in the production of appliances, Wilson's duties expanded rapidly. In 1928 he became assistant to the Vice President in charge of the Merchandise Department, and in 1930 Vice President in charge of all appliances. As these lines lengthened — sun lamps, electric clocks, washing machines, irons, heaters, air conditioning — Charlie Wilson's role in GE's management broadened.

In December 1937, Wilson was elected executive vice president of General Electric, a new position involving responsibilities for all Company departments. Two years later he was elected President of the Company, succeeding Gerard Swope.

For two and one half years, Wilson served as a vigorous and imaginative president. Then, in September 1942, with the United States struggling to increase production of war material, Wilson went to Washington, at the request of President Roosevelt, to become vice chairman to the War Production Board. Mr. Swope came out of retirement to resume the duties of GE President.

As wartime boss of the huge U.S. production effort, Wilson achieved some spectacular successes. Aircraft, shipbuilding and munitions programs boomed under his direction. He served in this capacity until August, 1944, when he returned to GE and was again elected a director and President.

He is particularly well known for his industrial production achievements, and for his demonstrated interest in expanding distribution of goods to absorb unemployment and to promote higher living and working standards.

In 1946, President Truman named Wilson chairman of the Civil Rights Committee, whose members studied and recommended new civil rights legislation to protect "all parts of our population."

Because of the worsening international situation, an Office of Defense Mobilization was set up in 1950 and in December, President Truman asked Wilson once again to come to Washington and become its director. Concurrently, Wilson resigned his GE presidency and all his directorates.

After having completed 51 years of continuous service with General Electric, Wilson took on a job which was described in Washington as second in importance only to the Presidency of the United States. His public service did not end with that position. In 1956, he became President of the People-to-People Foundation, a non-partisan program promoting international friendship and understanding.

John G. Forrest, writing in the *New York Times*, said, "Charles Wilson is a big man by any standard, physical moral, or mental." Mr. Wilson died in 1972 at the age of 85.

Philip Reed found his way to the helm of General Electric in an altogether different way from that traveled by Charles Wilson. He was born in comfortable circumstances in Milwaukee in 1899, the year Wilson went to work as an office boy.

Reed attended the public schools of Milwaukee and in 1917 entered the University of Wisconsin, but quit in his freshman year to join the Army. An appendix operation kept him out of the American Expeditionary Forces; when the Armistice came he was at Fort Monroe, training for the heavy artillery.

Reed returned to Wisconsin to complete his degree in electrical engineering. GE, then scouting for engineering talent, offered Reed a job at $115 a month, but he refused it. Instead, because he wanted to marry Mabel Mayhew Smith, he got a $2,000-a-year job with a firm of patent lawyers in New York. Reed had no special desire to be a lawyer, but the salary looked "as large as the setting sun." By studying nights at Fordham, he got his law degree in 1924, and in due course was admitted to the New York Bar.

In 1926, a lawyer friend of Reed's told him that Judge C. W. Appleton, a GE vice president, was looking for an assistant. Contact was made, and as a result, Reed went to work for Appleton in GE's law department in New York. There he had frequent contact with Swope and Young, who gave him an assortment of special assignments.

Reed was transferred to the Incandescent Lamp Department in 1927 and became its general counsel in 1934. Because he was an effective speaker and had Owen Young's gift of grasping the essentials of problems and stating them lucidly, he was invited by plant managers to talk on labor relations, Company policies, and pension plans. In December 1937, he was appointed assistant to the President and two years later, Reed was elected Chairman of the Board.

In February 1941, Mr. Reed began his government wartime service, becoming senior consultant to the Priorities Division of the Office of Production Management, which later became the War Production Board. He was subsequently named Chief of the Bureau of Industries, War Production Board, and in July 1942, went to London as deputy to W. Averill Harriman who headed a

PHILIP D. REED

lend lease mission to England. In 1943, the President created the United States Mission for Economic Affairs in London and appointed Reed its chief, with the rank of Minister. He returned to private life on January 1, 1945.

A month later, Reed, who had resigned all his posts with General Electric when he went abroad, was again elected a Director and Chairman of the Board. In addition, he was elected Chairman of the Board of the International General Electric Company.

Reed continued to take part in public affairs. In 1945, he was consultant to the U.S. delegation to the United Nations Conference on International Organization. From February 1945 to July 1947, he was chairman of the U.S. Associates of the International Chamber of Commerce, which submitted the Montreux Plan for Economic Stability to the State Department.

Reed was elected chairman of the Research and Policy Committee of the Committee for Economic Development in August 1948. It was a private research organization supported by contributions from individuals for the purpose of studying and attempting to solve the economic problems of the United States.

Philip D. Reed retired from GE in 1959 after 32 years of service.

1950-1951

NATIONAL DEFENSE

The Korean War starts and the Ordnance Systems Department begins production of the MK 56 gunfire control, the first fully automatic system to become a vital part of the Navy's anti-aircraft strength.

INDUSTRIAL EQUIPMENT

The successful development of a commercial xerographic unit by Haloid (forerunner of the Xerox Corporation) results in the first production of copy machine power supplies by the Specialty Transformer Department.

Design and material improvements result in ½-hp motors that are smaller and weigh almost 50% less than similarly rated units manufactured twenty years earlier.

Two 65,000-hp synchronous motors, the world's largest, are installed at the pumping plant of the Grand Coulee Dam.

Pittsfield-built MK 56 gun director.

POWER GENERATION

The Steam Turbine Department delivers the first single shaft 3600-rpm, double-flow, reheat steam turbine-generator to the Dunkirk, New York, station of the Niagara Mohawk Power Company. The 80,000-kw unit introduces a unique construction which is especially compact and efficient.

80,000-kw, single shaft, double-flow, steam turbine-generator for Niagara Mohawk Power Company.

C. Guy Suits (left), Vice President and Director of Research, accepts the key to the new home of the Research Laboratory from Charles E. Wilson, President of the General Electric Company, at dedication ceremonies on October 9, 1950.

ORGANIZATION

Completing 51 years of service, Charles E. Wilson resigns his position as President of General Electric to become Director, Office of Defense Mobilization. Ralph J. Cordiner is elected as his successor.

The buildings of the new site of the Research Laboratory are dedicated on the fiftieth anniversary of its founding. They constitute one of the world's largest and most modern research laboratories.

The new main building of the Research Laboratory.

MATERIALS

The introduction by the Hughes Tool Company of the first rolling cutter drill bit containing cemented carbide compacts marks the culmination of a five-year effort by Carboloy Co., a GE subsidiary, aimed at applying this material to hard rock drilling for mining and the drilling of oil and gas wells.

1950-1951

One of the first high-powered air defense radars.

Ceramic-metal microwave tubes.

ELECTRONICS AND COMMUNICATIONS

A new radar system for commercial airports is developed by the Electronics Department. By accurately positioning all aircraft within a 30-mile range and detecting larger aircraft up to 60 miles, the system will greatly aid air traffic control in times of both good and poor visibility.

The first ultra-high-frequency (UHF) transmitter for TV broadcasting is made possible by the development of a new klystron tube.

The polarization-twist duplexer, a new radar waveguide coupling system, is invented by Burton P. Brown of the Electronics Department. It makes possible the construction of the first high-powered air defense radars.

Fosterite ceramic planar microwave tubes are introduced by the Tube Department for high frequency, low noise, high gain applications.

Robert N. Hall, pioneer in early semiconductor research.

Robert N. Hall of the Research Laboratory finds that indium and germanium can be used to make alloyed P-N junctions—the basic elements of power rectifiers and some transistors.

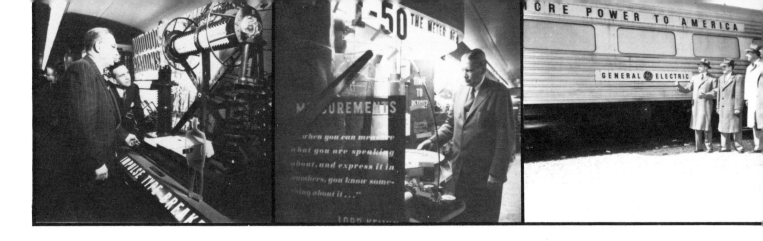

THE MORE POWER TO AMERICA SPECIAL

General Electric's "More Power to America Special," a ten-car exhibit train, begins a nationwide tour which will continue through 1950 into 1951. Visiting principal industrial centers, it displays opportunities which the electrical industry offers for increasing the nation's productivity. The quarter-mile long travelling showcase, of which the 4500-hp diesel-electric engine itself is a part, contains more than 2000 products and ideas for commerce and industry, for civic improvement, and for national defense.

The "5-star" line of high performance electron tubes.

ELECTRONICS AND COMMUNICATIONS

The Tube Products Department introduces the 5-star line of high reliability, rugged electron tubes for military and other high performance applications. The Electronics Division starts mass production of semiconductor diodes (low-power rectifiers) to replace vacuum tubes in many of its electronic products, including television receivers.

MATERIALS

Carboloy is cited for its hitherto top secret role in the development and production of armor-piercing tungsten carbide cores for anti-tank shells during World War II and the Korean War.

Seeking an improved wire enamel, chemist Daniel W. Fox makes discoveries leading to the development of Lexan® polycarbonate resin—a transparent plastic of unsurpassed impact resistance.

DANIEL W. FOX

The invention of Lexan® polycarbonate resin and Alkanex® wire enamel were but two of Fox's many valuable contributions which merited him induction into the Plastics Hall of Fame as its youngest living member (1976).

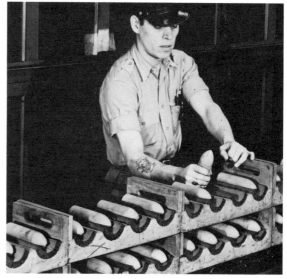

Carboloy production line for armor-piercing cores for anti-tank shells.

NATIONAL DEFENSE

Push-button control of the Navy's high-speed jet interceptors is brought closer to realization with the development of a new automatic pilot which relieves pilots of 90 percent of their "stick and rudder" work.

Two modified turbojets are provided to power the cargo-carrying XH-17, the world's largest helicopter, built by Howard Hughes Aircraft Company for the U.S. Air Force.

INDUSTRIAL EQUIPMENT

Canadian General Electric develops electrical equipment for the world's largest hydraulic dredge.

The new Form "G" line of fractional horsepower motors is 25 to 50 % lighter and up to 40 % smaller than previous motors of similar power ratings.

Matching motor parts at Taylor Street plant, Ft. Wayne, Indiana.

World's largest circuit breakers for 300,000-volt transmission line.

POWER GENERATION AND TRANSMISSION

KAPL, under the direction of the Division of Naval Reactors, AEC, develops the major containment concept for nuclear reactors, including the philosophy and equipment for design safety. This concept is used to design the West Milton Hortensphere which houses the prototype plant for the submarine Seawolf.

The Switchgear Department builds the world's largest circuit breakers for a 300,000-volt transmission line, highest in the United States.

Research and development leading to the reduction of power losses in steels for transformers results in a power transformer weighing 35 tons less than similar units of half the capacity shipped only three years earlier.

The first regenerative cycle heavy-duty gas turbine, the MS 3002, rated at 6200 hp, is delivered to the El Paso Natural Gas Company's Pecos River Station in New Mexico. It will be used to provide power for natural gas pipeline pumping.

1954

MATERIALS

Arthur M. Bueche and Elliot J. Lawton develop a method of cross-linking polymers by irradiation with an electron beam. This work leads to the widespread recognition of the value of irradiated polymers for such uses as insulating materials and food wrappings.

The Medium Transformer Department pioneers the use of Formex wire insulation in power transformer windings manufactured at its newly opened plant at Rome, Georgia. This tough, long-life insulation makes for smaller, lower-weight designs.

Arthur M. Bueche (l.) and Elliot J. Lawton exhibit their method of cross-linking polymers by irradiation.

LIGHTING

With the introduction of quartz bulbs, Incandescent Lamp Department engineers increase the power of tungsten filament infrared heat lamps while significantly reducing their size. Initial applications for the new lamps are in the reprographic industry.

The all-weather headlamp is developed as a result of innovations in reflector design. Driver visibility is dramatically improved in all types of inclement weather.

The first all-glass baseless miniature lamp for auto instrument panels is introduced. It provides lower socket and lamp cost as well as simplified installation.

New all-weather headlamps improve drive visibility. Val Roper (shown here) and Marv Riggert were key contributors to the expanded use of more effective exterior and interior lighting for automobiles.

APPLIANCES

The first truly automatic portable dishwasher, the Mobile Maid, is shipped from the recently completed (1952) Appliance Park facility in Louisville, Kentucky.

The new Mobile Maid automatic dishwasher.

30,000-hp propeller test stand built by Medium Steam Turbine Department for U.S. Air Force.

TRANSPORTATION

A 30,000-hp propeller test stand for developing and testing high horsepower, turbo-prop aircraft propellers is designed and built by Medium Steam Turbine Department for the Wright-Patterson Air Force Base in Ohio.

The Locomotive and Car Equipment Department develops a 4000-hp rectifier locomotive utilizing electronic tubes to convert ac power to dc power, promising many new railway applications.

INDUSTRIAL EQUIPMENT

The Kinamatic 1 small dc motor is produced at the recently completed dc motor manufacturing facility at Erie, Pennsylvania. Kinamatic motors are designed for use in applications requiring continuous adjustable motor speed.

The newly formed Specialty Motor Department introduces the 39-frame motor, used primarily in central heating and air conditioning units where its high reliability makes it particularly suitable.

POWER GENERATION

The Foundry (later, Engineered Cast Products) Department establishes the Applied Research and Development Laboratory to develop new processes for the production of high quality, large turbine castings.

Construction of rectifier freight locomotives at the Locomotive and Car Equipment Department in Erie, Pennsylvania. Each car weighs 120 tons.

1955

POWER GENERATION

America's first commercial nuclear power is distributed over the Niagara Mohawk Power Company system. A GE turbine-generator and the Seawolf submarine nuclear reactor prototype are used to produce electric power from a plant at West Milton, New York.

A new air-blast circuit breaker for 138,000-volt transmission lines is the first of its rating in the U.S. It uses high-pressure compressed air to "blow out" a hot electric arc and, for a split second, interrupt flow of electricity when lightning strikes or a fault occurs on a transmission line.

The first large generator with liquid cooled stator is completed by the Turbine Division. Rated at 260,000 kva, the unit is capable of supplying the household electrical needs of 700,000 people.

Portion of 260,000-kva generator with liquid-cooled stator.

Ceremonies marking first commercially distributed nuclear power at West Milton, New York.

KENNETH A. KESSELRING

At the Knolls Atomic Power Laboratory, "Kess", was a man whose organizing abilities and technical contributions played a major role in many early successes in atomic power development. His involvement in the development of nuclear propulsion plants for the submarine Seawolf and the destroyer Bainbridge contributed to the foundations for GE's participation in the growth of the nuclear Navy.

NATIONAL DEFENSE

The free world's largest, most powerful radar is installed in central Turkey for the U.S. Air Force. The GE FPS-17 radar is part of the Air Force's SPACETRACK global surveillance system.

As part of Project SABRE, a major effort in upgrading the radar of the U.S. fighter aircraft, Aerospace Electronic Systems Department equips the F-106 all-weather interceptor with its advanced electronic counter-countermeasures equipment.

F-106 all-weather interceptor carries Project Sabre with electronic counter-countermeasures equipment.

MATERIALS

The Research Laboratory announces the invention of the first reproducible process for making diamond — a landmark achievement that had eluded some of the world's top scientists for centuries.

The development of Alkanex® magnet wire insulation by Daniel W. Fox and Frank M. Precopio permits the operation of motors at higher temperatures, setting new standards for the motor industry in operating efficiency and size reduction.

Research Laboratory industrial diamond synthesis team. From the left are Francis P. Bundy, Harold P. Bovenkerk, Robert H. Wentorf, Anthony J. Nerad, and Herbert M. Strong (not shown, H. Tracy Hall).

1000-ton press in which GE man-made diamonds were produced.

HERE'S HOW THE FILTER-FLO SYSTEM WORKS . . .

1. Dirt loosens as clothes are individually cleansed by thorough Activator® washing action.
2. Lint and soap scum are carried out of washbasket as wash water continuously overflows into the outer tub.
3. Heavy sand and silt drop out here.
4. Pump continuously forces water up and through the filter and 5. only cleansed sudsy water flows back into the wash basket.

APPLIANCES

John Bochan of Appliance Park invents the Filter-Flo System for automatic clothes washers. It removes lint from the wash as it is generated.

Phillip Hughes invents the safety start switch for use in home clothes dryers. By interlocking the timer with a separate "start" switch, access to the dryer can be safely obtained by the user without altering the drying time cycle.

1955

INDUSTRIAL EQUIPMENT

Numerical control of machine tools is demonstrated at the Chicago Machine Tool Show using a punch card controlled Sundstrand shaft-turning lathe. The development is referred to as "the greatest innovation in metalworking of this century."

The hermetically sealed micro-miniature relay is introduced for aircraft and aerospace applications. Numerous versions of this product are now in use in virtually every U.S. commercial and military aircraft.

An offshoot of diesel-electric locomotive technology, the GE 752 Drilling Motor/Generator System, is introduced as a self-contained power source for oil well drilling rigs.

Micro-miniature relays for use in aircraft and aerospace applications.

Oil well drilling rig with GE 752 Drilling Motor/Generator System.

ELECTRONICS

The first portable television receivers are built by the Television Business Department, Syracuse. Radios using transistorized circuitry in place of vacuum tubes are introduced by the Audio Electronics Department.

New voltage tunable magnetrons extend the tube's use to microwave relay systems, aircraft altimeters, electronic test equipment and telemetering.

TRANSPORTATION

The GTS John Sergeant, a converted Liberty ship, is the world's first large merchant ship to be propelled solely by a gas turbine. With the 6600-hp regenerative cycle, two-shaft gas turbine, coupled to a controllable-pitch propeller, the vessel's maneuverability is outstanding and its speed is improved from 11 knots to 18 knots.

Credited with developing GE's postwar reorganization and decentralization program which brought new flexibility and a sharper focus on specific markets, Ralph J. Cordiner was the fifth President of General Electric.

He was born in 1900 on a 1280 acre wheat farm in Walla Walla, Washington. He worked his way through Whitman College by doing odd jobs and selling washing machines. He graduated in 1922 with a degree in economics, and joined the Pacific Power and Light Company as a commercial manager. Within a year he joined the Edison General Electric Appliance Company, a GE affiliate, where he became Northwest manager and then Pacific Coast division manager in 1930. He transferred to Bridgeport, Connecticut, in 1932 and became a leader of the Company's expanding appliance business, rising to manager of the Appliance and Merchandise Department in 1938.

Cordiner left GE in 1939 to become president of Schick, Inc., and is credited by *Time* magazine with putting that company "back on its feet" in a brief three-year tenure. In 1942, he went to Washington to work with GE president Charles E. Wilson on the War Production Board, returning to GE in 1943 as Wilson's assistant. In 1950, he was elected the Company's President, succeeding Wilson who, at President Truman's request, resigned to become director of the Office of Defense Mobilization.

Cordiner was elected Chairman of the Board and Chief Executive Officer in 1958, and also served as President of the Company during 1961, prior to the election of Gerald L. Phillippe as President in August of that year.

To better cope with General Electric's burgeoning growth, Cordiner established a new organizational structure based on the concept of decentralization — an idea that had been adopted by some segments of American industry since Du Pont pioneered it at the time of the First World War. He made each of some 120 department general managers responsible for a particular segment of GE business, handling assignments that he described as "not too big for one man to get his arms around." The organization reflected the view that the natural aggregate of many individually sound decisions will be better

RALPH J. CORDINER

for the business than centrally-planned and controlled decisions. Cordiner outlined his decentralized management philosophy in the book *New Frontiers for Professional Managers* in 1956. He also established the GE Management Development Institute at Crotonville, New York, which opened an entirely new approach to the education of personnel for advanced management.

Cordiner was President of the Business Council, a group of business leaders who advised the government on business affairs. He also served as Chairman of the Defense Advisory Committee on Professional and Technical Compensation in the Armed Forces.

The first Gold Medal Award of the Economic Club of New York City was conferred on Ralph Cordiner in recognition of his contributions to "principles of management and to the strength and prosperity of the nation."

In 1963, Cordiner retired after forty years of service to General Electric. He died in 1973.

DISTRIBUTING THE PRODUCTS OF TECHNOLOGY

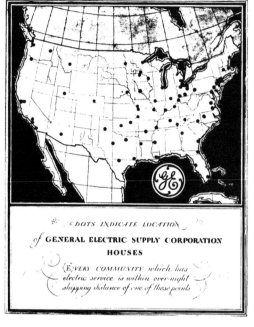
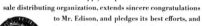
Electrification in the United States saw one of its most rapid periods of expansion during the decade after World War I. In 1919, 24% of America's homes were served by electric lines. By 1929, the number had grown to 65% and the increased need for electrical supplies in the newly equipped households presented General Electric with an opportunity to create a nationwide distribution network. In October, 1929, fourteen company-owned distributors and their 76 outlets were merged to form the General Electric Supply Company (GESCO). Headquarters were established at Bridgeport, Connecticut, with Gerard Swope chairman of the Board and C.E. Patterson president and director. Another director was Charles E. Wilson.

GENERAL ELECTRIC SUPPLY COMPANY

GESCO's network of supply houses, such as this one in Phoenix, Arizona stock over 85,000 different items.

GESCO sales representative reviews customer's needs outside the world's largest underground mine in San Manuel, Arizona.

In 1956, GESCO became a division of the Company, and two years later a young GE executive named Reginald H. Jones was appointed general manager. During the six years that he led GESCO, it experienced record growth and became firmly established as a full-functioning wholesale distributor of lamps, lighting equipment, electrical apparatus and supplies manufactured by GE and over 3000 other companies.

In 1976, GESCO's business took on an international flavor when the Saudi Electric Supply Company in Alkhobar, Saudi Arabia became an authorized distributor. Distribution centers were also opened in Riyadh and Jeddah.

In 1978, GESCO entered the Carribean market in Puerto Rico by assuming responsibility for General Electric del Caribe, Inc.

The General Electric Supply Company ranks high as one of the lesser known segments of General Electric. But it occupies a unique position in which it purchases products from some 46 GE manufacturing departments and seeks opportunities to sell its merchandise to all of GE's plants as well as to outside companies. Its 3300 people in 183 distribution centers in the United States and in growing international markets have built an unchallenged reputation for service to the customer and have made significant contributions to the Company's growth.

GESCO in Saudi Arabia.

1956

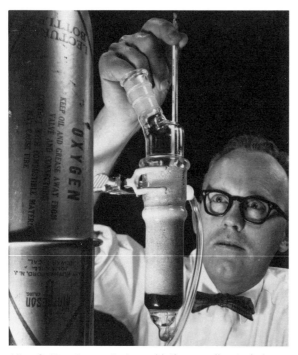

Allan S. Hay demonstrates oxidative coupling technique.

Fluid bed reactor for manufacture of silicones at new plant in Waterford, New York.

MATERIALS

Allan S. Hay of the Research Laboratory discovers a technique for polymerization by oxidative coupling. It leads to polyphenylene oxide and finally to Noryl® resin, a widely used engineering plastic with unusual strength at high temperatures and flame retardant characteristics.

The Waterford, New York, plant of the Silicone Products Department starts up its first fluid bed reactor with technology which becomes the basis for the worldwide economical production of silicones.

Copper-clad laminates for printed circuit boards are developed for radio and television applications, providing lighter weight, lower cost assemblies than had previously been possible.

INDUSTRIAL EQUIPMENT

Industrial Control Department announces the industry's first analog control system for a machine tool. It consists of electronic tube circuitry and amplidyne generator excitation for motor control.

The first motor specifically designed for appliance applications is the Form "R" produced by the Appliance Motor Department.

LIGHTING

The increased surface area offered by the "power groove" tube design leads to power outputs as much as twice those of straight tube fluorescent lamps.

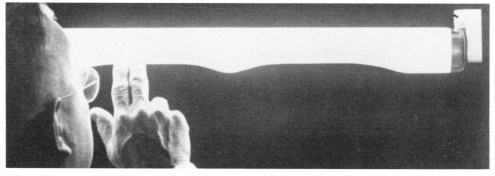

"Power groove" tube design doubles light output of fluorescent lamps.

NATIONAL DEFENSE

At the request of the U.S. Air Force, GE starts development of the reentry vehicle for the free world's first intercontinental ballistic missile, the Atlas. The system must house and protect payloads from the 12,000°F temperature encountered during reentry into the earth's atmosphere. Manufacturing will take place at Burlington, Vermont. Aerospace Electronic Systems Division develops the crucial radio guidance system for the Atlas.

Atlas intercontinental ballistic missile on launching pad.

Lead computing gyro and optical sight system for F-4 Phantom II fighter

TRANSPORTATION

The CJ 805 turbojet and turbofan versions of the J79 jet engine are selected to power the Convair 880 and 990 jetliners. The J79, with its variable stator compressor, is the free world's first Mach 2 engine. It is used on military aircraft such as the B-58 Hustler, the F-104 Starfighter and the F-4 Phantom II, enabling them to set 44 world records for time-to-climb, speed and altitude. The McDonnell/Douglas Phantom II, equipped with two Evendale J79 engines in addition to Binghamton's (AESD) lead computing gunsight and all-transistorized autopilot, is considered one of the most successful military fighter aircraft ever produced.

APPLIANCES

Housewares Division introduces the T-83 Toast-R-Oven, the first of a line which later will include broiling capabilities and larger toasting and baking capacity in a compact, energy saving appliance.

The first automatic drying termination cycle is devised for clothes dryers. It increases drying efficiency while bringing added convenience to home laundering.

1956

ORGANIZATION

The General Electric Management Development Institute is opened at Crotonville, New York. It resulted from a three-year investigation initiated at the request of Ralph Cordiner who saw the need to develop an expanded number of managers trained in additional skills to satisfy the requirements of the new decentralization program and to meet the predicted growth of the Company. From 1956 until 1961 over 1500 managerial and professional employees participated in the Advanced Management Course. It was unique-in the industry for its scope and length, and its approach to managerial work. During the same period, the Institute trained over 500 course leaders for the Professional Business Management Course conducted at many of the Company's locations.

Over the years, activities at Crotonville have reflected changing concepts in education and in management techniques and philosophy. Executive education programs have been complemented by learning opportunitites specifically appropriate to the individual's level of responsibility in a wide variety of disciplines.

GE President Ralph Cordiner addresses the first class of the Advanced Management Course at the newly opened Crotonville Management Development Institute.

A TRADITION OF EDUCATION

The recognition of the need for continuing, post-school education goes back to the earliest days of General Electric, when the Experts Course was organized to develop engineers who could deal with the new technologies that produced the Company's products. This was followed by the Apprentice Course, the Test Course, organized by Albert Rohrer; and the Business Training Program. "Test" as it is fondly and proudly referred to by its alumni, offered technically trained college graduates opportunities for a series of assignments at a variety of Company locations, augmented by formal classroom education, before a decision would be made on career concentration. Later, the Advanced Engineering Program was formulated to develop problem solving and analytical capabilities at levels equivalent to graduate engineering school educations. In the 1970's a number of programs were established which combine the best features of "Test", for example, with those of other courses of study in technological areas. The Edison Engineering Program is the most recent of such programs. The same has been true of non-technical areas -- as exemplified by the Financial Management Program, which has provided individuals with a broad base of familiarity with the Company's diversified operations, and has been a training ground for many of its business leaders.

The philosophy of career-long opportunities for development is centered not only in the formal training programs but in a great variety of technical and non-technical courses to meet the needs and interests of virtually every type of employee -- and where the pertinent educational opportunities do not exist internally, they are provided by financial support of external programs. In looking to the individual self-betterment of its employees General Electric is continually building the resources for its own progress.

Student Certificate issued the same year that the General Electric Company was formed—1892.

Static logic switching control panel for Inland Steel Company.

INDUSTRIAL EQUIPMENT

Silicon-controlled rectifiers are incorporated in a new class of small synchronous generators that eliminate brushes and add reliability and cost advantages.

Punched paper tape input for numerical control of machine tools is announced by the Industrial Control Department. This new industry standard is known as the GE "Mark Series" line.

Static magnetic digital switching and solid-state analog electronic amplifiers are introduced to the metal industry in the automation of an Inland Steel slabbing mill. Mill operation is controlled by a punched card program control system.

Tri-Clad brushless generator for computer power supply, under test by engineer E. H. (Ed) Perkins.

Continuous path tape control contouring and milling machine.

MATERIALS

GE announces the full commercial availability of manufactured industrial diamonds for use in metal-cutting and other difficult materials processing operations ranging from glass-grinding to commercial drilling and dentistry.

Robert H. Wentorf, Jr. synthesizes Borazon® cubic boron nitride, a material not found in nature and second in hardness only to a diamond. Its potential use in materials processing is enhanced by the ability to remain hard at temperatures where diamond will burn.

The first successful hydrostatic pressing of massive molybdenum billets is made by Howard Green, George Kaiser and Walter Brinn. Refractory Metal Products Department is the first commercial producer of large hydropressed tungsten and molybdenum billets used for forging rocket nozzle and other high temperature, high performance parts.

Robert H. Wentorf demonstrates that Borazon is hard enough to scratch diamond.

APPLIANCES

Housewares Division introduces the first commercially feasible combination spray, steam and dry iron, increasing the range of fabrics that can be conveniently handled with a single, household iron.

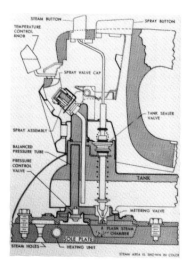

Cross-section of spray, steam and dry iron.

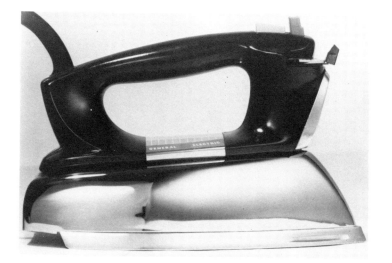

Model U9C diesel-electric locomotive for the Chilean State Railways.

TRANSPORTATION

The Erie Works makes its first shipment of a standard export universal locomotive to Chile. It is a 900-hp, six-axle U9C diesel-electric.

USS Seawolf, the U.S. Navy's second nuclear-powered submarine. (General Dynamics Photo)

POWER GENERATION

GE receives the U.S. Government's first nuclear reactor license for its five megawatt Vallecitos Boiling Water Reactor near Pleasanton, California. The unit goes into operation as a generator of electricity for the Pacific Gas and Electric Company and also serves as an operator training center and reactor component test complex.

Enriched uranium-oxide fuel pellets for nuclear reactors are first developed and produced by Carboloy (now the Metallurgical Products Department).

The Navy's second nuclear powered submarine, the USS Seawolf, contains a reactor plant designed by KAPL, under the direction of the Division of Naval Reactors, AEC; and uses the liquid sodium cooling concept. It is commissioned at the Electric Boat Division of the General Dynamics Corporation in Groton, Connecticut.

Vallecitos Boiling Water Reactor, recipient of first nuclear reactor license.

1958

POWER GENERATION AND TRANSMISSION

The Advanced Reactor Systems Department pioneers a fast breeder reactor theory indicating that such reactors can be economically viable. It also develops a ceramic oxide fuel for use in fast breeder reactors.

The Specialty Transformer Department introduces industry's first guaranteed noise level, high temperature transformer, the "QHT" (Quiet, High Temperature).

QHT dry type transformer, with old type D in background.

Testing the Vulcan gatling gun at Burlington, Vermont, firing range.

MATERIALS

The Wire and Cable Department announces Vulkene, an insulation utilizing cross-linked polyethylene technology. Vulkene's high temperature properties will revolutionize the cable industry and usher in a new generation of solid dielectrics for cable insulation.

NATIONAL DEFENSE

The largest operational radar laboratory in the free world is developed and operated for the U.S. Air Force on the island of Trinidad, down range from Cape Canaveral.

Armament Systems at Burlington, Vermont, produces the first linkless ammunition feed system, reliable at rates up to 7200 rounds per minute. It is used for the M-61 Vulcan gun installed on the Air Force F-105 fighter plane.

Trinidad radar laboratory, largest in the free world.

238

CJ610 turbojet-powered Gates Learjet.

TRANSPORTATION

Jet engine power is introduced for use in business aircraft with the development of the CJ610 turbojet. The J85, its supersonic military predecessor, was first used to power the F-5 Freedom Fighter.

SPACE EXPLORATION

The first payload ever recovered from outer space is a data capsule ejected from a Mark 2 reentry vehicle built for the U.S. Air Force. The vehicle also serves as the nation's first space laboratory, carrying scientific experiments which will help pave the way for future space exploration. Its precise, pre-determined path is controlled by a radio-guidance system developed by the Electronic Systems Division.

APPLIANCES

Housewares Division markets its automatic electric can opener, freeing consumers from the awkwardness of manual types.

Rotary compressors are developed for use in room air conditioners. The new design has fewer parts and its size, weight and quiet operation make it particularly suitable for window and wall mounting. The invention of the SPINE FIN heat transfer surface, with continuous refrigerant tubing and thousands of heat transfer spines, permits flexibility in design that results in the development of many new air conditioner applications.

SPINE FIN heat transfer surface developed for air conditioners.

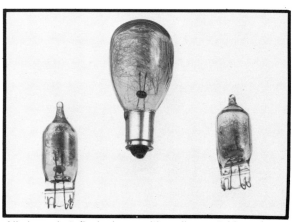

All-glass photoflash shown with earlier, metal base lamp.

LIGHTING

Development of the first all-glass photoflash, the AG-1, provides a smaller, yet more powerful lamp and is the forerunner of photolamp arrays that will bring a new dimension of automation and convenience to photography.

1959

LIGHTING

A team led by G.E. Reinker, E.L. Woodall and R.D. Jones is successful in the identification of a domestic source of quartz sand and the development of a purification process that ends U.S. dependence on imported quartz. This high temperature material is used not only in lighting and heating devices but for applications requiring good chemical resistance.

The Quartzline® halogen lamp is perfected as Ed Zubler, Stanley Ackerman, Al Foote and Fred Mosby develop the tungsten-iodine regenerative cycle, a chemical reaction that prevents blackening of the inside walls of the lamp bulb. The result is a compact lamp with greatly increased brightness and extended life. The Miniature Lamp Department introduces a 150-watt unit as a marker light for aircraft navigation.

The first totally integrated roadway lighting system is announced by Lighting Systems. Consisting of housing, reflector, refractor, lamp and ballast, the unit lowers the cost of outdoor lighting and increases driving safety.

As a consequence of fundamental sintering research, a new pore-free polycrystalline alumina oxide is invented by Robert C. Coble and Joseph Burke at the Research Laboratory. The material, called Lucalox®, will make higher efficiency discharge lamps a reality.

Integrated roadway lighting system lights the streets of Washington, D.C.

SPACE EXPLORATION

The first photographs of our planet taken from outer space are returned to earth in the Mark 2 data capsule.

The RVX-1, launched by a Thor-Able rocket, flies 4,939 miles and is the first re entry vehicle to be recovered in its entirety. The feat is made possible by a lightweight, ablative heat shield which replaces the heavier and bulkier copper shield of the original Mark 2 vehicle.

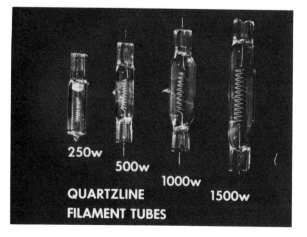

Quartzline halogen filament lamp for high intensity lighting.

World's first electro-hydraulic control system for steam turbines installed at Dow Chemical plant by Medium Steam Turbine Department.

USS Triton (GENERAL DYNAMICS PHOTO).

MK 73 guided missile director.

INDUSTRIAL EQUIPMENT

The world's first electro-hydraulic control system for steam turbines is introduced at Dow Chemical by the Medium Steam Turbine Department. The replacement of mechanical hydraulic controls provides greater accuracy and lower maintenance, making the new system the forerunner of all GE turbine control systems.

GE supplies the first integrated power control room (PCR) for a Jones & Laughlin Steel continuous annealing line. The self-contained, enclosed units include interconnecting wiring and ventilation and offer faster and less costly field installation.

NATIONAL DEFENSE

USS Triton makes the first round-the-world voyage without surfacing. During the 83-day, 36,000-mile trip, the nuclear dual reactor plant, designed by KAPL under the direction of the Division of Naval Reactors, AEC, demonstrates ample power to move the ship at cruiser task force speeds.

Pittsfield's Ordnance Systems produces fire control and guidance equipment for the Navy's Polaris Missile System, one of the nation's leading deterrent weapon systems.

The MK 73 director for guided missiles of the Navy's Tartar System goes into production at Ordnance Systems, which has been a continuous supplier of gun mounts and directors for 38 years.

Polaris missile launch.

SPACE EXPLORATION

On the threshold of manned space-flight — The Discoverer XIII is the first man-made object to be recovered from an orbiting space vehicle. The experimental reentry vehicle, RVX-2A, is the largest vehicle recovered from outer space and provides the first color photographs of earth from altitudes of up to 700 miles.

The Van Allen Radiation Belt is explored by the Nuclear Emulsion Recovery Vehicle (NERVA) built for the National Aeronautics and Space Administration. The satellite reaches altitudes as high as 1250 miles.

Center of attention is the U.S. Air Force Discoverer XIII capsule following its successful recovery August 11, 1960. President Dwight D. Eisenhower holds the 50-star flag recovered from the capsule. Looking on is Gen. Thomas D. White, Chief of Staff, U.S. Air Force.

For this rapid transit system in Chicago, GE supplies not only the streetlighting but motors and controls for the trains.

New electronic computers for business and scientific data processing.

LIGHTING

The "bonus electrode" makes a major improvement in mercury lamp performance, increasing the rated life to over 24,000 hours. The innovation helps trigger a massive conversion of incandescent street lamps to mercury vapor, producing an estimated annual energy savings of four billion kilowatt-hours or the equivalent of six million barrels of oil.

INDUSTRIAL EQUIPMENT

The first application of a high power static exciter is on a 25,600-kw generator for the International Paper Company at Bastrap, Louisiana.

The Computer Department announces its GE 225 system, filling the need for flexible, high speed, lower cost computers for business and scientific data processing.

Logic designs developed for the GE 200 series of computers are incorporated in the first all digital solid-state Mark Century series of numerical machine controls.

A new 43-inch bucket for 1800 rpm turbine is examined by Charles W. Elston (l.), Manager - Turbine Engineering, and L. M. Auchmoody, Supervisor - Motor and Diaphragm Engineering. Elston's career of more than 43-years with GE would include positions as general manager of the Gas Turbine and Large Steam Turbine Departments.

POWER GENERATION

The first large-scale, privately financed nuclear power plant goes into service. It is the 210-MW Dresden 1 unit of the Commonwealth Edison Company near Chicago, Illinois. The Large Steam Turbine Generator Department supplies the first turbine built to operate on steam from a nuclear reactor. The 192,000-kw unit operates at 1800 rpm and uses 950 psi saturated steam.

A new type of turbine is designed to drive boiler feed pumps supplying water to the boilers that produce steam for main-turbine generator units. The boiler feed pumps integrate into the total power plant cycle, resulting in greater efficiency of power output and water usage.

Turbine Department's Applied Research and Development Laboratory develops processes for producing turbine castings.

Anatomy of tandem-compound, double-flow reheat steam turbine-generator.

MATERIALS

Carboloy develops its tiniest product, cemented carbide balls for new ball-point pens. The result is a writing instrument with low cost, long life, and smooth perfomance.

Growth in Lexan plastics requires the construction of new facilities at Mount Vernon, Indiana. Lexan plastic is tough enough to replace metals in many applications and is expected to be in widespread demand in industry.

New facilities for the production of Lexan™ at Mount Vernon, Indiana.

Silicon control rectifiers promise to revolutionize machine control.

GE's smallest and possibly lowest priced product. Costing less than a penny apiece. Carboloy cemented Carbide balls (1 mm. diameter) are used for new ball-point pens.

ELECTRONICS AND COMMUNICATIONS

The advent of magnetic amplifiers and silicon control rectifiers provides opportunities to eliminate rotating exciters for ac generating machines and thereby make a major improvement in the reliability of utility power generation.

The National Academy of Television Arts and Sciences awards an "Emmy" to the Tube Products Department for outstanding engineering and technical achievement in developing an Image Orthicon TV Camera Tube with unsurpassed optical sensitivity in poor lighting conditions. Special credit for the development is given to Peter Wargo and Herb Hannan.

Communications Products Department introduces the first transistorized portable two-way radio for police and fire departments.

Semiconductor power rectifier system, world's largest, powers a chlorine generating process line.

TRANSPORTATION

Twin CT58 gas turbine engines, produced at Lynn's Small Aircraft Engine Department, are used to replace piston-driven types in their first application to commercial helicopters. The U.S. Navy awarded GE a contract to develop the XT58 in 1953.

The F-4 Phantom II with twin J79 engines—one of the most successful military aircraft ever produced.

Revolutionary J79 jet engines power the B-58 supersonic bomber and F104A fighter interceptor.

In 1959, Gerhard Neumann (left) and Neil Burgess, designers and developers of the J79 turbojet (above), were named to receive aviation's coveted Collier Trophy Award. They shared the award with the designer of the Lockheed F-104 Starfighter and two Air Force pilots who, in 1958, captured speed and altitude records for flying the F-104. Neumann would later become Vice President and Group Executive for Aircraft Engines.

S-62 commercial helicopter with twin CT58 engines shows its lifting power.

T58 engine at Lynn plant.

1961

APPLIANCES

The use of a powerful, compact motor and rechargeable battery leads to the introduction of an automatic toothbrush and is the forerunner of the development of other lightweight, handheld appliances such as electric hair dryers and an electric slicing knife, featuring twin reciprocating blades.

The newly established Battery Business Section of the Capacitor Department develops rechargeable nickel-cadmium batteries for a full range of portable products from toothbrushes to grass shears and hedge clippers.

A recognized need for larger capacity clothes washers leads to the introduction of the V-12 washer, the first automatic washer of 12-pound capacity available to the public.

Portable appliances with new rechargeable nickel-cadmium batteries.

New automatic washer handles 12 pounds of clothes, yet requires less floor space.

MATERIALS

Dallas T. Hurd, John Pugh and Lufti Amra, of the Refractory Metals Products Department, develop tungsten-rhenium lamp wire, the first new wire composition in over 40 years. The initial application of this new alloy as a photoflash lamp igniter wire produces superior flashability and improved reliability in flash photography.

Carboloy (Metallurgical Products Department) introduces Carb-O-Lock, a unique metalcutting tool combining a simple, rugged toolholder design with an economical, unground cutting insert produced by newly developed precision powder metallurgy techniques. Carboloy becomes the established leader in tool design as well as cutting alloys.

NATIONAL DEFENSE

The Navy commissions its first "quiet" nuclear ballistic missile submarine, the USS Jack. The Lynn-built steam propulsion turbines and gears are designed by Melvin A. Prohl and Erwin C. Rohde to meet the stringent requirements for quiet machinery to avoid enemy detection.

POWER GENERATION AND TRANSMISSION

The first "Package Power Plant" is supplied to the electric utility industry with a shipment to South Carolina Electric and Gas Company. The unit is a completely self-contained gas turbine-generator, almost entirely factory assembled and tested, and ready for installation as a peaking station to provide extra system capacity, or as a standby power source for emergencies.

The introduction of the high capacity vacuum interrupter for protection and control of medium voltage power systems enables the development of smaller, lighter, power breakers requiring less maintenance.

Two "Package Power Plants," each rated at 14,000 k w, operated by Gas y Electricidad, Mallorca, Spain.

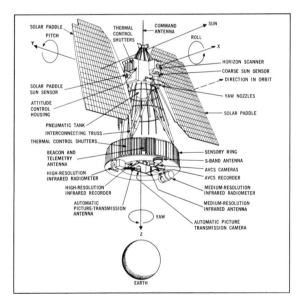

The NIMBUS meteorological satellite.

SPACE EXPLORATION

The Space Division develops NIMBUS, an earth-oriented meteorological satellite, the first of a series of seven that supply scientific data on atmospheric and environmental conditions.

Preparing NIMBUS prototype for test in Valley Forge space simulation chamber, one of the largest in the world.

1961

TRANSPORTATION

The Erie Works builds the country's largest diesel-electric loco-motive. The U25B is a 2500-hp four-axle unit designed for high speed freight service on domestic railroads.

The first railroad application of solid state silicon rectifiers is on New York, New Haven & Hartford Railroad commuter cars.

New York, New Haven & Hartford commuter car, first railroad application of solid state silicon rectifiers.

The U25B diesel-electric locomotive.

ELECTRONICS AND COMMUNICATIONS

The Compactron, an electron tube allowing multi-functional receiving capability within one glass tube, is introduced by the Tube Products Department.

The Federal Communications Commission approves GE's pro-posed standards for FM stereophonic broadcasting and GE's Schenectady station, WGFM, starts broadcasting in stereo.

Stereophonic table model radio with detachable speakers.

Gerald L. Phillippe, who became Chairman of the Board of General Electric in 1963, was widely known for his leadership in the nationwide effort to enlist the support of business in attacking urban problems, and unemployment. He was founder of the Urban Coalition.

Born in Ute, Iowa, September 27, 1909, Phillippe spent his boyhood in Basin, Wyoming. Early in his youth he acquired the nickname of "Flip," by which he came to be known throughout the business and financial communities.

During World War II Phillippe moved into his first managerial position as manager of the Statistics Division, with some 200 people reporting to him. He immediately won their admiration for his managerial skills.

GERALD L. PHILLIPPE

In 1947 Phillippe was appointed auditor for the Apparatus Department, and in 1950 was named comptroller for the department. In November, 1951, he was appointed manager-finance of the Apparatus Sales Division. Two years later he was elected Comptroller, chief financial officer of the Company. He served in this position and as general manager of the Company's Accounting Services until his election as President and a member of the Board of Directors on August 2, 1961. He became Chairman of the Board in 1963, succeeding the retiring Ralph Cordiner in that post.

Gerald L. Phillippe's term was cut short by his death in 1968, at the age of 59, but his astute leadership had left its mark on the growth of the Company. His service to humanity also left its mark on the spirit of the Company.

In honor of his leadership in public service, General Electric established the Gerald L. Phillippe Awards, recognizing outstanding social contributions by the award of a medal and an opportunity to designate a charity or educational institution for a $1000 grant from the General Electric Foundation.

GE Board Chairman Gerald L. Phillippe at dedication of new Power Transformer Department building in Pittsfield (1968). At his side is transformer invented by William Stanley in 1885.

PLANNING THE UTILITY SYSTEMS OF TODAY... AND TOMORROW

The first commercial central generating station in the United States was Thomas Edison's Pearl Street Station in New York City. Completed in 1882, it used six of Edison's "Jumbo" dynamos, with a capacity of 600 kilowatts, to provide electric current for lamps in the homes and businesses of 85 customers served via fourteen miles of underground cables. The success of that pioneering installation was due not only to Edison's inventive genius, but to his thorough planning of the overall system based on an understanding of the interactions of its components. This applications engineering expertise has taken many forms during the almost 100 years that General Electric has been supplying the needs of electric utilities.

Today, these services are centered in the Electric Utility Systems Engineering Department (EUSED) in Schenectady, New York. But the common denominator throughout has been the participation of people whose skills have been able to provide practical solutions to complex problems as well as the development of new theories and analytical methods to cope with ever-increasing equipment and utility system complexities.

In the space available here, it is possible to mention but a few of the many individuals who were part of EUSED's predecessor organizations and who made outstanding contributions in areas related to utility systems engineering.

Edith Clarke

Edith Clarke was the first woman to receive an electrical engineering degree from Massachusetts Institute of Technology (1919) and the first woman to be elected a Fellow of the American Institute of Electrical Engineers. A member of the GE Central Station Engineering Division from 1922 until her retirement in 1945, she made significant contributions to symmetrical component and circuit analysis theory and to the solution of long-distance power transmission problems.

A 1942 winner of the Coffin Award, Charles Concordia is the author of over 65 publications, including a textbook, which still serves as a foundation for the design and prediction of synchronous machine performance. He pioneered in the application of differential and digital computers to power system studies, and was the first chairman of the AIEE Committee on Computing Devices.

Charles Concordia

Selden B. Crary

Ten years after he joined GE, Selden B. Crary received GE's highest honor, the Coffin Award for 1937, for his work on the theory of performance of synchronous machines. He became an internationally known authority in the field of electric utility system design and made important contributions to the stability, reliability and economics of bulk power transmission systems.

ELECTRIC UTILITY SYSTEMS ENGINEERING DEPARTMENT

The Applications Engineering Department, a predecessor of EUSED, was an early leader in the use and application of computers and computer technology. As early as 1915, a dc network analyzer board was constructed to assist in the solution of power system problems. The General Engineering Laboratory supplied an ac network analyzer in 1937. These were followed by transient network analyzers and mechanical and electronic differential analyzers.

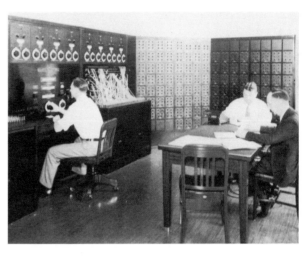

The ac network analyzer being used to solve a power company operating problem (1938).

Mechanical differential analyzer in use (1948).

The use of the CPC (card programmed calculator) and several generations of IBM computers heralded in the period of large scale digital studies as we know them today. EUSED continues to provide analytical leadership in the field of electrical utility systems by means of the development of new generations of equipment which can be used to model and simulate machine performance and system interactions – and by means of personnel whose combination of talents can provide a unique integration of technological and economic assessment of products and system operation.

EDUCATION -- A KEY TO FUTURE DEVELOPMENT

The ability of utility systems engineering to stay abreast of changing technologies and environments requires a broad educational service to General Electric and utility industry engineers. A major element in this service is the masters' level, thirty-week Power Systems Engineering Course. This course, established in 1949 at the recommendation of Selden B. Crary, has graduated nearly 1,000 utility engineers from the United States and various countries around the world. Many alumni have distinguished themselves, not only technically, but by advancing to leadership positions in the utility industry.

Homer M. Rustebakke, Manager-Power Systems Engineering Course, lectures before class of utility systems engineers.

1962

MATERIALS

The Silicone Products Department introduces the use of RTV sealants to industry and subsequently to construction and consumer markets. In 1958, room temperature-curing RTV silicone rubber was developed.

High power, solid state silicon rectifiers (SCRs) are made possible through the development of a tungsten substrate that matches the expansion characteristics of silicon yet serves as an excellent conductor of both heat and electricity. Produced by the Refractory Metals Department, these pressed and sintered tungsten discs serve as the basis for many new forms of power conversion.

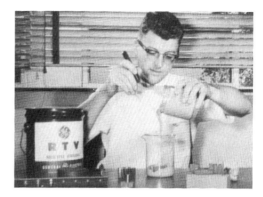
RTV silicone rubber is demonstrated by Silicone Products' Charles A. Berridge.

Metroliner service between New York and Washington, D.C.

TRANSPORTATION

Ernest F. Weiser invents a staged phase control rectifier propulsion system that provides smooth, stepless control for rail cars and reduces wayside equipment costs. It is first introduced in "Silverliner" cars for commuter service in the Philadelphia area.

The USS Bainbridge with its power plant designed by KAPL under the direction of the Division of Naval Reactors, AEC, is commissioned as the Navy's first nuclear powered missile frigate.

INDUSTRIAL EQUIPMENT

The Drive Systems Department pioneers the first successful application of digital computers to control hot strip steel mills at McLouth Steel Company. Use of the GE 312 computer provides the means for more accurate control operations, more uniform product quality and higher productivity.

Industrial Control Department builds industry's first solid state control and applies it to a battery-powered fork lift truck.

Launching of the USS Bainbridge, the US Navy's first nuclear powered missile frigate.

GE's new 18.8-cu. ft. Spacemaker Refrigerator-Freezer fits in same space as old 10-cu. ft. model.

APPLIANCES

The Mini-Basket washing system is added to the automatic washer to improve small load washing efficiency and to permit the handling of delicate handwashables. It uses 25 percent less energy than the small load setting on the same washer.

The first Package Terminal Air Conditioner is the ZONELINE which can be installed through the wall in apartments, motels, schools and other institutions to allow individually controlled heating or cooling at the touch of a button.

The first foamed-in-place urethane insulated refrigerator is built at Appliance Park. The new 18.8-cu. ft. capacity Spacemaker fits in the same space as the 1947 version of a 10-cu. ft. model.

LIGHTING

The Cool Beam dichroic reflector PAR lamp is developed for use in places needing increased light and reduced heat, such as food storage facilities. Its operation is based on a filtering process which permits all visible light to be reflected and more than two-thirds of the infrared (heat) radiation to be reabsorbed by the parabolic aluminized reflector.

POWER GENERATION AND DISTRIBUTION

The development of a patented system for detecting and locating corona sources (partial discharges) in power transformers significantly improves their reliability and life expectancy.

A standardized line of geared turbine-generator sets is developed for marine applications. These units drive electric generators to supply all electrical power aboard vessels ranging from LNG container ships to nuclear attack submarines.

Corona testing power transformers at Medium Transformer Department, Rome, Georgia.

1963

POWER GENERATION

A predecessor of GE's modern STAG combined-cycle generating system (in which steam and gas turbine generating units work together to achieve very high efficiencies) is built for Oklahoma Gas and Electric Company. The OG&E installation consists of a gas turbine-generator that produces 25,000 kilowatts of electricity and a steam turbine-generator rated at 194,000 kw. Rather than venting the gas turbine's exhaust to the atmosphere, these hot gases are channeled to the plant's steam boiler, where they serve as pre-heated combustion air. By making use of this otherwise wasted heat energy, the efficiency of the combined plant is significantly higher than that of a comparably rated plant of conventional design.

A world's record 100,000-gauss field is produced by a magnetic coil wound with niobium-tin superconducting wire developed by Research Laboratory scientists D. Luther Martin, Mark G. Benz, Charles A. Bruch and Carl H. Rosner.

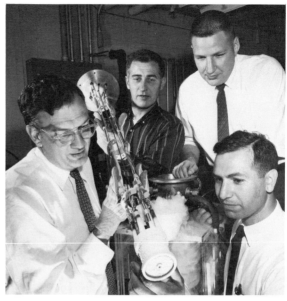

Research Laboratory scientists work on superconducting wire and coils: (l. to r.) D. Luther Martin, Charles A. Bruch, Mark G. Benz, and Carl H. Rosner.

ORGANIZATION

Fred J. Borch is elected President and Chief Executive Officer and Gerald L. Phillippe is named Chairman of the Board, as Ralph J. Cordiner announces his retirement.

TRANSPORTATION

William Speicher of the Transportation Equipment Products Department invents the first successful electric drive system for large off-highway haulage trucks. The motorized wheel propulsion system is introduced on 85-ton capacity Unit Rig Haulage trucks used at open pit mining sites, resulting in greatly increased productivity.

Electric Motorized Wheel propulsion of 85-ton capacity Unit Rig Haulage truck.

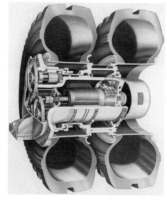

Anatomy of a motorized wheel.

Hot strip mill control room, with computer-directed position regulators, at Taranto, Italy.

INDUSTRIAL EQUIPMENT

The popular ½-hp motor reaches a stage in its evolution where it is about one sixth the weight of the same rating at the turn of the century.

The capabilities of the static exciter system (1960) are extended to the utility industry with the installation of a unit on a new 224,000-kva generator at Southwestern Public Service.

The first completely thyristor-powered rolling mill drive system is installed at Bethlehem Steel's Burns Harbor facility, with 28,000 kw of thyristor power supplies. Reductions in equipment size and weight are accompanied by increased reliability and efficiency.

Worldwide use of GE electronic controls with computer-directed, time-shared digital position regulators is initiated with installations in new hot strip mills in Taranto, Italy; Newport, England; and Abbey Vale, Wales.

Evolution of ½-hp motor.

Thyristor-powered rolling mill drive on Bethlehem Steel plate mill.

APPLIANCES

Mark P. Hogue of Appliance Park develops a unique, food waste disposer design incorporating an encapsulated series motor and the use of stainless steel throughout the water bearing components. The results set new standards for high reliability and long life, at a moderate price.

The P-7® self-cleaning oven is introduced. In developing the oven, which uses a pyrolytic system to remove food soil, GE engineers were granted some 100 patents.

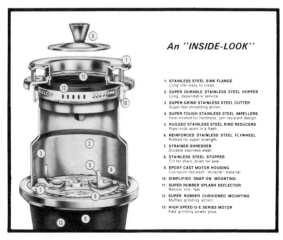

An "INSIDE-LOOK"

1. STAINLESS STEEL SINK FLANGE
   Long life—easy to clean.
2. SUPER DURABLE STAINLESS STEEL HOPPER
   Long, dependable service.
3. SUPER-GRIND STAINLESS STEEL CUTTER
   Super fast shredding action
4. SUPER-TOUGH STAINLESS STEEL IMPELLERS
   Heat-treated for hardness, jam-resistant design.
5. RUGGED STAINLESS STEEL RIND REDUCERS
   Rips rinds apart in a flash.
6. REINFORCED STAINLESS STEEL FLYWHEEL
   Ribbed for super strength.
7. STRAINER-SHREDDER
   Durable stainless steel.
8. STAINLESS STEEL STOPPER
   Tilt for drain, down for seal
9. EPOXY CAST MOTOR HOUSING
   Corrosion resistant "miracle" material.
10. SIMPLIFIED SNAP ON MOUNTING
11. SUPER RUBBER SPLASH DEFLECTOR
    Resists oils, fats.
12. SUPER RUBBER CUSHIONED MOUNTING
    Muffles grinding action.
13. HIGH SPEED G-E SERIES MOTOR
    Fast grinding-power plus.

Anatomy of the Disposall®.

1964

MATERIALS

A process for revealing charged particle tracks in minerals, plastics and glasses is developed by Robert L. Fleischer, P. Buford Price and Robert M. Walker. One application of particle track etching is the determination of the amount of cosmic radiation that would be encountered in space by future astronauts. A unique plastic filter with superfine holes is another offshoot of these studies.

The invention of the MAGVAR (Paper/Film) Capacitor dielectric system by E.B. Cox revolutionizes the design of power capacitors. Use of polypropylene film, which replaces a portion of the Kraft paper in the dielectric system, produces capacitors with a ten-fold reduction in internal electrical losses and permits the design of smaller, lighter weight units.

Engineers and metallurgists at the Research Laboratory and at the Wire and Cable Department develop the "Dip Form" process for continuously casting copper to form oxygen-free rod for wire making. The process converts copper cathode to high quality rod in long lengths without welds.

Walter L. Robb, of the Research Laboratory, invents a method of producing a silicone-based selective membrane which allows gases to pass through it at different rates. Such membranes would be installed in equipment to supply oxygen-rich air to patients needing breathing assistance and they could also be used in a number of industrial applications. Robb would later be appointed manager of engineering at GE Silicones and then General Manager of GE Medical Systems. In 1987 he would become Sr. Vice President - Corporate Research and Development.

New plastic filter is offshoot of research on fission fragment tracks in solid materials by (l. to r.) P. Buford Price, Robert L.Fleischer, and Robert M. Walker.

Dip Form system produces continuous oxygen-free rod for wire making.

Walter L.Robb demonstrates how a silicone-based membrane provides breathing air for a hamster in an underwater cage. The watertight membrane that makes up four sides of the cage extracts air dissolved in the surrounding water.

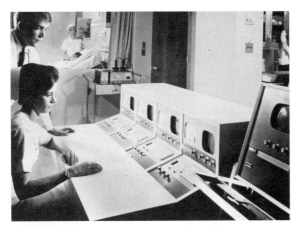

Electronic Patient Monitoring System.

Automatic Dial Paging System for doctors.

Vulcan Air Defense System (VADS).

MEDICAL EQUIPMENT

An electronic patient monitoring system for critical care applications is introduced by the Medical Systems Business Department.

A new automatic Dial Paging System is available for hospital and industrial use.

POWER GENERATION

Plans are formulated for SEFOR, the nation's first fast reactor fueled with plutonium-uranium oxide. This 20-MWe demonstration plant near Fayetteville, Arkansas, verified the theoretical work of GE scientists and demonstrated the feasibility of Liquid Metal Fast Breeder Reactors.

The first POWER BLOCK arrangement of gas turbines is built for Oklahoma Gas and Electric Company's Enid Station. These units, operating under a single control, consist of four General Electric MS 5000 units, rated at 14,000 kw each.

NATIONAL DEFENSE

GE receives U.S. Army authorization to develop the ground-based Vulcan Air Defense System. This rapid-fire system is a vital part of NATO and other U.S. ally anti-aircraft defense equipment.

INSTALLING AND SERVICING
THE PRODUCTS OF TECHNOLOGY

The concept of equipment installation and service and specialized engineering support for its products dates back to the early years of General Electric. The Thomson-Houston Company opened a field service shop in Philadelphia in 1882. A year later, in order to assure satisfactory on-site installation, adjustment and maintenance of its arc lamps, the Company trained and established an organization of "experts", ancestors of today's Installation and Service Engineering field engineers. The first "expert" was Edwin Rice who later became the Company's president.

APPARATUS SERVICE BUSINESS DIVISION

The Apparatus Service Business Division encompasses a network of more than 190 Service Shops in 19 countries worldwide – with the International Service Department headquartered in London. It employs more than 12,500 skilled technicians and craftsmen.

KEY EVENTS (1947-1978)

1949 The first International Service Shop is opened in Rio de Janeiro.

1955 One hundred Service Shop employees are flown into six Northeastern states to help repair electrical equipment at industrial plants and utilities damaged by record flooding after two hurricanes.

1959 Schenectady Instrumentation Service, begun in 1896, opens its first shop dedicated exclusively to instrument service.

1966 The introduction of the GEGARD® motor rewinding and insulation process sets a new standard in motor maintenance and repair.

1973 A mobile transformer test van, with portable generator rated at two million volts, is placed in service. It provides factory-quality dielectric testing on-site, saving down-time and costs involved in transporting the transformer to a test facility.

1975 A new Measurement Service helps locate invisible mechanical faults and potential equipment failures faster and more efficiently using state-of-the-art analytical tools such as thermographic surveys and acoustic emission tests.

Testing circuit board during electronic instrument repair.

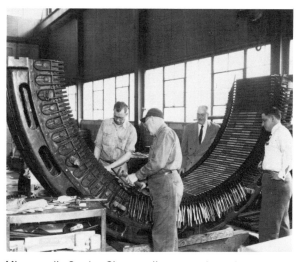

Minneapolis Service Shop applies new wire to heavy apparatus.

INSTALLATION AND SERVICE ENGINEERING DIVISION

The Installation and Service Engineering Division has evolved to a worldwide organization of 170 offices, with 20 located outside of the United States. Its staff consists of some 4,200 people, the majority of whom are engineers whose skills and talents match the profile of customer needs in the geographic areas in which they are stationed.

KEY EVENTS (1947-1978)

1951 An Aircraft Gas Turbine Section, predecessor of I&SE's Aviation Section, is established to install and flight-test General Electric jet engines.

1955 Twelve Field District Engineering components and a foreign Installation-Turbine Section are incorporated into the newly established Installation and Service Engineering Department. William M. Denny becomes its first manager.

1964 Transfer of the Power Plant Engineering Operation to I&SE adds utility and industrial plant capabilities and system design expertise.

1966 To help supply the growing need for field engineers, the Field Engineering Program for graduate engineers is established.

1970 The Pacific HVDC Intertie Project, the country's first high-voltage dc transmission line, is installed by I&SE.

1974 The Field Engineering Program moves to a new Field Engineering Development Center on Balltown Road in Schenectady.

W. G. ELY
1901 - 1927

F. P. WILSON
1927 - 1942

W. M. DENNY
1942 - 1964

I&SE Field Engineering Center houses classrooms and laboratories containing mechanical, electronic and electrical equipment that field service engineers are likely to encounter.

1965

ELECTRONICS AND COMMUNICATIONS

The first portable color television receiver, featuring the in-line picture tube, is marketed by the Television Business Department.

Closed circuit TV is introduced for viewing medical fluoroscopy.

The free world's largest ship sonar, the SQS-26, provides advanced high power, long-range capabilities for U.S. Navy submarines.

INFORMATION PROCESSING

GE announces the world's first commercial computer time sharing service, called "Mark I Service." In 1963, the concept of shared use of computers was developed jointly with Dartmouth College utilizing a new computer language dubbed "BASIC."

First portable color TV, the Portacolor.

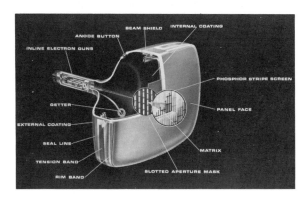

Anatomy of the in-line picture tube.

INDUSTRIAL EQUIPMENT

The Industry Control Department uses SCRs in place of contactors to obtain a highly reliable, stepless, solid state adjustable speed control for ac motors, the Tirastat II Control (TI-time, RA-ratio, STAT-static).

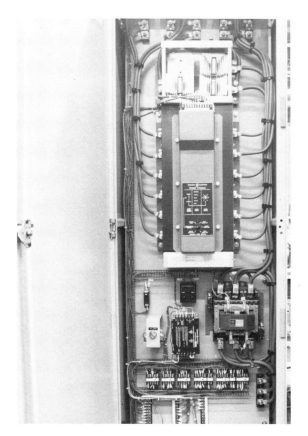

Heart of ac motor control, the Tirastat II.

New 500-kv air blast circuit breakers protect Arkansas Power and Light EHV line.

Underground distribution of power is more feasible with the development of new transformers.

NEW TRENDS IN POWER DISTRIBUTION

ORGANIZATION

The Research Laboratory and the Advanced Technology Laboratories (successor to GEL) are combined in a new organization to be called the General Electric Research and Development Center. Arthur M. Bueche is named to the newly created post of Vice-President-Research and Development. He is shown here, seated between his two predecessors, C. Guy Suits (left), Vice President and Director of Research, and George L. Haller, Vice President—Advanced Technology Services.

TRANSPORTATION

The high bypass turbofan TF39 jet engine is developed to power the world's largest aircraft, the Lockheed C-5 military transport. Its fuel consumption efficiency is 25 percent better than any previous jet engine.

1965

POWER GENERATION AND TRANSMISSION

Ten J79 type aircraft gas turbine engines are combined to provide hot gas to drive a single stage 1200-rpm gas turbine capable of producing 100,000 k w. The plant, built for the Cincinnati Gas and Electric Company's Dick Creek Unit #1, can burn either natural gas or liquid fuel by changing fuel nozzles and is designed for fully automatic, unattended operation.

The nation's first 500- kv power transmission system is protected by GE 500- kv Air Blast Breakers, the first power breakers of this rating. The breaker features the largest non-porcelain insulator column ever applied — a GEPOL unit, 4 ft. in diameter and over 15 ft. in length.

Canadian General Electric supplies EHV equipment for Quebec's 735,000-v transmission line, operating at the highest voltage of any commercial line in the Western World.

Introduction of the Load-Vac tap changer increases transformer operating levels and the time between required maintenance.

Fuel cells developed by the Direct Energy Conversion Operation are the first used in space flight as they power the Gemini 5 and Gemini 7 missions. An ion-exchange membrane, invented by Research Laboratory scientists Leonard W. Niedrach and W. Thomas Grubb, is a vital link in the construction of these highly efficient devices for converting fuel directly to electricity.

Power of 10 aircraft jet engines will drive new turbine-generator.

Leonard W. Niedrach (l.) and W. Thomas Grubb demonstrate fuel cell membrane.

General Electric's Progressland Pavilion at the New York World's Fair.

LIGHTING

Lucalox® lamps display the highest efficiencies known for a white light source. In 1961 William Louden and Kurt Schmidt developed this high-pressure sodium vapor discharge lamp which operated at pressures and temperatures never before possible in an electric lamp. The development was made possible by the invention of Lucalox polycrystalline alumina arc tubes in 1962 by Robert C. Coble and Joseph Burke of the Research Laboratory.

Multi-Vapor® lamps are introduced at the New York World's Fair. This new discharge light source, based on Gilbert Reiling's addition of other metallic vapors to a mercury discharge, improves color and efficiencies for lamps in commercial and industrial use. Process and equipment for continuous drawing of improved Type 214 fused quartz tubing used in the construction of these lamps was developed by M.C. Riggert and others at the Lamp Glass Products Department.

The first enclosed, high-intensity arc projection lamp, the MARC 300, is developed for use with sound projectors to produce greater screen brightness at long projection distances. A 300-w MARC lamp is up to four times as effective as a 1000-w incandescent lamp for screen illumination.

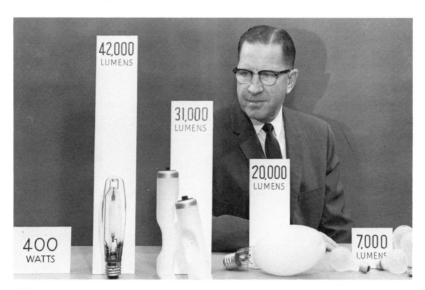

Efficiency of the new Lucalox® lamp is dramatized by Thomas M. Wallace, general manager of the Large Lamp Department. The relative light output (lumens) is shown for four types of light sources using 400w of electrical power: (l. to r.) a single Lucalox® lamp, two 96-inch-long Power Groove fluorescent lamps, a mercury discharge lamp, and four standard 100-w household lamps.

1966-1967

POWER GENERATION AND TRANSMISSION

The ALTERREX® excitation system for large steam turbine-generators is introduced to the electric utilities. By replacing dc exciters and amplidynes with an ac alternator and diode rectifiers, this system greatly increases the reliability of operation of steam turbine-generators and becomes a standard for other excitation systems.

The Power Transformer Department supplies transformers and power bushings for the Pacific HVDC Intertie Project, bringing power from the Pacific Northwest to Southern California in the first large scale demonstration in the U.S. of high voltage, direct current power transmission.

Hyper-Servo motors for use in computers.

INDUSTRIAL EQUIPMENT

The Large Motor and Generator Department develops zero leakage, "canned" (sealed) pump motors for use in the U.S. Navy's nuclear propulsion program.

Hyper-Servo® motors developed for computer uses are 50 times faster in response than standard dc industrial motors.

Japan Steel Company purchases "Man-Mate" to handle hot billets and improve mill efficiency. This new type of materials-handling machine simulates human motions while magnifying strength and reach capabilities.

Transformers and power bushings for the Pacific HVDC Project on the Columbia River in Oregon.

MEDICAL EQUIPMENT

Donald Graves of the Medical Systems Department designs the first 500-cycle, battery-powered mobile x-ray generator which makes possible fast response, high quality examinations at bedside in cases where it is inconvenient to move the patient. Improved x-ray tube loading, higher energy, faster exposures and significantly reduced radiation per exposure result from his development of the world's first solid state, three-phase x-ray generator.

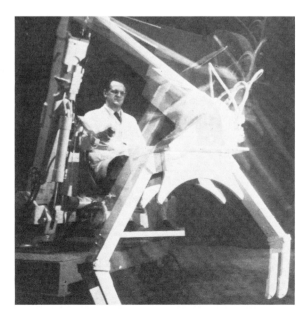

Man-Mate materials handling machine using new feedback and control technology.

Quartz blank for the 158-inch Kitt Peak Observatory mirror.

MATERIALS

The largest fused quartz mirror blank ever produced is supplied for the 158-inch Kitt Peak Observatory telescope.

ELECTRONICS AND COMMUNICATIONS

The first airborne laser ranging system is delivered to the Air Force. Experimental flight control equipment also used by the Air Force makes use of the first metal oxide semiconductor (MOS) circuits.

General Electric Cablevision Corporation, a wholly owned GE subsidiary, starts operations with four cablevision systems. Cable TV is expected to usher in a new era of home entertainment and communications.

SPACE EXPLORATION

The Biosatellite II primate-carrying space vehicle completes a successful two-day test in orbit, further demonstrating the possibilities for manned space flight.

APPLIANCES

Donald S. Cushing and Thomas E. Jenkins of Appliance Park design a dishwasher motor and water circulating pump combination whose improved efficiency reduces energy and operating costs to the consumer.

Vice President Hubert Humphrey (r.) discusses model of primate-carrying Biosatellite with (l. to r.) Mark Morton—General Manager, Re-entry Systems Department; V. DeLiberato, RSD; and Hilliard V. Paige—Vice President and General Manager, Missile and Space Division.

TRANSPORTATION

Research and Development Center engineers demonstrate the possibilities of personal transportation in an "electric car." Project results indicate the need for major improvements in batteries, motors and controls before a vehicle with general usefulness can be produced.

Research and Development Center experimental electric car.

Light valve television projector.

Integrated Engine Instrumentation System for aircraft use.

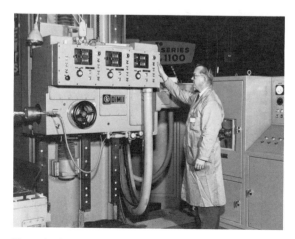

Numerical control machining center.

ELECTRONICS AND COMMUNICATIONS

The first commercial light valve television projector is announced. Capable of displaying color TV pictures up to 20 feet wide, the projectors are expected to find worldwide applications for military, commercial and educational uses.

An early spinoff of space technology, the integrated Engine Instrumentation System, is introduced by the Aircraft Equipment Division and accepted as standard equipment on wide-body transport programs, including the 747 and the DC-10.

Integrated circuitry, employed for the first time in the Mark Century series numerical control, makes possible machining centers, controlling both point-to-point positioning and continuous path contouring.

The Aerospace Control Systems Department develops VYRO, an angular rate sensor for flight control systems. With no moving parts to wear out or require lubrication, the result is essentially unlimited life and the high reliability required for aircraft use.

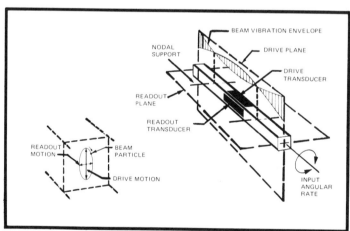

VYRO angular rate sensor for flight control.

(Electronics and Communications continued)

A Specialty Control Department team established by Lewis T. Rader produces the first of a series of high speed teleprinters using state-of-the-art electronics to operate at 30 characters per second. Dow Jones Company installs the machines in several thousand brokerage offices to take advantage of their rapid response. A similar product, the TermiNet 300®, is made available to the electronic data processing industry to complement the growing number of "time share" computers.

Mark II® Service is announced, with businesses in 42 cities in more than 20 metropolitan areas able to access GE 600 series computers via a local telephone call. Around the world, in 17 countries, over 100,000 customers can make use of the service.

GE mobile telephones are supplied for the high-speed Metroliner trains by the Communications Systems Division.

J. Kirk Snell, at the TermiNet 300 teleprinter, received the Steinmetz Award in 1978 for his contributions to the development of products which became the basis for the Data Communications Products Business Dept.

POWER GENERATION

The first GE combined steam and gas cycle Power Plant (STAG®) is shipped to the Wolverine Electric Cooperative. Overall thermal efficiency is the highest of any obtained with a fossil-fueled power plant.

The SPEEDTRONIC® governor for heavy-duty industrial gas turbines replaces mechanical governors with an all-electronic system that provides improved levels of speed, temperature and load control.

The first light water reactor simulator, a computerized hands-on Boiling Water Reactor (BWR) control room, is built as part of GE's BWR Training Center located at Morris, Illinois. It is used for training nuclear plant operators and qualifying them for Nuclear Regulatory Commission (NRC) operator licenses.

First light water nuclear reactor simulator.

Combined steam and gas cycle Power Plant (STAG) increases fossil-fuel power plant efficiency.

1968

MATERIALS

Jacob G. Rabatin develops a high efficiency x-ray phosphor permitting major reductions in patient exposure to medical x-rays.

Extruded Lexan sheet is developed for applications in glazing and sign materials. Improvement in its properties expands its use to include bullet resistant enclosures and virtually unbreakable windows for transportation and institutional use.

CF6 jet engines for new wide-body airliners.

TRANSPORTATION

The first solid state electronic train-running controls see use in the Metroliner service between New York and Washington, D.C. Propulsion systems are capable of 160-mph performance on adequate track.

GE CF6 engines with 40,000-pound thrust are chosen to power the McDonnell Douglas DC-10 trijet wide-bodied airliner. Increased thrust versions of the CF6 will be designed for the European-built A300 Airbus, the DC-10 series 30 and a number of Boeing 747 aircraft.

Chosen Businessman of the Year for 1970 by the *Saturday Review* (January 23, 1971), Fred Borch received twice as many votes as any other candidate for that honor in American business, finance, or government. He had been elected Chairman of the Board at General Electric only two years earlier.

Borch was born on April 28, 1910, in Brooklyn, New York, where his father was an electrical engineer with the Brooklyn Edison Company, now a part of Consolidated Edison Company of New York.

Most of Borch's schooling took place in Ohio, mainly in the Cleveland area. Schoolboy jobs included two summers as an office boy with *The Cleveland News.* Later, while a student at Case Western Reserve University, which he entered in 1927, he held a summer job as a timekeeper on a construction project for an electric power transmission line. In 1931, he received his B.A. in economics and went to work as an auditor with General Electric in the Lamp Division at Nela Park.

By 1940, Borch had become Manager of the Lamp Division's customer service organization and, in 1947, he was named manager of the Sales Operation Department. In 1952, he joined the administrative department of the Lamp Division, and later the same year undertook a special assignment with the Company's Management Consultation Services in New York.

In 1953, he was entrusted with the task of restructuring the Lamp Division into six operating departments as part of the Company-wide decentralization program. The following year he was named Vice President for Marketing Services, and from there on worked closely with Ralph J. Cordiner, the man he succeeded as Chief Executive of General Electric.

In September, 1959, he was appointed Vice President and Group Executive for the Company's Consumer

FRED J. BORCH

Products Group, the post he held until his election as Executive Vice President in July, 1962. In this position he was elected to the Board of Directors and given responsibility for the operating components of the Company on a worldwide basis, jobs he continued to handle after he was elected President and Chief Executive Officer in December, 1963, and Chairman on December 20, 1968. During his tenure Borch essentially added another General Electric to the one whose direction he assumed. Sales and earnings of the Company almost doubled between 1963 and 1972, the year that he retired. That phenomenal growth was, at least in part, due to Borch's keen judgement and motivation of people — his well recognized ability to choose "the right man for the job, for sizing up people and then getting the best out of them." (*World-Telegram and Sun*, December 22, 1964). The management team that Borch left in place at the time of his retirement was ample testimonial to this talent.

1969

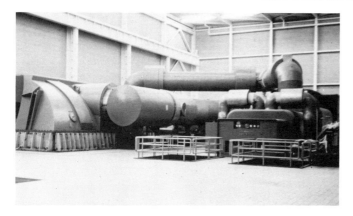

TVA turbine-generator, rated at 1,104,000 kw.

POWER GENERATION AND TRANSMISSION

The largest GE turbine for a plant using fossil fuel is built for the Paradise Unit No. 3 of the Tennessee Valley Authority. Rated at 1,104,000 kw, it has a 3600-rpm shaft driving one generator and an 1800-rpm shaft driving another generator.

The Big Sandy Unit No. 2 of the Kentucky Power Company, rated at 737,000 kw, is the Steam Turbine Division's largest double reheat turbine.

The first large scale production of nuclear fuel bundles and other components for boiling water reactors takes place at a newly opened manufacturing facility in Wilmington, North Carolina. Previously, such components were fabricated in laboratories and other prototype operations.

Nuclear fuel bundle production at Wilmington, North Carolina.

Big Sandy Station No. 2 of Kentucky Power Company, housing a 737,000-kw double reheat turbine.

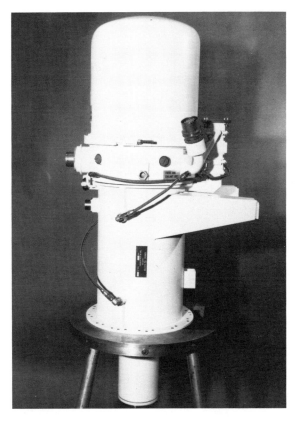

NATIONAL DEFENSE

A klystron tube, with very wide microwave frequency range and without mechanical tuning, is developed for the Airborne Warning and Control System (AWACS) by the Microwave Tube Operation in Schenectady.

MATERIALS

Neil Armstrong takes the first step on the moon with boots made from GE silicone rubber. Astronauts' helmets use visors fabricated from Lexan® polycarbonate.

The Specialty Materials Department announces the industrial availability of Borazon® CBN crystals, produced at its new plant in Worthington, Ohio (see 1957). Man-Made® diamonds are also manufactured at this location, now providing the two hardest materials known to man and made by man.

Klystron tube for Airborne Warning and Control System (AWACS).

INFORMATION PROCESSING

Regional computing centers are consolidated into GE's first Information Services "supercenter" near Cleveland, Ohio, providing computer power and remote batch and time-sharing services coast-to-coast.

SPACE EXPLORATION

The Space Division builds the first earth resources satellite system, the LANDSAT. This forerunner of a fully operational global system is being used by over 100 nations for earth resources inventory and management.

Information Services "supercenter" for time-sharing information processing.

1969

TRANSPORTATION

A special gear transmission system, based on design principles developed for both aircraft and marine gearing, is provided by the Medium Steam Turbine Department to meet the confined hull requirements of hydrofoil ships.

The first "Super Rapid Transit" propulsion system is introduced on the PATCO transit line from Philadelphia, Pennsylvania, to Lindenwold, New Jersey. High performance motors and controls and on-board automation equipment provide smooth acceleration, speed regulation and positioned station stops.

New "Super Rapid Transit" system with on-board automation equipment (above) sets new standards in commuter transportation.

APPLIANCES

Appliance Park announces the first side-by-side refrigerator-freezer with an automatic dispenser for ice cubes and chilled water through the door.

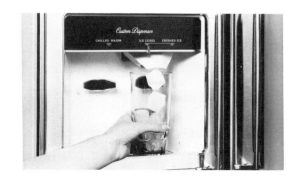

Side-by-side refrigerator-freezer with automatic ice cube and chilled water dispenser.

Four LM2500 turbines power Spruance-class destroyer.

Geared marine steam turbines drive U.S. Navy aircraft carrier, USS John F. Kennedy.

SHIPS AT SEA

General Electric jet engine, steam turbine, nuclear, and mechanical gear technologies help power and propel sea-going vessels for national defense (above), commerce (right), oceanographic research (bottom, left) and high-speed transportation (bottom, right).

LM2500 marine turbines first applied to roll on/roll off high-speed cargo ship, GTS Admiral William M. Callaghan.

Nuclear powered NR-1 deep submergence research vessel.
(General Dynamics Photo)

Hydrofoil ship uses special gear transmission system.

"The Eagle has landed".

Transatel TV system brings Apollo recovery to the world-live and in color.

GE IN SPACE

"That's one small step for man, one giant leap for mankind." Neil Armstrong-July 20, 1969. When Apollo 11 landed astronauts Neil Armstrong and Edwin Aldrin on the moon, 37 different GE operations and 6000 employees could take credit for having helped put them there. All manned flights through Apollo relied on GE radio command guidance equipment. The Space Division supplied overall quality control, systems engineering support, check-out equipment, Saturn launch vehicle test facilities and the ship-to-satellite system that provided the first live color TV pictures of splash-down and recovery.

SNAP-27 radio-isotope power generators provided the energy to run lunar surface experiments for years after the last astronaut left the moon.

STORY OF A SPACE RESCUE

During the lunar orbit phase of the Apollo 13 mission, a malfunction occurred in the Command Module power system. Specialty Control Department engineers were rushed from Waynesboro to Grumman Aircraft, builder of the Lunar Module. They worked out a procedure to isolate the faulty power supply (built by another contractor) and connect the Lunar Module power to the Command Module. Instructions were radioed to the astronauts and the heavily overloaded Specialty Control power supply helped bring the astronauts home.

Transporter with Apollo 11 atop Saturn moves to Cape Kennedy launch site.

Apollo Acceptance Checkout.

Barge Pearl River carries Saturn rocket stage at NASA's Mississippi Test Facility.

Japanese Broadcast Satellite.

Orbiting Astronomical Observatory

The nation's manned space program of the 1980's will be covered on the Space Shuttle, and the Space Division will play a key role in providing check-out and support facilities for the vehicle's factory, approach and landing test series, payload integration, and materials processing in space.

Man's ventures into space have been accompanied by unmanned satellites such as the Nimbus and Landsat series which are providing valuable information about our planet's weather and natural resources, on a daily basis. The Japanese Broadcast Satellite has advanced the state-of-the-art of television communications to remote locations.

In search of an increased knowledge of our universe, two GE-equipped Viking spacecraft made the long journey to Mars. And for Voyager, the U.S. mission destined to travel the farthest through the universe, GE-built thermoelectric generators power the two Voyager crafts and their ten scientific experiments.

Perhaps as important as the airborne achievements of space technology have been its earthbound offshoots, including solar and fuel cell energy research, microelectronics, information processing and communications.

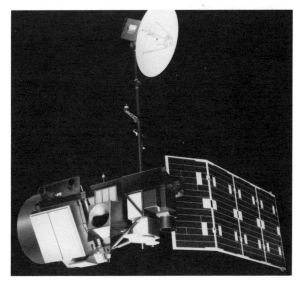

Landsat.

Space Shuttle on test pad.

1970

POWER GENERATION AND TRANSMISSION

Pittsfield's ultra-high-voltage program tests the world's highest voltage transformer, at 1,500,000 v.

Europe's largest hydroelectric plant is built at Alcantara, Spain, and supplies water pressure to turn hydro-generators built by the GE Spanish affiliate, GE Espanola.

Ten years after the installation of the 210-mw Dresden boiling water reactor and steam turbine-generator, Dresden 2 and 3 are supplied to the Commonwealth Edison Company. Each unit is rated at 809 mw.

The 1500-kv transformer for ultra-high-voltage research program at Pittsfield.

Dresden 2 nuclear power station, supplying 809 mw of electricity.

MATERIALS

Synthesis of gem-quality diamonds is achieved by Herbert M. Strong and Robert H. Wentorf of the Research and Development Center.

Carboloy introduces "500" Series titanium carbide-coated, cemented carbide cutting inserts to the metalworking industry. They increase productivity by allowing cutting speeds to be increased up to 50 percent without loss of tool life.

The Wire and Cable Department supplies the first crosslinked vinyl insulation, FLAMENOL XL. This new insulation provides superior flame and heat resistant properties and outstanding mechanical toughness.

Fred Holub (l.) of the Research and Development Center and Elwood Betts of the Wire and Cable Department lead development of Flamenol XL and other flame resistant insulations.

276

Tektite II undersea habitat for long-term oceanographic research.

UNDERSEA EXPLORATION

The Tektite II Program, an undersea habitat for prolonged underwater investigations, is the most ambitious of its kind ever attempted. Under the leadership of the Department of the Interior, GE makes contributions which include design, installation and maintenance of this habitat where over 50 scientists and engineer-aquanauts engage in scientific studies.

INDUSTRIAL EQUIPMENT

The first adjustable-speed ac drive is introduced, using solid state inverter technology.

NATIONAL DEFENSE

For the Air Force Minuteman ICBM program, the Re-entry Systems Department develops and produces the Mark 12 re-entry system. Modified versions of the Mark 12 will be used on the U.S. Navy's Trident ballistic missiles. In 1963, the Mark 6 vehicle became operational as part of the Air Force's Titan II deterrent missile system.

Synthesized gem diamonds created in the laboratory by subjecting graphite (dark powder) to extreme pressures and temperatures.

LM2500 gas turbine for ship propulsion.

TRANSPORTATION

Gas turbines based on the CF6 jet engine technology are chosen to power the newest Spruance-class Navy destroyers. A year earlier the LM 2500 heavy duty gas turbine demonstrated its capabilities on a merchant vessel. Other versions of the power plant are used for 25,000-hp drives for gas pipeline pumping.

1971-1972

LIGHTING

The first all-glass, baseless subminiature lamp is developed for automotive use. The lamp contributes to even smaller, lighter-weight and less costly instrument panel assemblies.

The Flashbar 10® multiple flash unit is developed and is initially used in Polaroid's new automatic SX-70 camera. The Flashbar combines electronics and lamp technology in the first of a new generation of compact, high performance photoflash lamps.

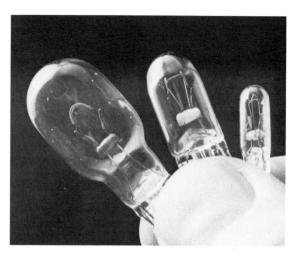

Subminiature baseless all-glass lamps.

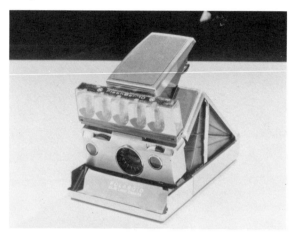

Flashbar 10 on Polaroid's new SX-70 camera.

MATERIALS

Valox® thermoplastic polyesters are introduced, offering special resistance to solvents, oil and gasoline, along with high strength and heat resistance.

Lexan®, Noryl® and Valox are all specially designed as structural foam resins for applications requiring extremely high strength in lightweight assemblies.

INFORMATION PROCESSING

A satellite link to London, extending to cities in western Europe, makes General Electric Information Services Mark II Service the only international computer time-sharing service. Growth of the network to Japan and Australia is planned for 1973.

Housings for computer readout terminal copiers and printers made of Lexan structural foam.

278

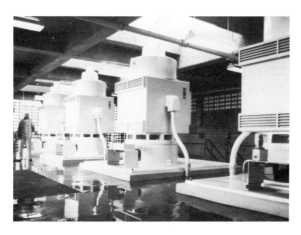

Power transformer being prepared for shipment to offshore oil well drilling rig.

INDUSTRIAL EQUIPMENT

The new AMRAC, computer-operated, two-way power-line communication system is introduced to the electric utility industry. The system provides communication for three options: load control, time-of-day metering and distribution automation. Its dial position meter encoder supplies billing information more reliably and accurately than can be obtained with manual meter reading.

The Large Motor and Generator Department participates in the modernization of U.S. steel manufacturing facilities with the construction of a 10,000-hp, 40-rpm dc mill motor, the largest ever built.

The Drive Systems Department supplies its first drive system control to the oil well drilling industry for an oil well drilling ship. The Specialty Transformer Department supplies transformers to power the drilling rig.

The Glomar Coral Sea oil well drilling ship with drive systems controls, power transformers and other components supplied by GE.

Nine-foot-high vertical motors drive massive pumps at San Jose-Santa Clara water pollution control plant.

POWER GENERATION AND TRANSMISSION

The new GECO method for the production of nuclear reactor fuel is placed in operation at Wilmington, North Carolina. Conversion of uranium hexafluoride to high quality uranium dioxide is accomplished pyrolytically without the complex wet chemical process required earlier.

The first prototype of a zinc-oxide arrester is installed as part of the development of systems for the improved protection of transmission lines and equipment.

Canadian GE and turbines help make Labrador's Churchill Falls hydroelectric generating station one of the largest single-site producers of electricity in the world. The station feeds ac power to the Eel River, New Brunswick, station, which converts it to dc and reconverts it to ac for transmission to eastern Canada's population centers. The conversion system, built in cooperation with Philadelphia's Power Delivery Group, overcomes synchronization problems between the adjacent ac transmission systems.

Canadian GE generator being installed at Labrador's Churchill Falls.

The Carry-Cool portable room air conditioner, low in weight and in cost.

APPLIANCES

The Carry-Cool® portable room air conditioner is introduced. Its light weight and rugged construction bring cool air in a package with convenience and cost previously unattainable. The extensive use of reinforced plastic produces, in one piece, an internal structure which would have required 27 formed and painted sheet metal parts.

NATIONAL DEFENSE

A new 1500-hp helicopter engine, the T700, developed for the U.S. Army, establishes a model for aircraft maintenance. It can be disassembled and maintained using only the ten standard tools included in the G.I. tool kit.

Ordnance Systems develops hydro-mechanical power trains which provide for rapid maneuvering and simplified operation at the high speeds required of the Army's infantry fighting vehicle. An electric stabilization system is also designed for the new combat vehicle.

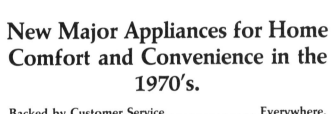

New Major Appliances for Home Comfort and Convenience in the 1970's.

Backed by Customer Service . . . . Everywhere.

PRODUCING AND DISTRIBUTING THE
PRODUCTS OF TECHNOLOGY ON A WORLDWIDE SCALE

Helping build Kenya's railway infrastructure, one of 26 GE diesel-electric locomotives being delivered at Indian Ocean port of Mombasa.

Speedtronic® solid-state control system for GE gas turbines in the Mid-East.

General Electric was international in scope before it formally became the General Electric Company. Roots of both the parent companies – Edison Electric Light and Thomson-Houston – were firmly implanted worldwide through licensing and patent agreements by Edison, and technical and manufacturing agreements by Thomson-Houston. By the time they merged in 1892 to form the General Electric Company, Edison and Thomson-Houston had developed sizable international sales and manufacturing operations in lamps, motors, generators and other electrical equiment. Edison dynamos were built and shipped worldwide from Schenectady in the 1880s. An 1893 GE publication proudly and almost accurately boasted: "Our incandescent and arc lamps extend in a unbroken line around the earth; they shine in the Palace of the Mikado as well as in the Opera House in Paris."

By 1900, manufacturing, selling or licensing agreements had been established in Canada, England, Germany, France, Italy, Spain, Portugal, Japan, Mexico, South Africa, and most of South America.

By 1919, the increasing scope of the international operations led to replacement of the "Foreign Department" by the newly formed International General Electric Company, with complete responsibility (except in Canada) for all foreign business. Under Gerard Swope, GE made enormous strides toward becoming a truly international company.

By 1945, IGE had 5,000 employees selling and manufacturing GE products abroad. In 1959, GE's International Business was organized as one of the Company's major Groups, and by 1970, international sales were 16% of all Company sales. In 1978, GE's international system employed over 100,000 people outside of the United States. It included 129 affiliated companies, manufacturing products in 23 countries and using more than 350 distributors who serve markets in 150 countries around the world.

GE's international business operates in several ways to sell and/or manufacture for world markets.

It provides exports from the U.S., such as consumer products, medical equipment, high technology, heavy electrical equipment for power generation, jet engines, marine propulsion gear, and industrial drive systems.

U.S.-made parts are sold to foreign manufacturers who construct the remainder of the product to GE specification and then independently market it.

Manufacturing affiliates produce and sell products in local markets, taking advantage of GE technology, trading, and marketing know-how. In some cases, these affiliates combine U.S. components and technology with their own to produce a variety of goods for export as well as for local distribution. Such products range from light bulbs to locomotives.

Joint ventures are formed for the manufacturing and/or marketing of products, abroad or in the United States.

The abundant flow of General Electric inventions provides a basis for the granting of licenses for use of know-how and technology on a fee or royalty basis.

The addition of Utah International to the General Electric family has provided a new international dimension in mining and export and natural resource development in Australia, New Zealand, South America, Canada, the United States, and wherever Utah's active exploration program may lead.

No other company in the world markets so many different products in so many different parts of the world. The role of these activities is critical, not only in General Electric's growth but in helping to offset the huge outpouring of U.S. dollars for imports, particularly for imported oil. GE Chairman Reginald H. Jones views the challenge as so vital to U.S. economic health that, in 1979, he agreed to serve as Chairman of the President's Export Council.

Mobile communications equipment such as that shown above is a product of Denmark's Storno A/S, Europe's leading producer of mobile radios and a majority owned affiliate of General Electric.

Incandescent lamps being manufactured for local markets at plant of Gevensa, GE's Venezuelan affiliate.

CANADIAN GENERAL ELECTRIC COMPANY LIMITED

Largest and most diversified of General Electric's multi-industry affiliates is the Canadian General Electric Company, Ltd. With a history of manufacturing experience that traces back more than a century, CGE has consistently been in the forefront of new engineering technology. It is one of the world's leaders in the development of nuclear and hydroelectric power generation and high-voltage transmission equipment. These and the manufacture of a broad spectrum of products, such as major appliances, housewares, defense radars, plastics, motors, marine propulsion equipment, transformers, communications gear, and heavy industrial equipment, have contributed to a record of growth which, in 1979, resulted in revenues in excess of $1.3 billion in Canadian dollars. A few of the highlights of CGE's history in the period after World War II are depicted below.

CGE's first major mobile radio production, for the Ontario Provincial Police (above), evolved into the development, in 1974, of one of the first computerized radio systems on the continent.

A vital link in the North American air defense system are altitude-monitoring radars, first built by CGE in Canada in 1959.

In 1978, CGE built the world's largest water-cooled hydroelectric generator for the Grand Coulee Dam. The 718-mva unit is shown above, being readied for assembly.

In 1955, CGE formed a partnership with Atomic Energy of Canada, Ltd. and Ontario Hydroelectric Co., Ltd. to develop the Candu nuclear reactor. The first such unit was built at Rolphton, Ontario (above).

New Audio Equipment and House-wares for the 1970's...a sampling

WILLARD H. SAHLOFF

In July 1967, *Business Week* nam-ed Willard Sahloff "Mr. House-wares" in recognition of his leader-ship in product innovation and marketing. As General Manager of the Housewares Division from 1953 to 1969 he made a significant im-pact on the growth of the small ap-pliance business in GE.

Arthur M. Bueche (l.) Senior Vice President Corporate Technology and Board Chairman Reginald H. Jones inspect one of many exhibits depicting GE technological achievements at the GE Centennial Hall of History exhibition at the Schenectady Museum in 1978.

Three "generations" of leaders meet. Ralph J. Cordiner (l.) with new Chief Executive Reginald H. Jones (c.) and Fred J. Borch, his predecessor.

The Corporate Executive Office in GE's centennial year. Chairman Reginald H. Jones (c.), with Vice Chairmen Walter D. Dance (l.) and Jack S. Parker (r.).

"What will be expected of managers in the future? Intellectual breadth, strategic capability, social sensitivity, political sophistication, world-mindedness, and above all, a capacity to keep their poise amid the cross-currents of change."

If anyone could serve as a model for this specification for the manager of the future, it is its author, Reginald H. Jones.

Mr. Jones' entire business career has been with General Electric. He joined the Company's Business Training Course in 1939. Three years later, he began an eight-year tour as a travelling auditor, an assignment that took him to nearly every plant in the Company. Then he moved into general management, serving as manager of various company businesses in consumer, utility, industrial, construction, and distribution fields. In 1968, he became the Company's Chief Financial Officer, and was elected Senior Vice-President two years later.

In 1972 he became President, then Chairman and Chief Executive Officer of General Electric. There he has brought fresh vitality and new strategic direction to one of the most diversified enterprises in the world. Most of that diversification has come from strong internal growth fostered by research and development, strategic planning and the introduction of the sector structure which "prepared the organization and the people to meet General Electric's long-range growth opportunities in the decade ahead". There have been exceptions to the pattern of internal growth, most notably the merger of GE with the Utah International Corporation in 1976 — at that date the largest acquisition in U.S. corporate history.

Under Jones' administration, the Company's sales have more than doubled ($10 billion to $22 billion) and earnings have grown even faster ($572 million to $1.4 billion) in seven years. A major thrust has been into international markets, and General Electric is now one of the nation's leading industrial exporter's, with a trade surplus of $2.5 billion at a time when the U.S. as a whole has a trade deficit of about ten times that amount. As Chairman of the President's Export Council, he has become an eloquent voice for the expansion of world trade and the restoration of U.S. competitiveness.

REGINALD H. JONES

But Mr. Jones is best known to the public for his role in changing the relationship between business and government. As Chairman of the Business Council and Co-Chairman of The Business Roundtable, he has been a leader in the movement to develop a constructive business-government dialogue. Three Presidents and their Cabinets have chosen to call on him frequently, for sophisticated counsel on economic policy. His most significant achievement in the policy arena is recognition in Washington of the nation's capital formation problem, but he has also been a powerful spokesman on the issues of tax policy, trade, monetary reform, unemployment, and human rights.

His work as a thoughtful and public-spirited counsellor on public policy has won him broad acceptance not only in the Administration, but also in both Houses of Congress, and both parties — a credibility most unusual for an executive of big business. *U.S. News and World Report*, in its 1979 and 1980 surveys of "Who Runs America", reported that his peers regard Jones as the most influential person in business today; and a 1980 survey by the Wall Street Journal confirmed that finding. He has used this well-earned influence to advance fresh ideas for the solution of economic and social problems.

If the corporation today is evolving into a more responsive — and responsible — element of the body social, it is due to the leadership of the people like Reginald Jones.

1973

TRANSPORTATION

The Locomotive Department delivers the world's first 50,000-v, 6000-hp thyristor-controlled locomotives for the Black Mesa and Lake Powell Railroad.

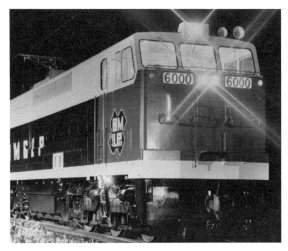

World's first 50,000-v, 6000-hp thyristor-controlled locomotive.

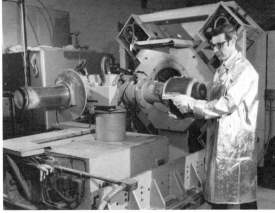

Engineer Bill Smith at SAC plant in Hendersonville, Tennessee, removes motor frame from fully automatic casting machine. It can produce a 10-hp frame, weighing 13 pounds, every two minutes.

INDUSTRIAL EQUIPMENT

The development of centrifugally cast aluminum alloy stator frames and end shields results in performance improvements and reductions in the weight of small ac motors produced at the recently completed plant at Hendersonville, Tennessee.

The Drive Systems Department makes the first application of large cycloconverter technology in a 16,800-hp wound-rotor induction motor, opening the way for the development of even larger ac drives.

Gerald J. Michon (l.) and Hubert K. Burke (r.) display solid state imager held by Michon. An experimental TV camera, built around the invention, is aimed at the imager and displays it on the television screen.

ELECTRONICS

The first solid state imager based on charge injected device technology is invented at the Research and Development Center by Gerald J. Michon and Hubert K. Burke. The stamp-sized device, which converts an optical image into an electrical video signal, replaces bulky video vacuum tubes used in conventional TV cameras.

IVAR GIAEVER WINS NOBEL PRIZE
1973 AWARD IN PHYSICS
RECALLS LANGMUIR'S 1932 PRIZE

In 1960, Ivar Giaever, a physicist at GE's Research and Development Center, conceived the idea of using electron tunneling to measure the energy gap in a superconductor. This technique, disclosed in a pathbreaking paper, both provided a new method for studying superconductivity and opened the possibility of a new class of electronic devices. The importance of the work was highlighted by the award of a 1973 Nobel Prize, shared with Leo Esaki and Brian D. Josephson.

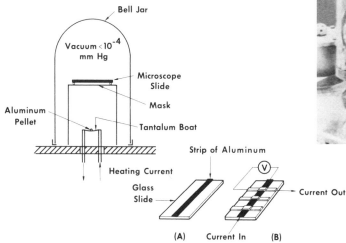

A bell jar in which Ivar Giaever performed his key experiments is shown in photo above and in diagram at left. At bottom of drawing, sketches A and B show how thin films were laid down, inside the evacuated bell jar, on glass slides.

"The Nobel Prize is the highest honor that a scientist can receive, and we are delighted that the Nobel Committee has this year recognized Dr. Giaever's outstanding contributions to the study of phenomena that occur at temperatures near absolute zero," said Dr. Arthur M. Bueche, GE vice president for research and development.

"The only other GE scientist to receive a Nobel Prize was the late Dr. Irving Langmuir, who won the award for chemistry in 1932," Dr. Bueche pointed out. "Dr. Langmuir was the first industrial scientist in the U.S. to receive the Nobel Prize."

GE Chairman of the Board Reginald H. Jones said: "It's poetic justice that today, October 23rd, the 100th birthday of one of General Electric's greatest scientists, Dr. William D. Coolidge, living in Schenectady, N.Y., that another GE scientist should also reach a significant milestone in his lifetime. We are proud beyond words. Dr. Giaever does honor to his profession, his associates, and his company."

Ivar Giaever accepts Nobel Prize from King Carl Gustav of Sweden in Stockholm ceremony.

100 YEARS OF TECHNOLOGICAL INNOVATION

*HATS OFF TO GE INNOVATION

THREE AND A FOURTH new U.S. patents every working day. That is the 1978 record for General Electric Co.; a total of 865 new U.S. patents last year. Little wonder, then, that GE has become the first organization in history to be assigned its fifty-thousandth U.S. patent.

One can hardly resist the temptation to refer to GE as being patent potent. Its giant Corporate Research and Development section has been structured and staffed by its present leader, Dr. Roland W. Schmitt, by Dr. Arthur M. Bueche before him, and by others to be what very likely is the world's most-productive research and development operation. They build on a history that goes back 101 years to the founding of GE's predecessor, Edison Electric Light Co. It is there that we find the start of this tradition of innovation and the first records of some individuals who helped GE to reach this innovation milestone.

[Ranking No. 1 and No. 3, respectively, on the list of the most prolific inventors in U.S. history were Thomas A. Edison, with over 1000 patents; and Elihu Thomson, with almost 700 patents. The evolution of the General Electric Company from the Edison Electric Light Company and the Thomson-Houston Company brought together the talents of these two men and the contributions of a number of others who were among the giants of invention of the late nineteenth and early twentieth century. William Stanley (transformers and electrical transmission); James J. Wood (motors and dynamos); Charles F. Brush (arc-lighting and dynamos); Charles J. Van Depoele (dc motors and electric streetcars); and Frank J. Sprague (motors and electric traction equipment), compiled upwards of 100 or more patents each during their careers.

One of the least well known of GE's early inventors was Hermann Lemp, who came to America from Switzerland in 1882 to work with Thomas Edison. He later became a long-time collaborator with Elihu Thomson and was a consulting engineer at the Erie Works. He was awarded more than 300 patents in areas such as welding equipment, x-ray apparatus, and components for transportation equipment. His design of automatic control systems for diesel-electric locomotives were considered by many to be among the most significant contributions in the history of railroad transportation.

Hermann Lemp

George B. Benander

Theodore A. Rich

During the last half of GE's first century there have been a number of its inventors who reached the 100 mark in numbers of patents. Perhaps the best known is radio and television pioneer, Ernst F.W. Alexanderson, with over 200 patents. Among the others are George B. Benander (switches and other small wiring devices); Frank M. Clark (motor insulations and capacitor and transformer insulating fluids); Theodore A. Rich (measurement and detection equipment); Burnice D. Bedford (electronics for motor control and power transmission); and David C. Prince (welding controls, switches and relays).

In 1978, the list was joined by John Bochan of Louisville, with 100 patents relating primarily to major applicance components; and Fred F. Holub, Research and Development Center chemist with 100 patents in organic and polymer chemistry and materials.]

Those performances are very impressive and worthy of much respect. After noting the tremendous patent accomplishments of these men, however, we are aware that in addition to their patents, there are more than 47,000 U.S. patents that were issued to thousands of other GE employees over the years. And two more points of interest: GE's 50,000th U.S. patent was issued in the name of Dr. Douglas E. Houston, a physicist, for a thermal migration process for creating fine grids in semiconductor devices. And, fully a third of GE's 50,000 U.S. patents are unexpired and are still in force.

On the 20th of this month we will present the 17th annual I•R 100 Awards for significant innovation. At that time it will be shown that GE has won more awards in this international competition for innovation during 1978 than any other firm. This performance will boost GE's total of I•R Awards to 124, more than twice the number earned by the next-highest contender.

Many excuses are given for declining U.S. innovation, a weakening of this nation's dominance in U.S. patents, and presumed technological stagnation. Let us remember that GE operates in the same world. At GE they don't know the meaning of technological stagnation. Innovation is alive and well at Schenectady and Syracuse and other GE lab sites.

Our hats are off to GE!

Robert R. Jones
editor
Industrial Research/Development

*Exerpts from an editorial in *Industrial Research/Development* magazine—September 1979. Insert, in brackets, prepared by *Pathways of Progress* editor.

Burnice D. Bedford

John Bochan

Fred F. Holub

Directo-Matic® Logic Control for steel plant process automation.

INDUSTRIAL EQUIPMENT

Directo-Matic® Logic Control is introduced for steel plant process automation. Its electronic memory stores an intricate program of instructions which can be easily expanded and changed to guide manufacturing or process equipment through sophisticated production sequences.

Microprocessor technology is incorporated in the GE Mark Century® 1050 numerical control. The great flexibility afforded by software design permits almost limitless control features and functions for automated large machining centers.

APPLIANCES

The first molded thermoplastic dishwasher tub is produced at Appliance Park. The one piece tub reduces the number of fabricated parts required and gives the consumer a longer-lived, maintenance free product than is obtained from coated metals.

COMMUNICATIONS

The first three-axis stabilized TV broadcast satellite, built for the Japanese government by the Space Division, is in orbit over the Pacific. The satellite provides the capability for TV distribution directly to home receivers, cable heads, or terrestrial broadcast systems.

New, one-piece thermoplastic dishwasher tub—being examined by John Vance (left), Edward McInerney (center) and Richard Butsch (right) of Appliance Park.

MATERIALS

Research and Development Center ceramist Svante Prochazka develops the first simple and inexpensive technique for fabricating ceramic parts from silicon carbide, one of the most heat resistant materials known to man. The new fabrication technique may significantly boost the efficiency of gas turbines.

POWER GENERATION

The first GENERREX static exciter system, a 377,000-kva unit, is installed at Colstrip, Montana, for the Montana Power Company. The GENERREX integrates the power transformer and reactor elements within the generator housing, resulting in major design simplification and improved performance.

The first nuclear power plant to generate more than 1,000,000 kw of electricity is the Tennessee Valley Authority's 1098-MWe Browns Ferry 1 BWR unit near Decatur, Alabama. The Large Steam Turbine Department also participates in the project as it supplies a single shaft turbine operating at 950 psi saturated steam.

Turbine vane made from silicon carbide is subjected to high temperature flame test by Svante Prochazka, inventor of the new fabrication process.

New General Electric Corporate headquarters at Fairfield, Connecticut.

ORGANIZATION

The General Electric Company officially transfers its Corporate headquarters from New York City to a new facility at Fairfield, Connecticut.

INFORMATION PROCESSING

The introduction of the Genigraphics® image generation system heralds the beginning of the world's largest computer slide art service. Working at a Genigraphics console, an artist can create and photograph up to 10 color visuals for slides in an hour. The material can then be stored in a minicomputer and returned at any time for corrections or updating.

1975

ELECTRONICS AND COMMUNICATIONS

The Space Division designs the DSCS III, the Defense Satellite Communication System, for unprecedented orbital life and operational utility, with features directly applicable to future commercial communications. Launch is scheduled for mid-1980.

The Aerospace Electronic Systems Department builds the GEOS-3 Radar Altimeter. GEOS, the Geodynamics Experimental Ocean Satellite, studies, measures, and maps the ocean from orbit, transmitting data from storage in earthbound computers.

GEOS-3 Radar Altimeter built by the Aerospace Electronic Systems Department.

APPLIANCES

The HOME SENTRY SMOKE ALARM is the first of a line of home protection devices produced by General Electric. Its detector is sensitive to the presence of small quantities of smoke produced in the earliest stages of a fire and emits a high pitched alarm, providing an extra measure of time for escape.

Home Sentry Smoke Detector and Alarm.

LIGHTING

The Photo Lamp Department develops FlipFlash lamp array for a new line of Kodak pocket cameras. Using automatically sequenced lamp triggering and a piezoelectric crystal as a power source, FlipFlash matches the compactness of the cameras and provides error-proof operation.

Fred F. Holub (l.) and Harold F. Webster (r.) demonstrate chemical-polymer switches that automatically sequence lamp triggering in FlipFlash photo lamp array.

POWER GENERATION

Introduction of the MS-9001 gas turbine, rated at 100 mw and designed for use in 50-Hz systems, opens the door for large-scale use of these units internationally.

Static excitation is adapted for use in hydro-electric generators at an installation of twelve generating systems for the Chief Joseph Dam on the Columbia River in Washington.

MATERIALS

PC-75 copper clad composite laminate is introduced to the electronics industry. The new printed circuit material combines the strength and electrical qualities of epoxy glass laminates and the cost advantages of phenolic paper.

Barge-mounted, self contained, gas turbine units ready for transportation to Brazil.

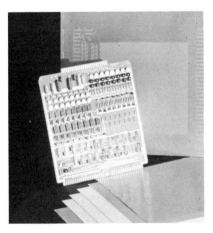

PC-75 copper clad laminates.

INDUSTRIAL EQUIPMENT

Energy $aver Serv-S-Line motors are introduced for heating and air conditioning replacement service. Efficiencies are up to 40 percent higher than shaded-pole design motors.

Let General Electric show you how high-efficiency motors can squeeze more profits from your plant operations.

HELPING TO FINANCE CONSUMER AND INDUSTRY NEEDS

The General Electric Credit Corporation has been part of the General Electric family since 1932. First known as General Electric Contracts Corporation, it was organized for the purpose of financing the purchase of consumer appliances. In that capacity it stimulated demand for appliances during a critical period of economic recovery from the nation's most severe depression.

Today, GECC is still a leading lender in the home products field, providing a broad spectrum of services to retailers and consumers, including casualty and life insurance through its Puritan Insurance Companies. In addition, it has become the largest non-manufacturing company in commercial and industrial equipment financing and leasing.

GECC is not a commercial airline. . .but in 1978 it had the ninth largest fleet of commercial airliners in the U.S., with 77 commercial aircraft on lease.

In 1967 GECC leased three DC-9 aircraft to Allegheny Airlines in the first such transaction in the aviation industry. In 1969, it signed a lease that provided United Airlines with 29 aircraft over a four-year period.

GECC is not a railroad. . .but it has accumulated more than 22,000 pieces of rolling stock–enough to make up a train 250 miles long.

In 1975, GECC participated in the largest leveraged lease in railroad history and provided some 9,500 boxcars for American commerce.

Over the years, the General Electric Credit Corporation has provided similar services to a wide variety of industries requiring large capital investments to remain viable. Through these activities it has also played a key role in the continuing development and application of the products of technology.

Administrative Offices:
260 Long Ridge Rd. • Stamford, CT 06902

One of the biggest names in almost everything.

GECC is not a maritime shipping company. . .but its fleet, leased to oil carriers, includes seventeen tankers that have an aggregate of 2,527,000 deadweight tons, the most of any fleet in the U.S. Merchant Marine.

The 368,000-deadweight-ton UST Atlantic, the largest tanker ever built in the Western Hemisphere, was acquired by General Electric and leased to the Shell Oil Company.

A Continuous Miner, shown here, is typical of equipment acquired by Quarto Mining, a subsidiary of North American Coal Company, through a lease by GECC. The lease arrangement allowed Quarto to acquire the equipment with no out-of-pocket investment and with much lower interest expenses than if Quarto had financed the venture conventionally.

1976

NATIONAL DEFENSE

The Electronic Systems Division demonstrates a new solid-state, computer managed radar, the AN/TPS-59 tactical air-defense radar, developed for the U.S. Marine Corps.

Installing grouted bolt reinforcement system in mine roof.

MATERIALS

A high-speed curing resin system is jointly developed by Carboloy and Laminated and Insulating Materials Business Department to improve the safety of underground coal mining. Used in a unique package, it provides efficient and economic grouted bolt reinforcement of mine roofs, minimizing the possibility of collapse under the most difficult of conditions.

Environmental concerns related to capacitor impregnants consisting of polychlorinated biphenyls (PCBs) lead to the development of a substitute fluid, DIELEKTROL. This achievement permits the Capacitor Products Department to lead the industry in the conversion to non-PCB capacitors.

APPLIANCES

The Food Service Equipment Department introduces the Cook-N-Hold convection oven for restaurant use. It uses stored energy that would otherwise go to waste to complete the cooling cycle.

DATA COMMUNICATIONS

A complete family of line printers, called TermiNet® 340, is introduced to provide printing speeds of 90 to 340 lines per minute. Used for "distributed data processing", the new printers enable remote minicomputers to handle routine chores and release main-frame computers for more sophisticated tasks.

Cook-N-Hold convection oven for restaurant use.

Computed tomography scanner takes detailed cross-section X-ray pictures of the body in less than five seconds.

MEDICAL EQUIPMENT

A computed tomography scanner developed by a team from the Research and Development Center and the Medical Systems Division takes detailed cross-section X-ray pictures of the human body in less than five seconds—four to 60 times faster than other total-body scanners in use. The high speed minimizes image blurring due to patient motion and provides superior detail.

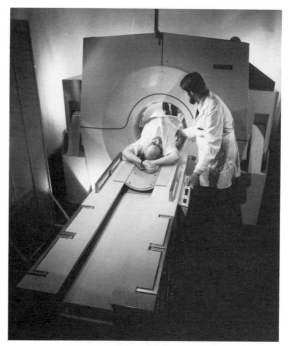

POWER GENERATION AND TRANSMISSION

The largest geothermal turbine in the world is the Turbine Division's 132-mw, four flow, low pressure unit. Representing another promising technology for energy production, the geothermal turbine operates on natural, underground steam from wells at 100psig and 338°F.

Power/Vac metalclad switchgear is developed for power systems ranging from five to 15 kv. Hailed as the most significant switchgear innovation in 40 years, the design was first to fully capitalize on the inherent space and maintenance saving features of vacuum interruption protection of medium voltage systems.

The world's largest hydraulic turbine is installed at the Grand Coulee Dam by Canadian General Electric's Dominion Engineering Works.

Power/Vac vacuum circuit breaker. Cover removed to show detail.

1977

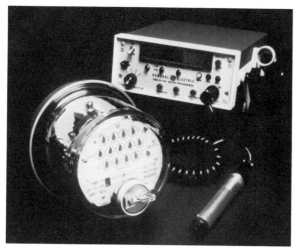

IR-70 programmable time-of-day watthour meter.

INDUSTRIAL EQUIPMENT

The first major breakthrough in the gearmotor industry since the 1930's is represented by the Helix 2000®. The Small AC Motor Department development, spearheaded by R.A. (Ron) Blair, reduces cast iron construction by 40% and utilizes a modular approach with plug-in motor designs so that off-the-shelf motors and gears can be mixed and matched for maximum machine flexibility.

The GE IR-70 programmable time-of-day watthour meter is introduced. Its self-contained integrated circuit chip allows virtually unlimited combinations for measuring kilowatt hours at time-of-day and day-of-week intervals. The IR-70 can also alert utility customers of their use of power during on-peak periods and can optionally limit such on-peak usage of high load appliances.

POWER GENERATION AND TRANSMISSION

The nation's first solid-state high voltage dc (HVDC) transmission system uses GE converter equipment to bring power to Duluth, Minnesota, from a generating station located 456 miles away, near lignite coal mines in North Dakota. The "coal by wire" project sets a pattern for others where natural resources are not conveniently served by means of transportation.

APPLIANCES

Microprocessor computerized cooking control is introduced to the fast food restaurant industry in the Dimension II series of fryers. Programming of the frying cycle provides food consistency, versatility and energy savings.

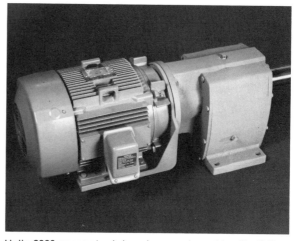

Helix 2000 gearmotor brings improved machine flexibility.

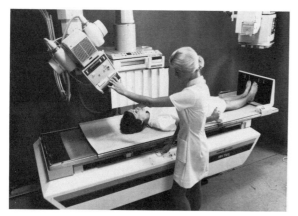

New RFX x-ray examination table.

MEDICAL EQUIPMENT

The Medical Systems Division announces the RFX x-ray examination table and MPX programmable x-ray generator for faster, more precise conventional radiography.

LIGHTING

The high output halogen "power plus" headlamp is developed for two and four headlamp systems. It provides up to twice the light straight ahead on high beam.

A new phosphor developed by Research and Development Center physicist William W. Piper, and produced at the Quartz and Chemical Products Department, results in the greatest single boost in fluorescent lamp efficiency since the 1950's. Used on the new 35-watt Watt-Miser II lamp, it enables it to produce 97 percent as much light as a standard 40-watt fluorescent light, and can cut lighting-system energy costs by as much as 14 percent.

INFORMATION PROCESSING

Computational capabilities for financial as well as technical applications are made available worldwide as the GE Mark III time sharing service opens its first overseas computer "super-center" in Amsterdam, the Netherlands. Linking Europe with the Cleveland, Ohio and Rockville, Maryland headquarters supercenters, the system now covers over 600 cities in 21 countries and 21 time zones.

William W. Piper and new phosphor for energy-saving Watt-Miser II lamps.

ELECTRONICS AND COMMUNICATIONS

GE is awarded an "Emmy" by the National Academy of Arts and Sciences for VIR automatic color control for television developed by the Television Department.

"Emmy" awarded for VIR automatic color control.

301

GE'S NEW DIMENSION IN NATURAL RESOURCES

Steam-powered shovels, mechanical marvels of the early 1900's, replaced the pickaxe and hand shovel.

Utah's railroad construction included trestles, tunnels, bridges, grading and track-laying.

Hoover Dam on the Colorado River required 5000 workers for its construction.

Utah International joined the GE family in December 1976 when a merger was approved by the share owners of both companies. This merger gave General Electric a new business dimension in natural resources and an acceleration of growth in international markets.

BEGINNINGS

Founded in 1900 as The Utah Construction Company, the enterprise spent the better part of the first 50 years of its existence as a heavy construction and engineering company. Most of the work in its first 20 years was the building of railroads, and the Company was the leading railroad contractor in the far West.

By 1920, the railroads were largely built, and the company turned its efforts toward heavy engineering construction efforts, such as dams, tunnels and earth moving. It was one of the leaders in the joint ventures that built such great structures as Hoover (1936), Bonneville (1940), and Grand Coulee (1942) Dams.

In the period shortly before and immediately after World War II, Utah's construction activities extended outside of the United States to Australia, Canada, Mexico, Peru, Brazil, Colombia, Indonesia, Guam, Korea and the Philippines. The Company utilized its earth-moving skills to enter into mining ventures in the U.S. and in many of these countries.

By 1971, Utah had removed itself from the heavy construction business and was committed mainly to natural resources -- on an international scale.

After World War II, Utah's earth-moving skills were applied in this Cedar City, Utah, iron ore mine.

UTAH INTERNATIONAL TODAY

- Utah's largest sphere of activity is in Australia — mining coking coal and iron ore for the steel industry.
- On Vancouver Island, British Columbia, it is developing the Island Copper Mine, producing copper concentrates and by-products such as gold, silver, molybdenum, and rhenium.
- Utah's domestic mining operations include steam coal in New Mexico and Colorado, iron ore in Utah, and a copper interest in Arizona.
- Uranium mining operations are conducted in Wyoming by the Lucky Mc Uranium Corporation, manager of all of Utah's uranium business.
- Through its interest in Samarco Mineracao, S.A., Utah is participating in a vast new iron-ore-producing venture in Brazil.
- Ladd Petroleum Corporation, a subsidiary, produces oil and natural gas in the U.S. and Canada.
- Utah engages in ocean transportation of ores and bulk cargoes through its subsidiaries.

In addition, a vigorous exploration program spans the globe and includes such areas as the western U.S., Australia, Canada, the South Pacific, Africa, and Brazil, seeking new sources of minerals traditionally mined by Utah.

Edmund W. Littlefield, Chairman of the Board and Chief Executive Officer of Utah International, Inc. "He has taken a relatively small construction company and turned it into one of the most exciting natural resources companies in the world today."
Reginald H. Jones, Dec. 16, 1976

Canadian GE motors power six grinding mills at Island Copper Mine in British Columbia.

Loading coal from Utah's Navajo mine in New Mexico.

Ladd Petroleum oil pumping well.

1978

LIGHTING

Laboratory versions of the Electronic Halarc lamp are developed as the forerunners to a family of high efficiency, compact discharge lamps for residential use. An evolution of the Multi-Vapor lamp, the Halarc produces more light than an ordinary 3-way 50/100/150-watt bulb, but uses one-third the energy and will last about four times as long.

Simplified mount, used on 60-, 75-, and 100-watt household lamps, eliminates supports for lead wires and filaments. In addition to large cost savings and productivity gains, there is a two-percent increase in lamp efficiency.

The first commercial all-plastic headlamp housing is designed using the Plastics Division's Lexan. Capable of cutting three pounds from the weight of a four headlamp assembly, it helps meet the needs of the automotive industry to produce lighter weight, more energy-efficient vehicles.

Cutaway model of Electronic Halarc bulb reveals electronic controls in base and arc tube in the top bulb area.

Mark III Distributed Data Processing and Mark-Link Terminal.

INFORMATION PROCESSING

The General Electric Information Service Company announces its Mark III® Distributed Data Processing and Mark-Link Terminal. This minicomputer system with software capability is designed for remote processing to be used in conjunction with the Company's worldwide network of computer supercenters.

INDUSTRIAL EQUIPMENT

Flexible automation units are placed in each domestic plant of the Specialty Motor Department. These units carry out potentially hazardous or less desirable work processes, such as casting with molten aluminum and unloading anneal furnaces.

ELECTRONICS AND COMMUNICATIONS

The Audio Electronics Products Department completes development of the first programmable digital clock radio. Using computer memory capabilities, the radio can store six stations with instant touch button recall.

"The Great Awakening" Programmable Digital Clock Radio.

APPLIANCES

Housewares Division completes development of the Versatron^T CTO-2000 countertop oven, featuring automatic, solid state electronic controls in a portable, energy saving appliance.

The FP-1 and FP-2 food processors are introduced, reducing the time for many food preparation chores to seconds. The powerful motor and attachments permit greater versatility in the types of food that can be processed rapidly.

The Major Appliance Business Group announces the first two-door combination refrigerator-freezer with automatically defrosted fresh-food section and separately insulated zero-degree freezer.

TRANSPORTATION

The new Series C30-7 diesel electric locomotives are delivered to the Norfork and Western Railroad. These six-axle 3000 hp units incorporate a GE turbocharger and over 60 improvements that produce significant advances in reliability, maintainability and fuel economy.

SPACE EXPLORATION

The first U.S. interplanetary mission to investigate the atmosphere and weather of the planet Venus is launched. The Reentry Systems Division designs and builds heat shields and separation systems for the four deceleration probes which encounter the planet.

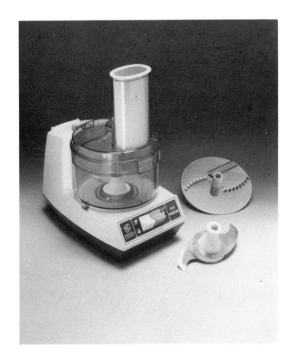

1978

MATERIALS

Vulkene Supreme[T], a development of the Wire and Cable Department and the Research and Development Center, is introduced as the first non-chlorinated high-performance, flame-resistant insulation.

The Laminated and Insulating Materials Business Department introduces a line of energy conserving thermosetting resin systems. These materials can be cured without the application of heat, by exposure to ultraviolet light. Energy required for curing can be as little as 15% of that required in a comparable thermal process.

A clear, silicone-coated glazing material with abrasion resistance approaching glass and high impact strength is announced by the Lexan Products Department. Properties of the new LEXAN-based product, called MARGARD™ sheet, make it ideal for glazing applications in transportation and building construction.

Lexan high impact resistance sheet used at rebuilt Yankee Stadium in New York City.

ORGANIZATION

Planning is initiated for the construction of a new $50 million addition to the facilities of the Research and Development Center. Over half of the new building effort will be devoted to assembling one of the U.S. industry's most modern electronic laboratories.

Roland W. Schmitt (left), Vice President for Corporate Research and Development, shows a conceptual model of the new construction to George B. Cox (center), Senior Vice President of the Turbine Group, and Porter W. Dobbins, manager of the Center Technical Services Operation.

Linden Pierce (l.), Thomas Nichols (c.), and Robert Gearhart (r.) stand in front of new Vapor Tran transformer at Medium Transformer Department plant.

POWER GENERATION AND DISTRIBUTION

The largest nuclear plant in the world is completed in Japan. The Fukushima 6 is a six-unit, 4700-megawatt Boiling Water Reactor station built jointly by GE and three of its licensees in Japan.

Vapor Tran®, the first practical vaporization-cooled transformer, is developed at the Medium Transformer Department. This long-sought-after concept has the added advantage of using a non-flammable insulation fluid.

The largest rated turbine-generator in the world, Palo Verde 1, is shipped to the Arizona Nuclear Power Project. The unit is capable of producing 1,559,100 kva.

The Space Division supplies vacuum tube solar collectors for one of the Department of Energy's largest commercial solar installations for hot water and space heating.

Fukushima 6 nuclear power station in Japan.

Celebrating General Electric's Centennial Year

The year 1978 was a special one for the men and women of General Electric. It was the Company's centennial year. In 1878, a small group of investors had the courage and vision to raise $50,000 to support Thomas Alva Edison's incandescent lamp experiments. They formed the Edison Electric Light Company, the earliest predecessor of General Electric.

Celebrations marking that event and the century of growth and achievement that followed were occasions for reflection, not only on the past, but also on the future of the General Electric Company as it entered its second century.

At the 1978 Information Meeting for Share Owners, Chairman of the Board and Chief Executive Officer Reginald H. Jones summed up these reflections as follows:

"If we were asked what business we are engaged in, we would have to say that we are fundamentally in the business of generating new businessess — and new sources of earnings — from our emerging capabilities. And our future, as our past, lies in the continuous extension of our capabilities into new applications, new markets, new products and services, new or contiguous industries where we can make a contribution that is profitable for our share owners, and profitable for the societies we serve.

What are some of the areas of opportunity, as we try to anticipate the most urgent needs of a changing world?

The energy revolution. Surely the world will need new ways to make and conserve energy.

The need for products and systems that increase productivity — not only in the United States, but in other nations at all levels of economic development.

The consumer desire for new lifestyles, new products and services for a new age.

The shift to a services economy in the United States and other major industrialized countries.

The demand for ever-increasing amounts of minerals and other natural resources, as the nations of the world press hard against available supplies.

The need for man-made materials, with special characteristics not found in natural materials.

And more broadly, the needs of an emerging worldwide economy that expands our strategic horizon as far as the imagination will carry.

How can we summarize what General Electric stands for at the threshold of its second century?

Corporations are responding as public expectations set new and higher standards of performance. We welcome these demands for change. Change is our birthright and our business.

And so our vision for General Electric, built on our heritage, is to be an innovative enterprise at the leading edge of technology, management, and social change.

The philosopher Eric Hoffer says that man is the unfinished creature, driven to continue the work of creation. So too, this very human organization called General Electric is an unfinished enterprise, always evolving, always new, and still — after one hundred years — extending the frontiers of human progress."

ADVANCED MATERIALS

Stratapac™ diamond compacts, set in drill bits, become a major contributor to the productivity of oil well drilling, and one more example of the success of GE Superabrasives at tailoring Man-Made™ diamond and cubic boron nitride products to a wide range of industrial applications.

Diamond compact drill bit.

AEROSPACE

GE's Radar Systems Department is selected by the U.S. Air Force to design and install over-the-horizon radar systems that rely on the refraction of radio signals by the ionosphere to provie long-range, all-altitude surveillance and detection of aircraft and cruise missiles. The first system will have a range of 1,800 miles out over the Atlantic Ocean.

Standing up to 135 feet high and three-fourths of a mile long, this transmitting antenna array in Maine is part of the new over- the- horizon radar system being built by GE for the U.S. Air Force.

APPLIANCES

The new GE Spacemaker™ microwave oven can be wall-mounted or hung from cabinets to provide a space saving alternative to counter-top microwave cooking. Installed over an electric cooktop or range, it frees up counter space, is easy to use, and has a built-in vent and cooktop light.

Hydroelectric generator rotor being lowered into place at Quebec's La Grande 2 power station, the world's largest underground hydro plant.

INTERNATIONAL

Canadian General Electric, Ltd. supplies eight of the sixteen turbine-generators for Quebec's 5,328-mw La Grande 2 power station. When completed in 1980, La Grande 2 will be the most powerful hydro plant in North America and possibly the world.

Wall-hung microwave oven saves counter-top space and has built-in exhaust.

1979

ORGANIZATION

General Electric Chairman, Reginald Jones, announces that the Board of Directors has elected John F. Burlingame, Edward E. Hood and John F. Welch as Vice Chairmen, effective September 1, 1979. All three are currently serving in the positions of Senior Vice President and Sector Executive. Commenting on the Board action, Mr. Jones said, *"These appointments are another step in the process, begun in December, 1977 with the Company realignment into Sectors, whereby we are preparing the reorganization and the people to meet General Electric's long-range growth opportunities in the decade ahead".*

Joining Chairman Reginald H. Jones (standing) in the Executive Office of GE are (left to right) Vice Chairmen John F. Burlingame, Edward E. Hood, Jr. and John F. Welch, Jr.

INFORMATION SYSTEMS

GE acquires Honeywell's international information systems business and combines it with its own remote data processing and distributed data processing services to create the General Electric Information Services Company (GEISCO).

MEDICAL SYSTEMS

The CT 8800 System for computed tomography, taking advantage of all the capabilities inherent in GE's "Fan-Beam Rotate Only" design, unlocks the competitive door and makes GE a true, worldwide supplier of advanced diagnostic imagery equipment.

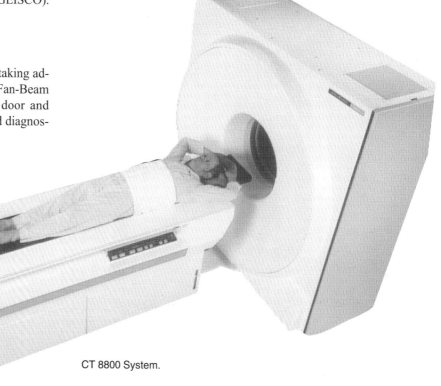

CT 8800 System.

AIRCRAFT ENGINES

The General Electric F404-GE-400 augmented turbofan engine enters service aboard the McDonnell Douglas F/A-18 fighter aircraft. It goes on to achieve unequaled performance and reliability records for the U.S. Navy and U.S. Marine Corps. Versions of this engine are selected for use on the F/A-18 aircraft by a number of governments around the world, with the first order coming from Canada.

During a period of over twenty years, Brian H. Rowe made significant contributions to the development of a number of innovative and successful engine programs. In 1968, he was named manager of the CF6 project Department, and, in 1979, he became Senior Vice President of GE Aircraft Engines.

Brian H. Rowe with new CF6-80A turbofan engine, designed for takeoff thrust of 48,000 pounds for the Boeing 767 and Airbus Industrie A310 transports.

GE aeroacoustics research leads to quieter commercial aircraft engines for the 1980s.

Testing of GE CF-6-80 engine at Evandale, Ohio, headquarters of GE Aircraft Engines.

GE and China Light & Power engineers discuss installation of "Dry Low NOx" system on 9F gas turbine at new Hong Kong power plant (1994).

POWER SYSTEMS

A 105-mw heavy-duty gas turbine the largest such unit ever built by GE, is installed at a combined cycle (steam and gas turbine) power system operating near Kirchlengern, West Germany.

Power Systems launches the development program for the gas turbine Dry Low NOx combustor. By applying a quiet combustor which utilizes six fuel nozzles instead of one, GE was the first to achieve 25ppm NOx without a selective catalytic reactor. This paved the way for future advances in technology to reduce plant emissions.

1980

INDUSTRIAL AND POWER SYSTEMS

GE Nuclear Services opens a training facility for the service and maintenance of nuclear power plants. The first of its kind in the industry, it uses actual equipment in operating GE-type boiling water reactor plants, training personnel to operate plants in an even safer and more reliable manner than ever before.

FINANCIAL SERVICES

As the Leveraged Buyout (LBO) business begins to flourish, the GE Credit Corporation becomes one of the nation's leading financers of LBOs, structuring hundreds of these complex, multi-layered deals; totaling many billions of dollars, and involving, in 1980, such companies as Baldwin Piano, Microdot, Inc., Tiffany & Co., and Farley Industries.

GE Nuclear Maintenance Training Center at San Jose, California.

1980 Lincoln Continental sedan with Lexan halogen headlamps.

POLYMERS

GE introduces the first plastic automotive headlamp. The new sealed-beam Lexan halogen lamp, product of a joint effort by the Plastics Division and the Miniature Lamp Department, weighs only one-third as much as a glass unit. It can reduce the weight of a four-headlamp vehicle by three pounds.

Construction of a new phenol plant is completed at GE's Mt. Vernon, Indiana polymer manufacturing facility. The plant will help provide a supply of vital feedstocks on a timely basis.

ORGANIZATION

John F. Welch, Jr. Named Chairman-elect of GE

On December 19, 1980, GE Chairman Reginald H. Jones announces that the Board of Directors has named John F. Welch, Jr., as Chairman-elect, effective January 1, 1981. Mr. Jones also announces that he plans to retire on April 1, 1981, at which time Mr. Welch will succeed him as Chairman and Chief Executive Officer. John F. Burlingame and Edward E. Hood, Jr. will continue as Vice Chairmen and Executive Officers.

Excerpts from 1980 Annual Report

"Innovation and self-renewal: these are themes that characterize General Electric as we enter a new era.

Your Company is engaged in a process of internal change that will transform the way we design, manufacture and distribute our products and services in the 1980s. We are encouraging our people to probe constantly for new markets, new techniques and new business opportunities.

We are in the business of creating businesses to anticipate and serve the needs of a changing world."

John F. Welch, Jr. - Chairman-elect
Reginald H. Jones - Chairman and Chief Executive Officer

CHAPTER FIVE

Building a Company Without Boundaries
1981-1999

Foreseeing the advent of global competition and rapidly changing markets, GE, under the leadership of John F. Welch, Jr., underwent a dramatic restructuring in the 1980s. Businesses that were not first or second in their global markets were improved, closed or sold. The company divested $10 billion of marginal operations and made $19 billion in acquisitions to strengthen the world-class businesses that would lead GE into the nineties. It also made large investments in its research and development and engineering facilities. From these facilities came a flow of innovative ideas and new products and services. The rapid and consistent growth of Capital Services and its ability to complement the expansion opportunities of GE's other businesses were a major factor in the company's strategy for growth. In 1998 alone, $21 billion was invested in 108 acquisitions in support of the company's growth initiatives. Even as it grew larger in size and in global presence, GE set out to instill in its people the "spirit and soul" of a small company. Self-confidence, simplicity, speed and a boundaryless outlook were emphasized and rewarded. Tools such as Work-Out and CAP (Change Acceleration Process) were developed to eliminate bureaucracy and solicit ideas from those closest to the problem.

As the 20th Century came to a close, GE's ongoing business strategy would revolve around four key growth initiatives – Globalization (of every aspect of the company's operations, from marketing and procurement to finding and attracting talented people from all around the globe); Services (that augment traditional repair, overhaul and reconditioning with the use of high technology methods to improve the performance of the installed equipment base); Six Sigma Quality (a disciplined, customer-focussed, methodology for improving quality in all existing and planned products and services by aiming to virtually eliminate all defects); and e-Business (the result of the revolution in digital technology and the availability of the Internet that makes it possible not only to achieve significant market growth but to accrue considerable savings in almost all aspects of doing business).

ORGANIZATION

At its meeting on March 27, the Board of Directors of General Electric confirm the previously announced election of John F. Welch, Jr. as Chairman and Chief Executive Officer. Mr. Welch is the eighth person to hold that office since the founding of the Company. Edward E. Hood, Jr., and John F. Burlingame continue as Vice Chairmen and Executive Officers with expanded responsibilities for realigned staff and operations.

John F. Welch, Jr., Chairman and Chief Executive Officer of General Electric.

In the 1981 Annual Report, Chairman John F. Welch, Jr., describes his concepts of the GE culture.

"There are three basic concepts we are emphasizing as part of the GE culture:

The first is *reality*. A sure grasp of marketplace realities and a clear understanding of corporate social responsibilities are essential in today's environment. Social expectations rightfully remain high, yet business faces intensified world competition and more rapid shifts in market structures. In this environment a company must be a lean, low-cost producer of quality goods and services in order to survive, let alone prosper.

Corporate social responsibility in the '80s begins with a healthy company, derived from satisfying customers with quality products and services. Worldwide competitiveness leads to jobs and job security and the ability to support effectively social, educational and cultural endeavors - support that is impossible without a healthy corporate balance sheet.

A second basic concept is *excellence*. This means reaffirming and enhancing the Company's tradition for quality goods and quality services in an increasingly skeptical and quality-conscious age. And it means excellence in people — calling for the best in all of us — in some cases being even better than we thought possible.

The third concept we describe as *ownership* — the call for GE employees to assume full responsibility for the decisions they make on behalf of you and the Company. It means moving more decision-making power to operations — to managers who know their markets best.

We intend to make *reality, excellence* and *ownership* the basis for a pervasive operational atmosphere in which people will dare to try new things, where their own creativity and drive will determine how far and how fast they move. Whether in revitalized core businesses, or in the newer growth businesses, the result will be an organization more high-spirited, more adaptable and more agile than companies a fraction of our size.

This decentralized entrepreneurial energy will be aligned and augmented by the very considerable central strengths of General Electric — not just *financial* (a very strong balance sheet), but also *technical* (a research laboratory that is a model of excellence worldwide) and *human* (a manpower development system acknowledged to be among the very best) — all bonded further by the unifying power of the GE monogram — our trademark and most enduring asset."

— *Excerpts from the 1981 Annual Report to Investors*

1981

PLASTICS

GE expands its plastics plant at Bergen op Zoom in the Netherlands as part of its plan to double its worldwide manufacturing capacity for engineered materials. GE Plastics Europe had been formed in 1969, following an alliance between GE and Akzo Chemical Co. In 1972, production of Noryl began at the Bergen op Zoom plant and, two years later, Lexan production was added.

Overall view of Bergen op Zoom facility in the Netherlands.

High purity fused quartz used in tubing for the lighting business is sold to the communications industry for fiber-optic applications.

ADVANCED MATERIALS

GE Lighting, as a by-product of its diverse materials manufacturing, produces 3 ft. long fused quartz ingots of such high quality and purity that a customer can draw them into fiber optic strands 25 miles in length. This helps make possible the fiber optics revolution in communications.

FINANCIAL SERVICES

Passage by Congress of the U.S. Economic Recovery Tax Act of 1981 gives a boost to strong efforts by the GE Credit Corporation to aid U.S. reindustrialization. GECC implements Congress' intentions and provides new funds to many of the nation's businesses, including the metals, chemicals, paper, natural resources, and transportation segments. Aggregate original cost of GECC leased equipment rises from $3.1 billion in 1978 to $13.3 billion in 1984.

A cogeneration system at this paper mill in Maine was financed by the General Electric Credit Corp. The mill burns sawdust, bark and other wood waste by-products to drive its GE steam turbine-generator, which supplies power to a local utility and enough process steam for the mill's needs.

AEROSPACE AND DEFENSE

The USS Ohio, first of the TRIDENT class ballistic missile submarines, is commissioned. Powered by nuclear reactors designed at GE's Knolls Atomic Power Laboratory, major components of that propulsion system are built by GE Power Systems. This class of ships, which will provide the nation's undersea strategic missile defense in the ensuing decades, is quieter, faster, and better equipped than its predecessors.

The USS Ohio, first of the TRIDENT class of ballistic missile submarines. (photo courtesy of Electric Boat Company)

Designing new integrated circuits at Intersil.

INDUSTRIAL ELECTRONICS

GE re-enters the semiconductor business through the purchase of Intersil, Inc., an established Silicon Valley electronic circuit manufacturer. The newly formed GE Semiconductor Division also constructs a $55 million Microelectronics Center at Research Triangle Park, North Carolina.

GE acquires the Calma Corp., Milpitas, California, a leading manufacturer of computer-aided design systems. In 1988, the semiconductor businesses will be sold to the Harris Corporation and Calma will be sold to the Prime Computer Corporation.

The Drive Systems Department introduces the load commutated inverter, a major breakthrough in alternating current drive technology, offering significantly higher efficiency in applications such as compressor drives. Drives totaling more than 400,000 horsepower are installed in 1981 alone.

Chairman Welch discusses a philosophy that will guide General Electric's business planning in the 1980s

"The winners in this slow-growth environment will be those who search out and participate in the real growth industries and insist on being number one or number two in every business they are in - - the number one or number two leanest, lowest-cost, worldwide producers of goods and services or those who have a clear technological edge, a clear advantage in a market niche."

– Excerpt from a presentation to Financial Community Representatives on December 8, 1981

1982

APPLIANCES

GE Appliances introduces the GE Answer Center® providing a state-of-the-art information service via a toll-free telephone number. By calling (800) 626-2000, at any time of the day or week, the consumer can get information on any aspect of GE's more than 100 consumer product lines.

The dishwasher factory in Louisville, Kentucky is turned into one of the most productive facilities of its kind as a result of a $38 million investment in state-of-the-art manufacturing, materials and inventory management and testing processes.

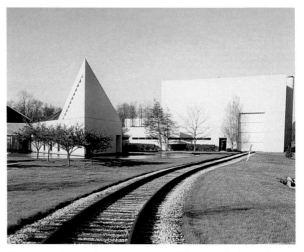
Transportation Systems Learning and Communications Center.

Computer control center monitors flow of materials and models and continuously reports status of all automated equipment to help assure quality and productivity at GE's new dishwasher factory in Louisville, Kentucky.

MEDICAL SYSTEMS

GE Medical Systems and Japan's Yokogawa Electric jointly create Yokogawa Medical Systems, with GE owning a 51% stake in the new venture. It soon becomes one of the key players in the Japanese diagnostic medical imaging market, the second largest national market for such products. In subsequent years, Yokogawa Medical Systems would produce a full array of medium and lower priced medical diagnostic systems to complement the higher performance products produced by GE.

TRANSPORTATION

The Transportation Systems facility in Erie, Pennsylvania., opens a Learning and Communications Center to provide training and retraining programs for its employees as well as technical service for the Company's railroad customers. The centerpiece of the $316 million investment in facilities is a fully automated locomotive motor frame machining line to meet the growing overseas market which accounts for more than 50% of the locomotives produced in Erie.

Automated locomotive motor frame machining line.

PLASTICS

GE Plastics-Europe completes development of XENOY™ resin, an exterior automotive material that combines impact strength with chemical resistance. XENOY™ is used on the first U.S. cars with all-plastic bumpers, introduced in 1983. By 1985, more than 35 automotive models worldwide have bumpers made of XENOY™ resin.

GE introduces ULTEM® resin, the first totally new polymer developed in almost a decade. Based on an invention made by Joseph L. Wirth at the GE R&D Center, and developed jointly by the R&D Center and GE Plastics, it combines outstanding processability with toughness and resistance to heat and solvents. Markets range from injection molded printed circuit boards for electronics applications to structural parts for aircraft interiors.

Special grades of Lexan® resin are developed for the fast growing audio and video disc markets.

Audio discs manufactured with special grade of Lexan resin are inspected at the GE Plastics applications labs in Bergen op Zoom.

ORGANIZATION

To expand on its export sales, which, in 1981, stood at nearly $4 billion, GE announces the formation of a wholly-owned trading company. The General Electric Trading Company (GETC) will engage in worldwide marketing of company products as well as marketing for U.S. companies whose products complement those of GE.

RESEARCH AND DEVELOPMENT

The GE R&D Center in Schenectady, New York, completes a three year, $130 million expansion in buildings and equipment that increases its size by almost 50% to more than 1 million square feet of floor space.

Dedication ceremonies held in the atrium of the new wing of GE's expanded R&D Center facility.

Large steam turbine generator being loaded aboard ship for delivery to an overseas customer.

1983

LIGHTING

GE announces a $250 million lighting leadership program for the revitalization of facilities and equipment. It includes development and application of a new high-speed horizontal fluorescent lamp manufacturing system, the most advanced cost-efficient system in the industry. The new PRO 80 system doubles the capacity for incandescent lamp manufacturing.

High-speed horizontal fluorescent lamp machine at GE plant in Bucyrus, Ohio.

Section of PRO 80 lamp manufacturing system.

ENGINEERED MATERIALS

GE Silicones introduces Sealant X1, a high performance neutral cure one-part sealant, which provides a low-odor, high-performance sealant material. The business is a leading supplier of silicones for industrial, commercial and consumer markets

Construction workers use GE silicones to seal glass panels.

CONSUMER ELECTRONICS

GE Consumer Electronics incorporates into 12 color television models a channel block-out system that can restrict up to 112 channels simultaneously, including cable channels and channels used for video cassette recorder playback. This gives parents the discretionary ability to block out any undesirable viewing material on television channels for a period of up to 12 hours, or until the parent cancels the restriction.

320

MEDICAL SYSTEMS

Scientists at GE's Research and Development Center and GE Medical Systems develop the Signa® Magnetic Resonance Imaging system. This makes GE a leader in this technique, which is having a revolutionary impact on the field of medicine. Based on a giant superconducting magnet with a highly uniform field 20,000 times as strong as that of the earth, the system uses radio waves and computer information processing to produce cross-sectional images of internal body structures. Because of the unprecedented detail and clarity of the Signa®MRI, it is particularly suited to "soft" tissues which are difficult or impossible to image by X-ray methods.

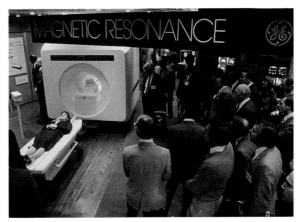

Signa® Magnetic Resonance Imaging system is introduced at meeting of the Radiological Society of North America.

GE cellular telephone.

COMMUNICATIONS

GE Mobile Communications enters the cellular telephone market, the most rapidly expanding segment of the commercial 2-way mobile communication industry. With the introduction of Synthesized Radio Products, radios move from the realm of crystal frequency control to state-of-the-art microchip frequency control.

A GE programmable controller helps increase productivity at the Weirton Steel plant in West Virginia, where it automatically controls the welder in a tandem cold-rolling mill.

INDUSTRIAL ELECTRONICS

The new Series Six® programmable controller is one of a new family of products introduced for accurately monitoring and controlling industrial drives and motors in factory automation and other applications.

1984

AEROSPACE

Landsat 4, an earth observation spacecraft designed, assembled and tested by the GE Space Systems Division for NASA, goes into orbit. It has since imaged most of the earth many times, providing data for oil and mineral exploration, identifying geological faults, cataloging crops, and locating forest fires. The Landsat series of satellites has been one of the most socially beneficial developments of the entire U.S. space program.

MOTORS

One of the world's most highly integrated systems for motor insulation and winding is installed at the DeKalb, Illinois Motor plant - replacing 10 separate machines and several manual operations. Completion of a $290 million modernization program, begun in 1983, will strengthen GE's position as the world's leading supplier of electric motors in sizes ranging from fractional horsepower to several thousand horsepower.

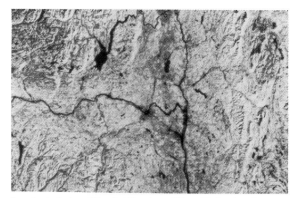

Landsat photo of Capitol Region of New York, showing Mohawk River, from left, flowing into the Hudson.

Headquarters of Employers Reinsurance Corporation in Kansas City, Kansas.

FINANCIAL SERVICES

GE Credit Corporation acquires Employers Reinsurance Corporation. Founded in 1914, this "insurance company's insurance company" is one of the three largest property and casualty reinsurance companies in the United States. The acquisition also leads to the formation of a new entity, General Electric Financial Services Inc., to oversee both the GE Credit Corporation and Employers Reinsurance.

AIRCRAFT ENGINES

General Electric begins full scale production of the F110 augmented turbofan engine. Derived from the GE 101 propulsion system for the B-1B bomber, the F110 engine, rated at 27,000 pounds thrust, is specified for the General Dynamics F-16 and Grumman F-14 fighters. In the first three years of the "Great Engine War" (the competition for powering the F-16), the F110 engine receives the majority of orders.

New motor insulation and winding system at GE motor plant.

PLASTICS

GE Plastics opens a new technology center in Pittsfield, Massachusetts, to support its world leadership in developing high-performance plastics as alternatives to metal, wood, and glass.

POWER SYSTEMS

The world's first integrated gasification combined cycle (IGCC) plant enters service at Southern California Edison's Cool Water facility, using a Texaco gasification process and a GE combined-cycle system. Initially designed as a power generation technology to burn coal in a more environmentally acceptable manner, IGCC power plants have the added flexibility to cleanly burn heavy oils, petroleum coke, orimulsion, biomass, and waste fuels while meeting stringent emissions standards.

In a joint venture with Big Three Industries, Inc., GE brings on line the 300-megawatt Bayou Cogeneration Plant in Texas. It is one of the largest of its kind and the first of several cogeneration plants designed and constructed by Power Systems in the 1980s.

New GE Plastics technology center in Pittsfield, Massachusetts.

APPLIANCES

The use of electronics in major appliances is extended with the introduction of dishwashers that can be programmed to "remember" when to start, microwave ovens that fit under a kitchen cabinet, and electronic refrigerators that "beep" if a door is left ajar.

In order to concentrate its Consumer Products resources in the large-scale consumer business, GE sells its Housewares Operations, consisting of its small appliance businesses, to Black & Decker Manufacturing Company.

NATURAL RESOURCES

GE completes the sale of its natural resource subsidiaries, Utah International, Inc. and Utah-Marcona Corp., to The Broken Hill Proprietary Company Limited, of Australia. Commenting on the transaction, GE Chairman John F. Welch, Jr., said, "The sale of Utah reflects our strategy to focus on our key businesses where we believe GE's unique technological, financial and managerial strengths can add the most to value."

Bayou Cogeneration Plant, southeast of Houston, Texas.

1985

INFORMATION SERVICES

GE's information services business shifts its primary focus from timesharing and computing to applied teleprocessing, with emphasis on specialized network-based application services, such as Electronic Data Interchange (EDI), international trade, shipping, health claims processing, and marketing and distribution systems.

Chemical reactor tower for starting materials used in the production of silicones, at GE Silicones worldwide headquarters, Waterford, New York.

GE Information Services Electronic Data Interchange.

PLASTICS AND ENGINEERED MATERIALS

GE introduces NORYL GTX® resin, the first thermoplastic developed to withstand the heat of automotive paint ovens.

SILTEM®, the first of a family of copolymers combining the strength of organic materials with the flexibility of silicones, is introduced by GE Silicones. It offers higher performance characteristics for use in high technology applications such as optical fiber coatings.

FACTORY AUTOMATION

The Drive Systems Operation installs the first fully digital power conversion and control system for a paper mill at the Union Camp Plant in Savannah, Georgia. Drive Systems is the world's leading supplier of customized drive and automation systems for the paper, mining, drilling, automotive testing, ship propulsion and metals industries.

In recognition of his many contributions to the development of controls for drive and automation systems, Charles E. Konrad received GE's 1985 Steinmetz Award for excellence in engineering. He is co-inventor of the GEnius Input-Output System, a major breakthrough in the distributed control of factory equipment.

GE drive systems control slab-casting operations at LTV Steel's Indiana Harbor Works in Whiting, Indiana.

AIRCRAFT ENGINES

CFM International, a 50/50 joint venture between GE Aircraft Engine and SNECMA of France, delivers its 1000th aircraft engine. The company was formed in 1974 and delivered its first turbofan engine, the CFM56, in 1981. The CFM56-3 aboard Boeing's 737-300, -400, and -500 series aircraft, would become the bestselling engine/aircraft combination in the history of commercial aviation.

The GE CF6-80C2 high bypass turbofan engine enters service for medium-to-large commercial aircraft. The highest thrust and most commercially advanced engine offered to date by GE, it incorporates advanced technology features derived from the successful NASA/GE Efficient Energy Program.

The Unducted Fan (UDF™) engine, also developed with advanced technology derived from a NASA/GE program, successfully completes its first test flight. Configured with two sets of counter-rotating unducted fan blades driven by a counter-rotating turbine, this revolutionary new propulsion system is expected to offer fuel savings of 40 to 70 percent over conventional turbofans.

GE CF6-80C2 aircraft engine.

TRANSPORTATION

Transportation Systems ships its first Dash 8 diesel-electric locomotives. Designed for increased productivity, this new, ultra-efficient generation of locomotives provides 109,000 lb. of continuous tractive effort, 78,000 lb. of dynamic braking effort and up to 3,900 (traction) horsepower.

GE Unducted Fan (UDF™) engine.

Front and side views of Dash 8 diesel-electric locomotive.

1985

ORGANIZATION

The sector structure of GE is replaced by a direct report structure in order to give the leaders of GE's various businesses significantly more responsibility. This "de-layering" will enable the businesses to compete more effectively in world markets.

AEROSPACE

The Upper Atmosphere Research Satellite Observatory, designed and developed by GE Space Systems Division for NASA's Goddard Space Center, provides the capability to achieve new insight into the nature of the ozone layer. Ozone is a more active form of oxygen which protects people from excessive exposure to the sun's ultraviolet radiation.

Upper Atmosphere Research Satellite will include 10 scientific instruments for studying the ozone layer and atmospheric conditions.

POWER SYSTEMS

The first unit of a 2000 MW combined cycle steam turbine and gas (STAG™) plant of the Tokyo Electric Power Co. enters commercial operation. When completed in 1988, this facility, sitting on a man-made peninsula in Tokyo Bay, Japan, will be the world's largest and most technically advanced station of its kind - featuring 14 GE STAG™ combined-cycle systems.

Tokyo Electric Power Plant, Tokyo Bay, Japan, the largest power plant in the world, uses a combined cycle steam turbine and gas system.

Welcome **RCA**

The merger of General Electric and RCA, first announced in 1985, was completed on June 9, 1986. Here, reprinted from RCA's 1986 Annual Report, are highlights of the company's contributions to electronics, communications, and entertainment.

1932

RCA became an independent company when the U.S. govern-ment decreed that it should be separated from GE. The memory of GE lingered on in the notes of the famous NBC chimes - G,E,C - which stands for the General Electric Company.

1968

A tiny RCA space camera, weighing less than five pounds, was used by the astronauts on Apollo 7 to transmit the first live pictures from space to American viewers. Miniaturized integrated circuits enabled RCA to build a camera small and light enough for use in space.

1939

Although this RCA Victor television console stood almost four feet high, its screen measured only nine inches. The set, which also included a radio, was an ancestor of today's high-tech "Dimensia" system.

1974

RCA produced the world's first 164,000 - element chip. Research in semi-conductors and integrated circuits has earned RCA a worldwide reputation in this field.

1950

RCA introduced the first international telex service. This technological advance in telecommunications made possible a two-way exchange as well as a printed copy of all messages.

1978

After nearly 60 years as an RCA trademark, Nip-per had a face-lift. He emerged with a sleek new look that reflected RCA's modern image while re-calling the history of qual-ity and reliability long as-sociated with the little ter-rier.

1966

RCA's TK-44 television camera became the bestselling camera in the industry. RCA cameras set the standard for color broadcasting in the late 1960s.

1986

RCA comes full circle by rejoining GE in a historic merger. While RCA will no longer be an independent company, its world-famous brand name will live on.

1986

MEDICAL SYSTEMS

Medical Systems introduces the CT Max™ computed tomography system. With its price and performance, this new CT scanner makes GE the first supplier to place advanced CT capabilities within the reach of smaller hospitals and clinics. In recognition of contributions by Yokogawa Medical Systems, GE increases its stake in its Japanese joint venture from 51% to 75%.

Gary Glover, a senior physicist at Medical Systems' Applied Science Laboratory, received the 1985 Charles P. Steinmetz Award on the basis of his many creative technical contributions in the fields of computed tomography and magnetic resonance imaging.

Rowland Redington led the development efforts at the GE R&D Center that resulted in both the first computed tomography system and the Signa Magnetic Resonance Imager. In recognition of his accomplishments he was elected to the National Academy of Engineering.

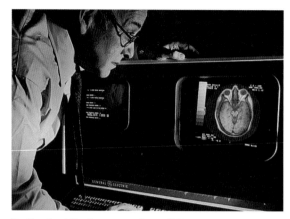

Dr. Rowland Redington studies a CT image of head.

As General Manager of Medical Systems, Walter L. Robb led GE's move into the computed tomography and magnetic resonance areas, transforming the business from a supplier of x-ray equipment to a world leader in medical diagnostics. In 1986, Dr. Robb became Sr. Vice President - Corporate Research and Development.

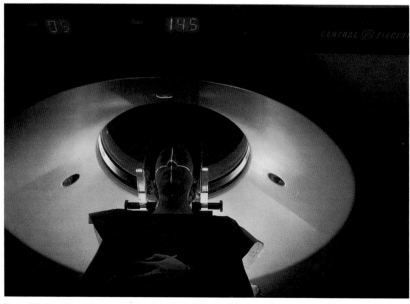

New CT Max™ system places advanced CT capabilities within the reach of small hospitals and clinics.

PLASTICS

GE Plastics builds a $325 million Lexan resin plant at Burkville, Alabama, the largest single plant and equipment investment in GE Plastics history, to date.

The 1986 Ford Taurus and Mercury Sable represent a landmark for GE Plastics. Each of these models contains some 70 pounds of GE resins.

GE Plastics Manufacturing Plant, Burkville, Alabama.

Bumpers being produced at a Ford plant in Milan, Michigan, use GE high-performance plastics.

AUTOMATION SYSTEMS

GE and Fanuc Ltd. of Japan create GE Fanuc Automation Corporation, with subsidiaries in the United States, Europe and Asia. The new company offers a full range of high technology factory automation systems and equipment, including numerical controls and programmable controllers.

FINANCIAL SERVICES

GE Financial Services acquires Kidder, Peabody & Co., Inc., a leading investment banker, market maker in fixed income and equity securities, and financial adviser. The firm traces its origins to a predecessor formed in Boston in 1824. Placed under the umbrella of GE Financial Services, Kidder would operate as an independent unit until 1994, when its brokerage assets were sold to Paine Webber in return for a 25% equity in that firm.

Through such businesses as life insurance, mutual funds, long-term care insurance, auto insurance and warranties, and supplemental accident and health products, GE Financial Assurance would become involved in providing financial security solutions that help consumers create, preserve and protect their lifestyles and personal wealth.

GE Canada and GE Fanuc team up to supply motors, drive systems and these programmable controllers that operate the paper-making machinery at Domtar's fine papers mill in Windsor, Quebec.

1986

APPLIANCES

The Space Center 27 electronic refrigerator is now the largest refrigerator offered by GE. It features a refreshment center, automatic ice maker and dispenser, and an electronic control center that tells users if the appliance is working properly .

GE Appliances further strengthens its ability to serve consumers by combining its service and parts operation with RCA's consumer service units, forming one of the largest and most widespread consumer service organizations in the United States.

GE Space Center 27 electronic refrigerator.

The torch of the newly restored Statue of Liberty.

LIGHTING

GE Lighting devises an entirely new lighting system for the Statue of Liberty. Now, when the sun goes down, the appearance of natural light created by combining the cool and warm light effects from two new Multi-Vapor® lamps turns the Great Lady into an instant spectacle worthy of her rich significance.

Engineer inspects new Multi-Vapor lamps for the restored Statue of Liberty.

1986

POWER SYSTEMS

The 7F gas turbine is ordered by the Virginia Electric Power Company. Incorporating advanced materials, coatings and cooling techniques from GE's aircraft engine technology, the "F" machines are the first land-based gas turbines designed to operate above 2300 degrees F. Because of this higher firing temperature, the F technology gas turbines set new standards in fuel utilization, thermal efficiency and power output.

The first F technology gas turbine installed at Virginia Electric Power Company.

Tom Brokaw interviews Soviet dissident, Anatoly Sharansky on "NBC Nightly News with Tom Brokaw".

NBC

The Peacock is returned to its place as NBC's symbol, with six feathers representing the network's six divisions. Thirty years earlier, an eleven-feather, six-color peacock ushered in the age of "living color" with the first color telecast.

At the end of 1986, NBC-TV was first in prime-time ratings, first in late night programming and first in Saturday morning children's programming.

The NBC peacock returns.

1987

MEDICAL SYSTEMS

GE and Thomson S.A., of France, agree to the acquisition by GE of Compagnie Generale de Radiologie (CGR), the leading producer of medical diagnostic imaging equipment in France. The addition of CGR will significantly strengthen GE's presence in Europe and Latin America and will complement Medical Systems' engineering, marketing, and manufacturing operations in the United States and in Japan, where it holds a majority stake in Yokogawa Medical Systems. As part of the transaction, Thomson will acquire GE's consumer electronics business.

Medical Systems introduces the MR Max™ magnetic resonance imaging system which provides a more economical approach to magnetic resonance imaging and can be used in mobile MR units shared by several clinics or hospitals. It features electronics from Japan and GE's new self shielded superconducting magnet made in South Carolina.

Technician inspects new Senograph™ 600TS x-ray systems in production at Stains, France.

FACTORY AUTOMATION

GE Fanuc Automation Corporation, completing its first year of business, is selected as single-source supplier of programmable controller and numerical control products for General Motors' Saturn manufacturing complex in Tennessee. The new Series 15™ computer numerical control enables machine tools to operate faster and more accurately, while its new Series 90™ programmable controller can do the same for a variety of factory floor processes.

At GM's Saturn plant, controls from GE Electrical Distribution and Control and GE Fanuc automate the process for casting engine heads.

ELECTRICAL DISTRIBUTION & CONTROL

GE will provide the entire electrical system – switchgear, panelboards, transformers, safety switches, motor control centers, substations and several miles of busway, for the new Saturn facility in Tennessee.

Completed circuit breaker panelboards move down conveyors at new, highly automated GE Electronic Distribution and Control plant in Salisbury, North Carolina.

PLASTICS

A joint project with BMW creates the world's first production car with all vertical body panels made with thermoplastics. The GE materials provide lighter weight, more design flexibility and better resistance to impact and corrosion than metal.

For the rapidly growing personal computer market, a number of tailored materials are designed to replace internal and external metal structures with plastics. The new IBM Personal System 2®/Model 50, for example, uses Lexan® polycarbonate resin for the base, screen bezel and inner support structure — combining them into an easily assembled, lightweight and durable unit.

A new grade of crystal-clear Lexan also is developed specifically for beverage containers. For this application, other grades of Lexan could be sterilized as many as one hundred times before recycling.

New crystal-clear grade of Lexan is suitable for use in beverage containers.

APPLIANCES

A new "Satisfaction Guaranteed" program is introduced, allowing consumers to exchange or return GE or Hotpoint appliances up to 90 days after the purchase if they are dissatisfied for any reason.

BMW production car has vertical body panels made with GE thermoplastics.

Launching ceremonies at Ingalls Shipbuilding in Mississippi for the CG59 cruiser Princeton, the 13th U.S. Navy cruiser to be equipped with GE's Aegis fleet air defense system.

AEROSPACE AND DEFENSE

The U.S. Navy's CG59 cruiser *Princeton,* is launched. It is the 13th U.S. Navy cruiser to be outfitted with GE's Aegis fleet air defense system and the first to incorporate the improved AN/SPY-1B radar array. GE is prime contractor on the Aegis system for U.S. cruisers and destroyers.

1988

MAJOR APPLIANCES

The acquisition of the Roper Corporation and its range manufacturing facilities enhances the new lines of GE and Hotpoint gas ranges introduced in 1985 and 1986, respectively. Additions to the new Monogram line of appliances for the growing designer kitchen market include gas-fueled cooktops, downdraft modular cooktops, and 24-inch counter-depth refrigerators with ice and water dispensers in the doors.

Totally GE-equipped kitchen includes a gas cooktop and other newly introduced major appliances.

GE Americom's large dish-like antennas in New Jersey and California keep track of GE's fleet of orbiting communications satellites.

COMMUNICATIONS

GE American Communications (Americom) is awarded a long-term contract with Alascom, the Alaskan longlines phone company, for 16 transponders on a new satellite to replace Alascom's existing satellite by 1991. Americom pioneered commercial satellite services in the United States and operates seven communications satellites, more than any other carrier. In 1986, its Satcom K-1 and K-2 were the two most powerful domestic communications satellites in orbit.

AIRCRAFT ENGINES

The U.S. Air Force unveils the B-2 Advanced Tactical Bomber, powered by F118 engines from GE.

1988

FINANCIAL SERVICES

GE Capital forms a joint venture with the Penske Corporation in the business of truck leasing. When combined with GE Capital's existing fleet, the resulting business has more than $1.5 billion in assets and 55,000 vehicles. The number of vehicles in the fleet would more than double by 1998. In other full-service leasing businesses, GE Capital leases more than 47,000 railcars, while its Genstar Container Corporation is the world's largest lessor of shipping containers, and Polaris Aircraft Leasing is the world's largest lessor of commercial jet aircraft. By 1998, GE Capital Aviation Services would have more than 900 planes and 125 customers in over 60 countries and 350 additional aircraft on order or option from Boeing or Airbus Industrie.

With the acquisition of the Montgomery Ward Credit Corporation, GE Financial Services increases its leading position in the private-label credit card business. In an average week, it authorizes more than three million consumer credit card purchases.

GE Capital arranges to acquire FGIC (Financial Guaranty Insurance Company). FGIC provides financial guaranties for municipal bonds so that local governments, school districts, and other public entity agencies can raise funds to improve their infrastructure.

PLASTICS

GE Plastics acquires Borg Warner's chemical businesses, the world's largest producer of ABS thermoplastics. ABS is one of the industry's most versatile materials and has properties and applications that significantly broaden the scope of GE's high performance plastics portfolio. Included in the acquisition is Polymerland, a world leader in the distribution of thermoplastic resins.

INFORMATION SERVICES

GE Information Services launches its Automated Cargo Expediting System (ACES) as part of its Electronic Data Interchange (EDI). The new network increases productivity and reduces costs by enabling businesses and other organizations to streamline and electronically exchange data on all aspects of freight movement, as well as other business-to-business transactions on a global basis.

GE Capital expands its truck and container leasing businesses.

POWER SYSTEMS

GE introduces packaged industrial steam turbines. These factory-packaged 10 to 100 megawatt steam turbine-generators can be shipped pre-assembled to a site for quick connection, reducing both installation time and cost. Ready to produce power in weeks, instead of months, they can meet short term needs for electricity.

Installation of packaged industrial steam turbine.

1989

LIGHTING

The development of the Halogen - IR™filament tube leads to floodlights and spotlights with energy efficiency more than twice that of conventional incandescent lamps. A large part of the efficiency gain is due to the incorporation of a dielectric, multi-layer, infrared-reflecting coating on the surface of an elliptically shaped tube. This coating captures the normally dissipated infrared energy and converts a portion of it into visible, useful light, thus producing more light for less energy.

The introduction of the revolutionary forward discharge lighting system gives automotive designers more freedom to create sleek front-end designs for cars. By using an initial high current xenon gas discharge to almost instantaneously provide a light output that is nearly the same as that of the fully warmed up metal halide lamp, a constant light level can be maintained. An added benefit is longer lamp life and higher reliability.

Arc-discharge lamps being tested in sleek new automobile front-end design.

GE Research and Development Center chemist, Dr. John Ackerman, examines the infrared-reflective coating on the small inner bulb that fits inside one of GE's new 60-watt Halogen-IR lamps.The lamps provide as much light as a 150--watt incandescent lamp.

PLASTICS

GE Plastics opens its Living Environments concept house in Pittsfield, Massachusetts. The house showcases current and future applications of engineering polymers in the building and construction industries. Several products already commercialized include house siding coated with Geloy™ resin and a concrete aggregate containing Valox™ resin.

NBC

NBC launches CNBC, the Consumer News and Business Channel — a 24-hour, consumer-oriented business news program service. By the end of its first year the new cable TV channel was producing 17 hours a day of original programming for 13 million subscribers.

NBC-TV becomes the first network in television history to rank first in every week of the 52-week broadcasting year running from September to September. NBC's weekly winning streak had reached an unprecedented 68 weeks before being interrupted by ABC's coverage of the World Series.

The new Living Environments concept house in Pittsfield, Massachusetts.

1989

The Pace of GE's Globalization Efforts Continues to Accelerate

By the end of 1989, GE operating profits from outside of the United States had grown to $2.8 billion, 40% of the Company total, and exports by GE had helped increase its positive contribution to the U.S. balance of trade from $2.1 billion in 1987 to $4.8 billion in 1989. As the decade came to a close, events in Eastern Europe and elsewhere accelerated the pace of globalization, offering sudden opportunities and growing challenges. Examples of some of the global business ventures that were launched during the closing years of the decade are reviewed below.

COMMUNICATIONS

GE Mobile Communications and Ericsson of Sweden form a joint venture to service the growing communications equipment market. The business, owned 60% by Ericsson and 40% by GE, will produce mobile radio systems and cellular telephones for the international market and will serve the U.S. and Canadian markets for cellular telephone systems.

LIGHTING

GE forms a joint venture with Toshiba of Japan to produce fluorescent lamps in Ohio for the U.S. and Asia-Pacific markets. The two companies also will cooperate in market development programs aimed at the growing Asia-Pacific region.

MEDICAL SYSTEMS

GE acquires the medical equipment sales and service activities of General Electric plc (GEC), an unrelated corporation in the United Kingdom. It also forms an alliance with Scanditronix AB of Sweden under which GE acquires that company's Positron Emission Tomography (PET) scanner business. To further support the newly acquired business, GE enters into a joint development agreement with Hamamatsu Photonic of Japan involving light detection devices for use in PET scanners.

CGR, which joined GE in 1987, introduces the Stenoscop II™ mobile surgical system and the compact Saturne™ 41 linear accelerator for radiation oncology.

INDUSTRIAL AND POWER SYSTEMS

GE reaches an agreement with the joint venture between GEC of the United Kingdom and Alsthom of France to form the European Gas Turbine Company (EGT). The EGT alliance will provide GE with long-sought-after access to the European Economic Community.

APPLIANCES

GE and GEC of the United Kingdom agree to combine their interests in European appliances and electrical controls. This joint venture elevates GE Appliances to the number two position in major appliances, worldwide.

ELECTRICAL DISTRIBUTION & CONTROL

GE's Italian-based affiliate (COGEMEC) is combined with GEC's Belgian-based Vynckier NV and French-based Unelec to create a European business that manufactures and markets distribution and control equipment for the European market.

MOTORS

BG Automotive Motors, a new joint venture between GE and Robert Bosch of West Germany, begins production of electric motors in the United States for a variety of automotive applications. It is now shipping blower and engine cooling fan motors for Ford in the U.S. as well as exporting power window motors for BMW in Europe.

Boundaryless; Work-Out; Speed; Simplicity and Self-Confidence - keywords of the GE management philosophy for the 1990's

In the 1989 Annual Report, Chairman of the Board and Chief Executive Officer, John. F. Welch, Jr., (right); Vice Chairman of the Board and Executive Officer Lawrence A. Bossidy (center); and Edward E. Hood, Jr., (left), took the opportunity to look back at the changes that had taken place within GE during the 1980s and to paint a vision of the landscape of 1990s and the corporate qualities that would be necessary to allow the Company to grow in that decade and beyond.

Excerpts from 1989 GE Annual Report

Our dream for the 1990s is a boundaryless Company, a Company where we knock down the walls that separate us from each other on the inside and from our key constituencies on the outside.

The boundaryless Company we envision will remove the barriers among engineering, manufacturing, marketing, sales and customer service; it will recognize no distinctions between "domestic" and "foreign" operations — we'll be as comfortable doing business in Budapest and Seoul as we are in Louisville and Schenectady. A boundaryless organization will ignore or erase group labels such as "management," "salaried" or "hourly," which get in the way of people working together.

A boundaryless Company will level its external walls as well, reaching out to key suppliers to make them part of a single process in which they and we join hands and intellects in a common purpose — satisfying customers.

This is an admittedly grand vision, requiring unprecedented cultural change, and we are nowhere near achieving it. But we have an idea of how to get there — an idea that is rapidly becoming reality across the Company. It's called Work-Out.

Work-Out is a fluid and adaptable concept, not a "program." It generally starts as a series of regularly scheduled "town meetings" that bring together large cross sections of a business — people from manufacturing, engineering, customer service, hourly, salaried, high and lower levels — people who in their normal routines work within the boxes on their organization charts and have few dealings with one another.

The initial purpose of these meetings is simple - to remove the more egregious manifestations of bureaucracy: multiple approvals, unnecessary paperwork, excessive reports, routines, rituals. Ideas and opinions are often, at first, voiced hesitantly by people who never before had a forum — other than the water cooler — to express them. We have found that after a short time those ideas begin to come in a torrent — especially when people see action taken on the ones already advanced.

With the desk largely cleared of bureaucratic impediments and distractions, the Work-Out sessions then begin to focus on the more challenging tasks: examining the myriad processes that make up every business, identifying the crucial ones, discarding the rest, and then finding a faster, simpler, better way of doing things. Next, the teams raise the bar of excellence by testing their improved processes against the very best from around the Company and from the best companies around the world.

We have progressed well into the first stage of Work-Out in most of our businesses, and some are beginning the transition into the second — or best-practices — phase; but we are under no illusions that this is anything less than a decade long crusade. We have hardly scratched the surface of the enormous mine of productivity and innovation that we know exists in the intelligence of our 300,000 employees, but we are excited beyond measure by what we are discovering. The natural cynicism that accompanies the announcement of new corporate campaigns and slogans has largely been dissipated as progress and momentum have begun to grow. Work-Out is working.

The hardware of this Company — its businesses and its management structure — is now largely the way we want it. Work-Out is our decade long vehicle for the software. Restructuring is a road, not a destination. A company can boost productivity by restructuring, removing bureaucracy and downsizing, but it cannot sustain high productivity growth without cultural change, without totally involving the individual who is closest to the work and therefore knows it better than those who "manage" it. The individual is the fountainhead of creativity and innovation, and we are struggling to get all our people to accept the counter cultural truth that often the best way to manage people is just to get out of their way. Only by releasing the energy and fire of our employees can we achieve the decisive, continuous productivity advantages that will give us the freedom to compete and win in any business anywhere on the globe.

Our Company will be making exciting business moves in the 1990s — ventures, new product lines, acquisitions, alliances — but the most important campaign will be the daily one we wage to inspire and enlist our employees in the cause of shared excellence and winning.

In the 1980s, we changed the Company. We also challenged the bureaucracy and generally got the better of it. In the 1990s, our task will be to challenge each other and, in doing so, to get the very best out of ourselves. The cool efficiency that many have always associated with business leadership must give way to personal skills and traits like empowering, listening, passion, energy and the capacity to

transmit that energy to others. Being "on top of things," controlling them, must give way to sharing, trusting. Most of the bureaucracy that infects business institutions— the reviews, layers, routines and reports — stems largely from a lack of trust. We have seen, with the demolition of the control superstructure we once imposed on our business, and we are beginning to see even more clearly as Work-Out starts to blossom, that controlling people doesn't motivate them. It stifles them. We've found that people perform better, even heroically, when they see that what they do every day makes a difference.

When they see that — when they are allowed to make real contributions to win they quickly develop increased *self-confidence.* That self-confidence in turn promotes *simplicity* — of action, of design, of process, of communication — because there is no longer a psychic need to wrap oneself in the complexity, trappings and jargon that, in a bureaucracy, signify sophistication and status. And that simplicity will radically increase the *speed* of our businesses and their ability to react to a world whose pace of change will become astonishing in the 1990s. *Speed, simplicity and self-confidence* will be the operative characteristics of the winning companies of the 1990s and beyond.

Discussing global Work-Out strategies for GE Medical Systems are (left to right) Nobuko Schlough, Steve Patscot and Wendel Barr of the United States, Yoshiaki Fujimori of Japan and Shereyar Vakil of India.

1990

AIRCRAFT ENGINES

GE announces plans for the development of the new super-thrust GE90 turbojet engine. Designed for tomorrow's widebody airliners, the GE90 will address growing demands for greater thrust, better fuel efficiency and quieter, cleaner operation. SNECMA of France, Fiat-Avio of Italy and IHI of Japan are major revenue-sharing participants in the project.

GE Aircraft Engines and Pratt & Whitney agree to study the feasibility of developing a propulsion system for a long-range, high-speed civil transport capable of Mach 1.5 to Mach 3.5.

Aeroflot, the Soviet Union's national airline, selects CF6-80C2 engines from GE as the first Western-built high by-pass turbofans for its new fleet of aircraft.

MEDICAL SYSTEMS

GE introduces the new L/C™ cardiac positioner x-ray system. Its unique 3-axis rotation can produce the widest range of viewing angles into a patient's cardiovascular system.

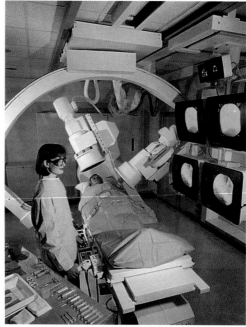

The new L/C™ x-ray system for unrestricted views into the human body.

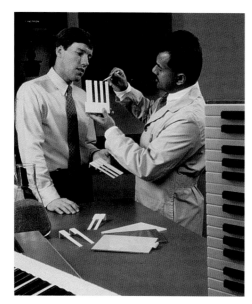

Heavy Valoxa® resin being evaluated for use in piano keys.

PLASTICS

GE Plastics introduces Heavy Valox® resin, a mineral-filled polymer with the density of steel or brass. The material can have the touch, feel and aesthetic qualities of glass, ceramic, porcelain, metal or ivory yet it has the productivity and the design advantages of engineering thermoplastics. Potential applications range from piano keys to kitchen counter tops.

ELECTRICAL DISTRIBUTION & CONTROL

A new national service and training center is opened in Charlotte, North Carolina, by the Electrical Distribution and Control business. Its purpose is to provide all employees with hands-on training in state-of-the-art customer services.

LIGHTING

GE Lighting acquires Tungsram, one of Hungary's largest companies, with twelve manufacturing plants. It allows GE and Tungsram to merge their European distribution and sales operations, significantly strengthening GE Lighting's position in Europe.

GE-Thorn Lamps, Ltd., newly formed by the acquisition of the Thorn Light Source business from Thorn EMI, gives GE Lighting added manufacturing capacity in the United Kingdom, Germany and Italy, and makes it number one in the world lamp market.

NATURAL RESOURCES

Consistent with the Company strategy of striving for a number-one or number-two position for each of its major businesses, GE announces the sale of Ladd Petroleum, originally acquired as part of the purchase of Utah International.

APPLIANCES

A state-of-the-art gas range facility is brought on line as a result of a joint venture with MABE, Mexico's leading appliance manufacturer. The plant, in San Luis Potosi, produces GE's new line of top quality XL44™ gas ranges for the Mexican and American markets.

Compact fluorescent lamps are transferred to electronic mounting unit at Tungsram facility in Nagykanisza, Hungary.

Harrod's is one of many London landmarks illuminated by Thorn, GE's new lighting acquisition.

New facility at San Luis Potosi, Mexico, produces GE gas ranges for the Mexican and American markets.

FINANCIAL SERVICES

GE Capital acquires the private label credit card operations of The Burton Group, Britain's largest specialty apparel retailer. The mortgage insurance business acquires a Travelers unit that services some $14 billion in home mortgages. GE Capital's Fleet Services, one of the world's leading corporate fleet management companies, adds the 50,000-vehicle fleet of McCullagh Leasing. By 1998, there would be over 940,000 vehicles under lease or service management.

1991

AIRCRAFT ENGINES

Aircraft Engines announces that British Airways will be the first customer for the GE90, the world's largest and most powerful high bypass turbofan engine. British Airways specifies the GE90 for its new Boeing 777 twin-engine aircraft, ordering 15 of the 777s with options for 20 more. Lauda Air of Austria follows by selecting the GE90 for its four new 777s. An ambitious development program is underway to certify the GE90 in 1994 and introduce it into active service in 1995.

GE Aircraft Engine Services adds to its worldwide network of overhaul and component repair centers by acquiring a facility in South Wales. The service centers accommodate both GE and non-GE aircraft engines.

GE Aircraft Engine Repair and Maintenance facility at Nantgarw, South Wales.

FAMAT, a joint venture between GE and SNECMA, produces frames for CFM56, CF6 and GE 90 series jet engines at St. Nazaire, France.

INDUSTRIAL AND POWER SYSTEMS

Power Systems introduces the 9F — the world's most powerful gas turbine, rated at 226 megawatts and designed for 50-hertz markets in Europe and Asia.

TRANSPORTATION SYSTEMS

GE's reputation for reliable and high performance DC transit propulsion systems results in contracts for its new AC propulsion systems from the Massachusetts Bay Transportation Authority and the San Francisco Municipal Railway.

NBC

NBC acquires the Financial News Network (FNN) and merges it with the Consumer News and Business Channel (CNBC). The combined service is available in about 49% of the television households in the United States and also has moved into international distribution.

NBC News and its affiliates begin a new era in television news when they launch the NBC Channel as a separate around-the-clock service for affiliated stations. The service provides video, original reports and customized packages to over 200 affiliated stations.

The design, materials of construction and higher firing temperature of the new 9F gas turbine being built in Greenville, South Carolina, will result in high fuel efficiency, record output and high reliability.

342

GE CORE VALUES DEFINE A COMPANY CULTURE

In 1989, after having largely concentrated on restructuring, the removal of layers of management and reductions in bureaucracy, the leaders of General Electric identified Work-Out as the process for transforming the Company to a boundaryless, agile organization capable of growing and prospering in a challenging environment of rapid change. In the 1991 Annual Report (February 14, 1992) Chairman, John F. Welch, Jr., and Vice Chairman, Edward E. Hood, Jr., summarized the success in the implementation of the process and the effect on productivity in what otherwise might have been a more difficult year. They also emphasized that continuing success would depend on the ability of all leaders within the Company to share a common set of values if they were to "walk the talk" of the vision encompassed by the term Work-Out. These values had been selected after extensive discussions at the Crotonville Leadership Development Center and other Company locations. Over the years that would follow, they would be refined somewhat and streamlined so that the list could fit on a wallet-sized card, but the basic tenets would remain the same.

The GE Values

GE Leaders ... Always with Unyielding Integrity:

- *Have a passion for excellence and hate bureaucracy*
- *Are open to ideas from everywhere ... and committed to Work-Out*
- *Live quality ... and drive cost and speed for competitive advantage*
- *Have the self-confidence to involve everyone and behave in a boundaryless fashion*
- *Create a clear, simple, reality-based, customer-focused vision ... and communicate it to all constituencies*
- *Have enormous energy and the ability to energize others*
- *Stretch ... set aggressive goals ... reward progress ... yet understand accountability and commitment*
- *See change as opportunity ... not threat*
- *Have global brains ... and build diverse and global teams*

Leaders of General Electric
John F. Welch, Jr.

In 1981, when John F. Welch, Jr., became the eighth Chief Executive Officer and Chairman of the General Electric Company, he was, at the age of 45 years, the youngest appointee to that office. He reached that position by establishing an impressive record of successes in a number of GE businesses where he spearheaded the development of innovative products and aggressively built high-growth markets for them. Some of the traits that most likely contributed to these successes were demonstrated early in Jack Welch's life. Childhood friends and teammates recall him as an intelligent, industrious and highly competitive young man who was passionate in the pursuit of his goals both on and off the playing field.

Born on November 19, 1935 in Peabody, Massachusetts, John Francis Welch, Jr., attended nearby Salem High School and went on to study chemical engineering at the University of Massachusetts at Amherst. In 1958, a year after graduating from college, he received a master's degree in engineering from the University of Illinois and, in 1960, he earned his doctorate in chemical engineering from that school.

The first professional job, which he took later that year, was as a process chemical engineer at General Electric's small but innovative plastics operation in Pittsfield, Massachusetts. He chose to work on PPO (polyphenylene oxide) a polymer that had been invented by GE Research Laboratory chemist, Allan S. Hay in 1956, This material was exceptionally strong at high temperatures, but its major drawback was that it was very difficult to mold. Welch took on the PPO project because he saw it as a chance to build a business from the ground up. Working with only one chemist to assist him, he spent his first year setting up a pilot plant in Pittsfield. Within a few years his team grew to five and they succeeded in eliminating the molding problem by blending PPO with a low cost polymer, polystyrene. The resulting material came to be known as Noryl.

In 1963, Welch was promoted to the position of manager of Polymer Products Manufacturing and he soon started construction of a production plant for Noryl in Selkirk, New York. In 1966, when he became manager of the Polymer Products Operation, Welch was still faced with the challenge of developing markets for this new product. He enlisted the help of scientists at GE's Research and Development Center in Schenectady. They replaced the metal casing of an electric can opener with a lighter weight and lower cost molded Noryl housing. Welch then used this sample to market Noryl to potential customers and it was not long before it became a commercial success.

In recognition of his success in developing and marketing Noryl, Welch was given similar responsibilities for all GE polymers. In 1968, he was appointed manager of the Chemical Development Operation which became the Plastics Business Department the following year. At that time, with a business of about $40 million in hand, Welch predicted that potential sales for GE plastics could grow to more than $200 million/year and he pushed hard to meet that goal. In 1971, he became general manager of the Chemical and Metallurgical Division and after two years was made vice president and group executive of the Components and Materials Group. By the end of 1977, when Welch moved to a new position, the Plastics business had grown at an average annual rate of 50% and its sales were $500 million, more than fulfilling his prediction. At the same time, he had convinced the Company leadership to increase its investments in the development of Medical Systems' CT - scan technology, which would turn that business into a world leader in medical imaging.

As senior vice president and sector executive of the Consumer Products and Services Sector and vice chairman of the GE Credit Corporation, one of Welch's most notable achievements was an increase in the pace at which GE expanded in the rapidly growing financial services field. GE Credit (later to be called Capital Services) was to become one of the fastest growing and most profitable segments of the Company. These and other successes could not be ignored, nor could the traits of the man whose entrepreneurial spirit had helped accomplish them. In 1979, Welch became a vice chairman of GE and in 1980 it was announced that he would succeed Reginald Jones upon his retirement as Chairman and Chief Executive Officer of GE.

After taking office, Welch was quick to implement his strategy for growth in the 1980s and beyond. In 1981, he announced the criteria by which GE businesses would be judged. They would either have to be number one or number two in terms of industry leadership in goods and services or they would have to hold a clear advantage in a highly profitable market niche. Businesses that could not meet these criteria would either be closed or sold. To back this up, GE made massive investments in expanding and modernizing its strong or promising businesses; it shed its weaker units; made hundreds of new acquisitions; and expanded the capabilities of its Research and Development Center. To create a leaner, flatter, more market-driven business structure, it revised its organizational structure, reducing the number of layers of management by 50%.

The results of these changes during the 1980s were: a doubling of revenues to $54.6 billion; an increase in earnings from $1.5 billion to $3.9 billion; an increase in total growth productivity from 1.6% to 5%; an increase in operating margin from 9.0% to 11.3%; and an increase in the Company market value from $12 billion to $58 billion.

Looking forward to the challenges of the 1990s, Welch believed that an acceleration of growth at GE would require additional changes in its culture. In 1989, he put forth the vision of a boundaryless organization where bureaucracy and other internal and exterior barriers to communications and cooperation would be eliminated. The process that would be used to simplify and speed up decision making was called "Work-Out". One of the early products of Work-Out was a set of core values which characterized the traits of those who occupied leadership positions at GE or aspired to be leaders.

Another opportunity for competitive advantage that Welch identified was the reduction of costs that could be achieved by lowering the levels of defects in all of the Company's processes, products and services. In 1995, he announced an initiative aimed at quantitatively evaluating and improving all of those factors that influenced quality. This initiative was called "Six Sigma" and Welch stood behind it by investing in the training of tens of thousands of employees in the rigorous processes of Six Sigma. He predicted that the savings resulting from these efforts would approach $1.5 billion by the end of 1999. As usual, his projections proved to be on track.

Welch also recognized that GE's customers would not care very much about all the claims made for the benefits of Six Sigma unless it resulted in direct benefits in the form of increased performance, productivity and profitability for their own businesses. Six Sigma was soon expanded to include improvements that GE businesses would make in the design of all of their new products and services while methodically taking into account the desires of their customers. This process became known as Design for Six

Sigma (DFSS) and the result was the onset of a flow of exciting new products that drew enthusiastic reception in the commercial and consumer marketplaces.

Welch saw long term product services as a natural extension of the GE-customer interaction. The very large and growing, worldwide installed base of GE products represented a tremendous area of growth in the service area. GE invested heavily in developing technology for on-site and remote monitoring and diagnosis of its major products and it built the infrastructures necessary to support long term service agreements. Welch described his vision of GE in the 21st century as that of "a global service company that also sells high-quality products." If any part of the company could help make that vision real, it would be Capital Services which, by the end of 1998, contributed 40% of GE's earnings. Welch supported its expansion and that of other GE organizations into what others thought to be risky global markets. As a result of this focus on globalization, international revenues grew from $13.9 billion at the beginning of the 1990s to $43 billion in 1998.

Early in 1999, seeing the tremendous opportunities for market growth and cost reduction offered by the rapidly spreading use of the Internet, Welch called for a company-wide initiative in e-Business. As in previous initiatives, that call brought a degree of urgency, intensity and focus that would mobilize the resources of the company, including all of the aspects of the GE culture that he had been instrumental in creating.

As the decade of the 1990s was drawing to an end, Jack Welch had several milestones to be proud of as he met with shareholders at the 1999 Annual Meeting in Cleveland, Ohio. For the first time in history, GE had crossed the $100 billion mark in revenues; earnings had grown at a rate of 13% for the year to a record $9.3 billion; operating margin had grown to 16.7% compared to 11.3% at the beginning of the decade; and over $21 billion had been invested in new acquisitions in 1998.

But one of the milestones of which Welch was also proud was the fact that GE volunteers had reached, one year ahead of schedule, the goal that they had promised General Colin Powell at the President's Summit in 1997 — one million volunteer hours per year delivered to America's youth by the year 2000. What was not said was that this could not have happened without Welch's dedicated support to this effort.

Also not mentioned was the fact that, for the second consecutive year, *Fortune* magazine had named GE "Most Admired Company in America" and that Jack Welch had, for the fourth consecutive year, been named "Most Respected Executive of the Year" by a majority of his peers who had been surveyed by *Industry Week.*

1992

AEROSPACE

The Mars Observer spacecraft is successfully launched on a Martin Marietta Titan 3 launch vehicle for a 1993 rendezvous with Mars. Built by GE for NASA, the Mars Observer will study Martian geology and climate and will map the planet's surface in preparation for a landing in the future

NASA and the Department of Defense award GE Aerospace contracts to design, build, launch, and operate the Landsat 7 Earth Observer Satellite. A contract to provide a satellite for direct-to-home television programming is received from the Echostar Satellite Corp.

Mars Observer spacecraft.

AIRCRAFT ENGINES

A new low emission, dual annular combustor is developed. Based on combustor technology from NASA's Energy Efficient Engine program, the new combustor design will be a key element in the world's cleanest burning engines. It will see first application in the super-high-thrust GE90 and in the CFM56-5B, both of which will enter service in 1995.

New low-emission, dual annular combustor for jet engines being prepared for component testing.

POWER SYSTEMS

Korea Electric Power's 2,000-megawatt Seoinchon combined-cycle plant enters commercial service. Equipped with eight GE 7F gas turbines, it is the world's most efficient power plant.

The 2,000-megawatt Seoinchon plant near Seoul, Korea.

MOTORS

GE Motors introduces the ECM™ programmable motor for heating and air conditioning applications. The motor is 20% more efficient than regular induction motors and its operating characteristics can be programmed after assembly to serve many applications, thereby reducing customers' cycle times and inventory requirements.

POWER SYSTEMS

The first commercial demonstration of a new remote electronic metering system takes place at Mississippi Power and Light. The system was co-developed by GE Industrial and Power Systems and Ericsson/GE Mobile Radio.

The memory chip inside a new ECM™ motor is programmed for use in a geothermal heat pump unit made by WaterFurnace.

CAPITAL SERVICES

GE Capital Services (formerly GE Financial Services) introduces the GE Rewards MasterCard which offers consumers a variety of rebates and savings. Through direct distributors, GE already services 61 million private-label credit card holders in more than 300 private-label credit and commercial programs for retailers and manufacturers on two continents.

MEDICAL SYSTEMS

The Advance imager, a new generation of Positron Emission Tomography (PET) scanner, is introduced by Medical Systems. Physicians can use PET images to evaluate a variety of diseases including cancer and epilepsy.

GE Rewards MasterCard offers a variety of high-value savings to consumers.

LIGHTING

GE and Hitachi form a joint venture in Japan to combine the technology strengths of GE Lighting with Hitachi's extensive Japanese distribution network. The Hitachi GE Lighting partnership will allow the companies to consolidate Japanese sales and distribution into one that can more effectively take advantage of the growing $2 billion Japanese lighting market.

In India, GE and Apar create GE Apar Lighting Private Ltd, a joint venture which will combine Apar's existing manufacturing skills and 14 sales offices with GE's technology skills and full product line, to serve India's growing consumer and commercial markets.

GE Medical Systems team with a new generation Advance™ PET Scanner designed for improved image quality, faster scans and ease of use.

347

1993

NBC

NBC acquires control of and relaunches NBC Super Channel, the largest general programming television service in Europe, watched in more than 70 million homes. It also starts operation of Canal de Noticias NBC, a new 24-hour Spanish-language channel delivered by satellite in South America.

Lindsey Hanson monitors the satellite transmission of NBC Super Channel programming to 60 million homes and other locations across Europe.

The GE90 is readied for its maiden flight on GE's 747 flying testbed aircraft at the GE flight test facility in Mojave, California.

AIRCRAFT ENGINES

The GE90 engine attains an unprecedented 105,400 pounds of thrust during the first day of ground testing. The first of its kind, wide-chord fan blade for this engine is comprised of 685 layers of a graphite fiber and epoxy composite. The light weight and high stiffness of this composite fan blade result in improved engine performance and reduced engine noise.

TRANSPORTATION SYSTEMS

The Amtrak Genesis I is the first new U.S.- designed and built diesel-electric passenger locomotive in over 40 years. With its light weight and aerodynamic design, it delivers increased power and fuel efficiency while offering features that enhance performance and crew comfort, including a fully insulated, ergonomically designed cab.

The first Dash 9, advanced DC propulsion, microprocessor-controlled locomotive, is delivered to CSX. With its ratings of 108,600 lb. of continuous tractive effort, 78,600 lb. of dynamic braking effort and up to 4400 traction horsepower, this freight locomotive can travel at speeds up to 65 m.p.h..

The first Dash 9 locomotive, CSX road number 9000.

MEDICAL SYSTEMS

Clinical investigations begin on a new Magnetic Resonance-guided Therapy (MRT) system developed by researchers at GE Medical Systems and the Company's R&D Center. MRT provides direct access to the patient during the imaging process, giving physicians a real-time view of internal organs. The technology may be used one day to plan, guide and monitor surgical procedures in a minimally invasive manner, which could significantly reduce hospital stays and costs.

The LOGIQ™ 700 is the first in a new line of totally digital ultrasound systems. It features 128 digital channels for higher image quality, instantaneous switching among probes for faster examinations and an adjustable keyboard for simpler operation.

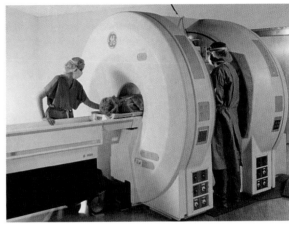

Magnetic Resonance-guided Therapy system provides direct access to patient while imaging.

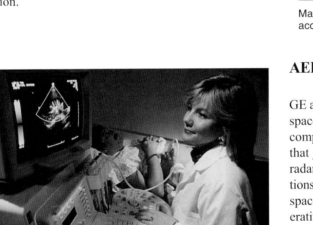

The fully digital LOGIQ™ 700 ultrasound system being used for a kidney examination.

AEROSPACE

GE and Martin Marietta complete the merger of GE's Aerospace businesses into Martin Marietta, nearly doubling that company's annual revenues. The GE Aerospace businesses that join Martin Marietta are major suppliers of satellites, radar and sonar systems, simulation systems, communications systems, government technical services and other aerospace and defense systems. As part of a continuing cooperative agreement between the two firms, GE's Research and Development Center will support Martin Marietta's R&D activities.

LIGHTING

GE Jiabao Lighting Company, Ltd. is formed as a joint venture in China. It will manufacture, distribute and sell a full line of lighting products in China's fast-growing, $550 million lighting market.

The recently formed Hitachi GE Lighting joint venture expands to 100 distributors serving about 10,000 Hitachi retail outlets with the first co-branded product (GE/Hitachi) in Japanese markets.

The GE/Hitachi brand can now be found on light bulbs made by GE and Hitachi for sale in Japan.

1994

APPLIANCES

GE introduces the Profile™ 30 side-by-side, the world's largest freestanding refrigerator, and a 27-cubic-foot Profile side-by-side that is completely free of chlorofluorocarbons in the compressor refrigerant.

Profile halogen/radiant cooktops offer consumers the option of halogen or radiant cooking, and the new 30-inch wall ovens have the largest capacity in the consumer market.

New Profile™ radiant convection range with its glass-ceramic cooktop.

GE's AC 4400, the first 4,400-horsepower AC locomotive.

TRANSPORTATION SYSTEMS

The first alternating current 4,400-horsepower locomotive, the AC4400, is delivered to Union Pacific. This high horsepower, heavy haul locomotive provides more tractive effort because of its greater electrical capability and the ability to control each of the six low-slip traction motors independently. Other features include electronic fuel injection, integrated function computer and displays, and enhanced microprocessor controls.

LIGHTING

GE Lighting introduces the energy efficient Genura™, the world's first self-contained electrodeless reflector lamp. Genura features 10,000 - hour life and provides light output similar to that of a 100-watt incandescent for only 23 watts of energy. Produced in Hungary, it is first being distributed in European commercial and industrial markets, with expansion into the U.S. and other markets to follow.

Other expansions internationally include the purchase of Focos S.A., more than doubling Lighting's market share in Mexico; the purchase of Lindner Licht in Germany; the formation of PT GE Angaska in Indonesia; and the acquisition of 100% ownership of Sivi Illuminazione and the Ilesa brand of lighting products in Italy.

Group of Genura lamps being examined by Martin Scott who put together the multinational team of GE Lighting and Corporate R&D scientists and engineers that created this innovative and energy efficient lamp.

NBC

NBC introduces NBC Desktop Video™, a new generation in business and financial news services delivered directly to existing personal computers, "live" or "on demand".

AIRCRAFT ENGINES

The CF6-80E1 high bypass turbofan engine, rated at 67,500 pounds of thrust, enters service powering the Airbus A330 twinjet. The first of the CF6 series of engines were developed in 1968 to power the new generation of wide-body airliners being introduced by the aircraft industry (see 1968).

POWER SYSTEMS

GE acquires Nuovo Pignone of Italy, one of Europe's leading designers and manufacturers of gas and steam turbines, centrifugal, axial and reciprocating compressors, pumps, and other highly engineered products used in oil and gas pipelines, refineries, and the petrochemical and power generation industries. The GE-Nuovo Pignone partnership expanded GE's portfolio of power generation equipment and services to meet growing requirements for smaller blocks of power in the 2 to 50 megawatt range, including applications such as industrial cogeneration and oil and gas production.

First-stage wheel of an axial compressor being inspected at Nuovo Pignone prior to assembly and shipment to the oil and gas fields of Russia.

The first Nuovo Pignone PGT 10 (10 megawatt) gas turbine production unit, installed in a refinery cogeneration plant in Japan in 1989.

1995

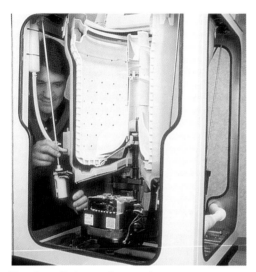

The Auto Balance System for the new line of Profile clothes washers uses an off-the-floor rod and spring floating suspension (shown here) with a fluid-filled balance ring on the basket to allow the basket to move with the load being washed. The result is reduced vibration and noise from off-balance loads and improved washing performance.

LIGHTING

GE Lighting introduces the Heliax™ energy-saving compact fluorescent lamp with a unique helical shape that virtually matches the size of an incandescent light bulb. Its open spiral design makes it one of the most durable and optically efficient compact fluorescent lamps. A 32-watt Heliax™ lamp offers nearly the same light as a 150-watt incandescent light bulb.

AC Dual Mode locomotives can operate in diesel or third rail power.

APPLIANCES

An agreement with Kojima, Inc. one of the largest retailers in Japan, marks the first time that GE Appliances will be able to sell products directly to Japanese retailers, cutting through the traditional layers of distribution.

The new Profile line of clothes washers, built at the completely redesigned home laundry plant in Louisville, Ky., offers the largest capacity available in North America. Their new Auto Balance system virtually eliminates noise and vibration from off-balance loads.

GE-Harris Railway Electronics demonstrates a new Railway Control and Management System' capable of coordinating movement of all trains and work crews across an entire rail-road network to optimize traffic flow and labor workloads.

TRANSPORTATION

The first AC Dual Mode locomotives, with the ability to operate both on diesel and electric rail, are delivered to Amtrak and Metro North. This advanced design delivers unsurpassed performance in either mode, quickly accelerating to over 110 m.p.h. in diesel and over 60m.p.h. when operating on third rail mode. The system computer automatically controls the transition between power modes without the need to stop the train or any of the train services, as in previous designs.

GE Transportation Systems forms a partnership with the Harris Corporation, creating GE Harris Railway Electronics. GE Harris develops advanced train control electronics and software systems designed to increase on-time arrivals, improve asset utilization, and reduce operating costs. One of its products, LOCOTROL®, enables a railroad to haul longer trains faster, and with less fuel consumed, by distributing locomotives throughout the train.

PLASTICS

GE Silicones develops a new silicone material for cushioning keys in computer keyboards. Worldwide growth in the use of silicones leads to the construction of new capacity at the headquarters plant in Waterford, New York.

The resins business acquires 100% ownership of its Tampico, Mexico, and Copen, Brazil, operations in order to increase flexibility and expand sales in those regions.

A manufacturing facility is started in Nansha, China, and is scheduled to begin operations in the third quarter of 1996. It incorporates the same global standards for environmental health and safety employed by all GE Plastics plants in the United States, Europe and Japan.

Ed Jeram (left) and Prakash Pawar of GE Silicones developed this new material for cushioning the keys of these computer keyboards, which are also made of GE resins.

The first GE90-powered Boeing 777 twinjet enters service with British Airways.

AIRCRAFT ENGINES

The GE90 high bypass turbofan engine is certified at 84,700 pounds of thrust by the FAA and a GE90-powered Boeing 777 twinjet enters service with British Airways.

The CF34-8C high bypass turbofan engine, rated in the 13,000-pound-thrust class, is selected to power Bombardier's 70 to 76-passenger Canadair Regional Jet Series 700 airliner.

F101-GE-102 engines power two U.S. Air Force B-1B aircraft in a world-record fastest around-the-world flight of 36 hours and 13 minutes.

ELECTRICAL DISTRIBUTION & CONTROL

The Low-Voltage business of AEG of Germany is acquired to strengthen the line of International Electrotechnical Commission products, which are being used increasingly worldwide. The relay business acquires the world -class electronics and industrial marketing capabilities of Multilin of Canada.

GE Power Controls, formerly a joint European joint venture with GEC of the United Kingdom, becomes 100% GE-owned.

A test rig of miniature circuit breakers is operated at the Hameln plant in Germany, part of the AEG Low-Voltage business acquired by ED&C in 1995.

GE Launches Six Sigma Quality Initiative

In 1995, the leaders of GE concluded that World Class Quality was the next great challenge and one of the major opportunities for growth acceleration by the Company. Customers were demanding better quality as they were trying to provide better quality to their customers; and important competitive advantages could by gained by defect-free products and services that would lead not only to improved customer satisfaction, but higher total cost productivity.

Be it lamps, dishwashers, turbines, broadcasting, insurance or financing, **quality** is measurable, and it can approach near perfection by an unyielding devotion to a disciplined procedure. The procedure is called *Six Sigma* and the devotion extends across the board to all GE employees. Until the current emphasis on Six Sigma, GE and most U.S. companies typically measured about 35,000 defects per million operations performed. In the language of statistics, that level of occurence of defects denotes about 3.5 Sigma. Attainment of Six Sigma means that 3.4 defects are produced per million operations. Clearly, this means that to move from 35,000 defects to 3.4, the process must be improved by 10,000 times!

The Process Previous major programs at GE, namely restructuring, Work-Out, and Change Acceleration Process, laid the groundwork for the current Six Sigma program to reduce defects, launched by GE in 1995. The concept of a formalized process for defect reduction had been embraced by Japanese companies since the 1960s, and in this country by Motorola, Inc. in the 1980s, and by Texas Instruments and AlliedSignal, beginning in 1994. Six Sigma, as pursued by GE, consists of five basic activities: Defining, Measuring, Analyzing, Improving, and ultimately, Controlling the process.
Defining identifies the characteristics that are critical to quality (CTQs) in a process. The aim is to place in evidence all factors that influence not ony the quality of the procedure but the requirments of the customer.
Measuring creates a relation between the number of defects and one or more of the factors which influence quality. Defects are defined as CTQs that are out of tolerance.
Analyzing explores why defects are generated. What exactly is there about the procedure that generates a defect? This phase may involve brainstorming, statistical tools,electrical or mechanical theory, etc. The output is a list of causes, ordered in their relative ability to reduce quality.
Improving leads to quantifying the identified variables which control quality, setting acceptable ranges for variables to attain Six Sigma quality, and taking steps to stay within those ranges.

Controlling sets procedures so that the process stays within the acceptable ranges. These procedures may involve things as simple as checklists or as rigorous as statistical process control.

This structured approach, in its five phases, is similarly applied to all of GE's activities, manufacturing, transactions, software, and service.

The Implementers The backbone of the Six Sigma program are the Black Belts, a term taken from the discipline of the martial arts. Master Black Belts serve as teachers and mentors. Quality teams are led by Black Belts who are responsible for measuring, analyzing, improving and controlling processes which influence customer satisfaction and/or productivity growth. By the end of 1998, there were about 5,000 full-time, fully-trained Black Belts and Master Black Belts. Other working members of the team, trained by the Black Belts, are given the title of Green Belts. and are expected to serve on one or two teams each year. Some 60,000 Green Belts in the Company are engaged part-time on projects and it is expected that virtually all GE professional employees will start training as Green Belts within one month after they are hired. To top this cadre, the Business Champions are senior management leaders ultimately responsible for the success of the Six Sigma effort. They approve projects, fund them and alleviate road blocks to project success.

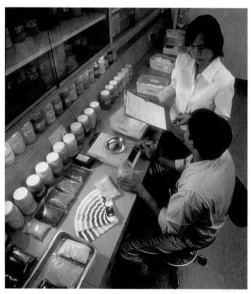

Shown here in a color lab at the GE Plastics plant in Singapore, are two members of a Six Sigma team that reduced by 85%the lead time for matching colors of GE resins to customer requirements, a distinct competitive advantage in the fast-paced global market for plastics.

The Commitment   Commitment to the Six Sigma program by GE is totally and utterly sincere. From its launching in late 1995, with 200 projects and massive training, this program grew to 3,000 projects with an investment of $200 million in 1996. In 1997, over $300 million was spent to carry out an estimated 6000 Six Sigma projects; and in 1998, over $400 million was invested. It is expected that, during 1999, an additional $500 million will have been devoted to Six Sigma projects.

The Verification   Customer surveys determine the extent that customers perceive performance. Customers grade the results. The key here is a close relationship with the customer and constant feedback. Constant review of progress is available to Black Belts by the mechanism of "Dashboards." Taking an analogy from the instrument panel of an automobile, the standard gauges are replaced with quality performance gauges. One arrow indicating customer requested quality characteristic is placed on each gauge on the dashboard. Another arrow indicates how far the process of quality improvement has progressed relative to the goal. The challenge is to close the gap between. In addition to serving as an internal tool, dashboards are a way for GE businesses to share the results of individual programs with each other and with customers. Strategies effective for one business become available for all businesses.

In an evolution of the Six Sigma process, called Design for Six Sigma (DFSS), most new products would be designed with those items Critical to Quality identified. The goal is to <u>design</u> products and services to Six Sigma capability. Of the manufacturing designs reviewed, the aim is to make all the designs capable of yielding Six Sigma quality. The DFSS process and some of its initial results will be discussed later. (See page 364)

An administrative associate for GE Aircraft Engines in Canada used her Six Sigma training as a Green Belt to make the paperwork perfect every time GE Canada imports a marine and industrial engine, parts or tooling for a Canadian customer. In addition to cutting customs costs, her project has reduced border delays by at least 50%.

The Results   In the 1997 Annual Report some individual examples from GE businesses were chosen to demonstrate the effectiveness of the Six Sigma initiative.

- GE Medical Systems reported a 10-fold increase in the life of x-ray scanner tubes for Computed Tomography. These tubes convert x-rays to electrical signals to be processed by computers.
- The industrial diamond business, Superabrasives, quadrupled its return on investment by improving yields without increased cost for plant capacity.
- The railcar leasing business described a 62% reduction in turnaround time at its repair shops. The business has become two or three times faster than its nearest rival because of Six Sigma improvements.
- GE Plastics, through rigorous Six Sigma process work, added 300 million pounds of new capacity, saved $400 million in investment and will save another $200 million by the year 2000.

Precision assembly of the core of the new Performix 630 CT tube is done with the aid of computer quality control checks that ensure superior image quality.

The 1998 GE Annual Report summarized the monetary benefits to GE from its investments during the first three years of the Six Sigma initiative. It was estimated that, in 1999, the scores of thousands of Six Sigma projects that were underway would result in savings approaching $1.5 billion beyond the investment.

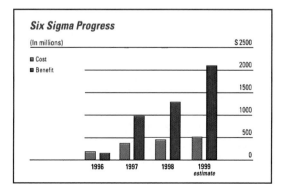

1996

TRANSPORTATION SYSTEMS

The first GE pre-production AC6000 CW™ locomotives are delivered to CSX and Union Pacific. The 6000 horsepower rating is the highest ever produced in a modern, single-engine freight locomotive and can generate up to 180,000 pounds of continuous pulling power.

AIRCRAFT ENGINES

GE Aircraft Engines and Pratt & Whitney establish an alliance to develop a new engine, rated at 72,000 to 84,000 pounds of thrust, to power larger versions of Boeing's 747 aircraft.

CSX puts into service the new GE AC6000CW locomotive - the most powerful, single-engine diesel-electric locomotive built by GE to date.

APPLIANCES

The GE Monogram Collection, a group of professional style, stainless steel appliances, is launched as part of the Monogram premium appliance line.

A 73% interest is acquired in DAKO S.A., Brazil's leading gas range manufacturer. This adds to GE's growing brand strength in Brazil and other countries in Latin America.

PLASTICS

The first stage of GE's new $700 million polycarbonate plant in Cartagena, Spain, begins compounding Lexan™ and Cycoloy™ resins for European markets. By 1998, global capacity for polycarbonate production will be double that available in 1993.

Night view of new Lexan™ polycarbonate plant in Cartagena, Spain. A second plant, announced in 1998, will double polycarbonate capacity at Cartagena to 260,000 metric tons annually.

INFORMATION SERVICES

Information Services introduces the GE Trading Process Network, an Internet-based procurement service capable of cutting purchasing cycle times by up to 80% and associated costs by 30%.

CAPITAL SERVICES

The Structured Finance Group forms precedent-setting joint venture with the Shanghai power system to fund and operate the Shanghai Zhabei Power Project, China's first long-term non-guaranteed, commercially financed project.

NBC

MSNBC, a 24-hour cable news and information channel, and MSNBC on the Internet, a comprehensive interactive on-line news service, are launched by NBC and Microsoft. MSNBC premiers with 22 million subscribers, the largest subscriber base ever for a new cable service. The network also debuts NBC Asia and CNBC Europe, and reintroduces the NBC Super Channel as NBC Europe.

1996

DOW JONES INDUSTRIAL AVERAGE MARKS 100TH BIRTHDAY!!

On May 26, 1896, the Dow Jones Industrial Average was inaugurated by Dow Jones & Co. to provide an index or barometer for measuring the change in the values of the nation's stock market, as represented by a composite of its leading publicly traded companies. General Electric was one of twelve companies chosen for inclusion in the list - and, 100 years later, in 1996, is the only original member of the group.

Stocks in the Dow Jones Industrial Average May 26, 1896

American Cotton Oil
American Sugar
American Tobacco
Chicago Gas
Distilling & Cattle Feeding
General Electric

Laclede Gas
National Lead
North American
Tennessee Coal & Iron
U.S. Leather (preferred)
U.S. Rubber

GE IS THE FIRST COMPANY TO REACH $200 BILLION MARKET VALUE

The Dow Jones Average at the end of the day on May 26, 1896, was 40.94. On its 100th birthday, it approached 5800 and, during 1996, GE became the first company to reach $200 billion in market value.

GE Chairman and Chief Executive Officer, Jack Welch (right) visits the New York Stock Exchange to join in the festivities marking the 100th anniversary of the founding of the Dow Jones Industrial Average. With him are Peter Kann (center), Chairman of Dow Jones, and Richard Grasso (left), Chairman and CEO of the NYSE. (photo courtesy NYSE Archives)

****

GE's Technology Management Services is a leading global provider of information technology solutions.

CAPITAL SERVICES

GE Capital Services acquires First Colony and Life of Virginia, adding to GNA, Harcourt General, AMEX-LT Care, Union Fidelity Life, Union Pacific Life and other members of its family of insurance and annuity companies dedicated to consumer wealth accumulation and protection.

With the acquisition of AmeriData in the United States and CompuNet in Germany, the size of GE Capital Services Technology Management Services businesses is doubled. Information Technology Solutions, a $5 billion global information technology company is created to provide integrated products, services and financial solutions to local, national and international commercial and global customers.

357

1996

GE Crotonville Leadership Development Center Marks 40th Anniversary

GE's Leadership Development Center at Crotonville, New York, passed its 40th anniversary in 1996 and approaches the 21st century with ever-increasing strength and vigor, characteristic of its many years of service in the education of GE managers. The company has long been known for developing some of the best leaders in business and for reinventing itself with the changing times. It invests almost $1 billion annually on training and education programs around the world to ensure this heritage continues.

Although the scope of its activities is global, the focus of GE's commitment to excellence in leadership development and cultural change is Crotonville, the world's first major corporate business school. Crotonville provides the forum for GE people to tackle new business problems from around the world and share their knowledge with customers, suppliers and colleagues throughout GE.

Crotonville came into being after Chairman Ralph Cordiner and a study group concluded that additional educational facilities would have to be provided to introduce GE leaders to the new management challenges and procedures necessary to successfully bring about decentralization of the Company. In 1954, GE purchased the 15-acre estate of the Hopf Institute of Management in Croton-on-Hudson, New York, and immediately began an expansion of the facility which now occupies 52 acres. Its core of instructional and hands-on courses were the Advanced Management Course (AMC), the General Management Course, and the Management Development Course. By far, most of the management courses conducted at the Company's many locations dealt with functional skills. The Advanced Management Course, however, was oriented primarily toward consideration of those generic skills - such as planning, organizing, integrating and measuring - that every manager needed, regardless of function or position. Among the texts used in AMC were the "Blue Books, seven volumes on professional business management that also explained GE's philosophy of decentralization.

As the years brought experience and the competitive environment changed, so did the courses. A Business Management Course and Executive Development Course were added. The decision to expand the Center to engage more managers meant going to many Corporate locations with an expanded curricula. Notable were the First Time Managers Course and the Foremen-Supervisor Program.

Out of stated management objectives grew the need for procedures to bring changes to the Company. Crotonville was the principal arena for teaching these procedures. In 1970, the emphasis shifted to people skills and specifically how to get the job done. The need for strategic planning led to Executive Workshops. GE created techniques such as MBO (management by objectives), SWOT (strengths, weaknesses, opportunities, threats) analysis and strategic planning. GE executives learned these and other methods, which have been widely adopted by businesses, governments, and organizations around the world.

GE's Leadership Development Institute at Crotonville, New York.

In 1981, the newly appointed Chairman of GE, John F. Welch, Jr., saw that the changing competitive global environment required dramatic changes in culture and thinking and Crotonville became instrumental in bringing this about. In the "Pit," the main auditorium and in the classrooms, give and take sessions between participants and top GE management defined, sometimes painfully, a set of concepts and core values for the Company.

One of the most significant of these was **"Work-Out,"** first publicly described in the GE Annual Report for 1989 (See 1989). Work-Out involved identifying an area in need of improvement and bringing people together from all sides of the process - design, marketing, production, sales, etc. - to identify a better method. The Work-Out team met outside the normal work environment to discuss issues and develop recommendations. Recommendations were then presented to management for immediate decision. The procedure remains an integral part of everyday life in GE.

Another initiative was **CAP (Change Acceleration Process)**. Participants are taught how to initiate, lead and manage significant change, using a variety of effective tools. Project, process, and personal change are all addressed in this program. CAP is currently playing a key role in the Company-wide implementation of Six Sigma Quality training.

Six Sigma projects aim to improve quality in products and services by using a well-defined framework of quantitative and analytical methodologies. Two courses are taught at Crotonville - Master Black Belt Training and Six Sigma Champion Training. These integrate with Six Sigma training offered by each of GE's business units. Master Black Belt Training is a one-week program to develop skills needed for the quality initiative. Champion Training is a 2-3 day program to give leaders a working knowledge of key Six Sigma and CAP tools.

Thousands of people each year come together to identify opportunities and debate the issues facing GE around the world. Everyone from newly-hired college graduates to the Chairman meet in classrooms and the "Pit". In 1997, the entire facility was renovated to upgrade the infrastructure and prepare for the educational challenges of the 21st century. Crotonville is equipped with the latest audio, visual and computer technology to facilitate learning. Excellent dining, fitness and recreational facilities, all available on the campus, create a relaxing atmosphere conducive to sharing ideas among all participants.

One of the larger classrooms at Crotonville.

Crotonville's **Core Leadership Development Program** traces its origin to earlier years, but, since the 1980s, an emphasis on personal analysis and GE's Leadership Values has led to the current sequence. This can include the **New**

Manager Development Course, for those in their first leadership positions, and the **Experienced Manager Course**, which emphasizes leadership and influence as well as the financial aspects of management. Senior professionals and executives identified as high-potential and capable of playing key roles in GE's businesses or functions attend the **Manager Development Course**.

The "Pit" auditorium at GE's Crotonville Leadership Institute.

In recognition of the importance of the increasingly global nature of the company's businesses, senior executives with the potential to manage a business are selected to attend the **Global Business Management Course**. This experiential three-week course, held at locations around the world, addresses the development of market-driven strategies and global leadership skills. In support of this course and other GE global education programs, 30% of the Leadership Institute staff is located outside of the U.S. Without the bricks and mortar, a virtual Crotonville is provided.

The **Executive Development Course** is the capstone of the Executive Education Sequence. It involves action learning with real business issues using projects sponsored by the CEO. Participants focus on creating boundaryless, customer-focused global businesses with a special emphasis on cultural diversity.

A relatively new role for Crotonville is to help the businesses improve relationships with strategic customers and other key constituencies. This entails visits on site with customers and their business partners to share the unique experience of Crotonville and to engage in open dialogue on how they can integrate with other key organizations and processes to contribute to their mutual success.

1997

MEDICAL SYSTEMS

GE announces a first-of-its-kind multiple purpose digital x-ray detector. The digital system offers the potential for more accurate, faster and more cost-effective x-ray examinations. It replaces conventional x-ray film and processing chemicals with computer images that can be reviewed instantaneously, stored, and transmitted electronically to remote sites. The new detector, which will be manufactured exclusively for GE by EG&G, Inc., is the result of a 10-year, $100 million R&D effort.

Medical Systems introduces the new Signa® Horizon™ LX MRI system, the first to combine advanced imaging technology with a high-performance, lightweight magnet for lower operating costs and easier installation.

The introduction of SmartView™ software makes it possible for GE's computed tomography systems to provide real-time monitoring of interventional procedures.

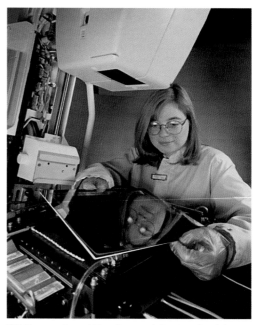

GE Research and Development Center physicist installs prototype digital x-ray detector in test apparatus.

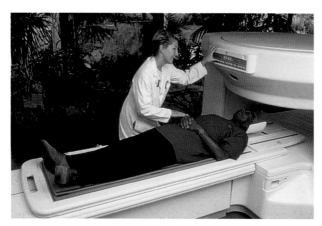

Open design of Signa® Profile™ Platinum MRI can make patients more comfortable and provides more room for monitoring patients.

AIRCRAFT ENGINES

GE acquires Greenwich Air Services, Inc. and UNC Inc., also an aircraft engine services company. The new additions will expand GE Engine Services' capabilities and markets into the business jet and aircraft accessories services sector. By 1998, the revenues of this segment of Aircraft Engines would be close to $5 billion, almost half of the total revenue of that business.

APPLIANCES

Responding to consumer demand for softer, cleaner, better tasting water, GE introduces SmartWater™ softeners and filtration systems. These are the first such products offered by a major appliance manufacturer.

Part of the new GE Profile Performance™ series, the SmartWater™ faucet provides high-quality, clean water for drinking or cooking.

1997

CAPITAL SERVICES

GE Capital, through the acquisition of Woodchester, one of Ireland's largest financial services companies, expands its auto and equipment leasing business in Ireland, Britain, Denmark and Portugal. Auto Financial Services now has a presence in 13 countries.

Railcar Services, a global leader in railcar leasing, makes its European debut with the acquisition of pan-European Cargowaggon. Railcar Services also provides railcar management, repair, refurbishment, conversions and other services to railroads and shippers in North America and Europe.

Before a leased car is returned to a customer, any repairs that have been made to it are recorded with a hand-held computer.

CNBC has become the "must-see" channel for business news, even in Manhattan, where the giant Astrovision™ screen looms over Times Square in Manhattan.

NBC

CNBC, the world leader in business television journalism, enters into a strategic alliance with Dow Jones to merge their European and Asian business news services under the CNBC banner. Dow Jones will provide CNBC with access to the editorial resources of The Wall Street Journal as well as other Dow Jones properties in the United States. By the end of 1998, the U.S. distribution of CNBC would rise to 68 million subscribers and the number of subscribers to MSNBC would more than double to 46 million since its 1996 launch.

Personnel at Minnesota Power use XA/21™ control system from GE Harris to automatically monitor and control the electric power grid across the northern tier of Minnesota.

POWER SYSTEMS

GE Power Systems significantly broadens its participation in the global energy management market by forming a joint venture with Harris Corporation called GE Harris Energy Control Systems. The new business designs, manufactures and markets computer control centers and other electronics to help utilities identify the most cost-effective methods of dispatching power, tracking power quality, simulating outages and recommending timely actions to optimize operations.

361

1998

Honduras installation of an LM6000 aeroderivative gas turbine power system packaged by Stewart & Stevenson Energy Products.

MEDICAL SYSTEMS

The new LightSpeed™ QX/i CT system is introduced. Completely designed and developed using Design for Six Sigma (DFSS, see p364), it is the world's first scanner that allows doctors to capture multiple images simultaneously and at a speed that is six times faster than traditional single-slice scanners. The savings in scanning time can save precious time in life-or-death trauma situations.

Medical Systems announces the acquisition of Marquette Medical Systems, a global leader in diagnostic cardiology and patient monitoring devices.

GE purchases the nuclear medicine and magnetic resonance imaging businesses of Elscint, Ltd., an Israeli medical imaging firm. Medical Systems and Elscint will continue their joint venture, ELGEMS, formed in 1997 to design and manufacture nuclear imaging products.

APPLIANCES

The Spectra True Temp gas range is introduced as the first GE consumer product built using the methodologies of Design for Six Sigma. It captures the first four positions in a consumer magazine ranking due to its extremely accurate electronic control of oven temperatures and other consumer-judged performance and quality features.

POWER SYSTEMS

GE acquires Stewart & Stevenson's Gas Turbine Division which becomes Stewart & Stevenson Energy Products. That organization is a world leader in packaging power generation equipment in the 5 to 50 megawatt range for the electric utility, cogeneration and gas compression markets. Packaged equipment enables fast, easy installation of small blocks of power at a site where that power is needed.

AIRCRAFT ENGINES

The LM2500 marine engine is selected for the world's first gas turbine-powered cruise ships being built for Royal Caribbean International and Celebrity Cruises. S&S Energy Products and GE Industrial Aeroderivatives combined forces to win the order for packaging and servicing these engines.

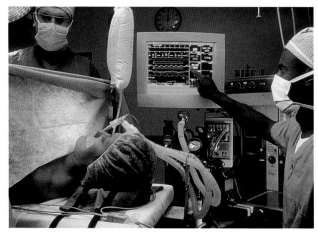

Marquette Medical Systems high-tech patient monitoring systems provide anesthesiologists with highly accurate patient data during surgery.

PLASTICS

Exatec, a joint venture between GE Plastics and Bayer AG of Germany, will develop polycarbonate automotive glazing technology and manufacturing systems at facilities in Wixom, Michigan, and Cologne, Germany, to pursue this high potential use of their materials. Another joint venture with Bayer, GE-Bayer Silicones Europe will strengthen their position in Europe.

The planned construction of a second 130,000 metric-ton polycarbonate plant in Cartagena, Spain, will double the capacity of that facility.

CAPITAL SERVICES

GE Financial Assurance acquires the infrastructure of Toho Mutual Life to form GE Edison Life, one of the fastest-growing life insurers in Japan. With more than 500 offices and 6,000 sales agents, it serves both corporate and individual clients throughout Japan. The acquisitions of Koei Credit and the consumer finance business of Lake Corporation also increase the ability to provide a variety of financial services to the Japanese consumer under the Koei Credit, NC Card Sendai and GE Capital Consumer Finance names.

In Europe, GE's globalization initiative continues with acquisitions of Agrabanka - a Czech financial institution - and the Polish American Mortgage Bank. Other acquisitions include mobile accommodations and modular unit businesses in Germany, Swiss consumer credit operations and International Wagon Services, a leading freight car leasing company in Great Britain. The latter transaction doubles the European freight car capacity of GE Capital Railcar Services. It also helps propel Railcar into the ranks of the top 20 businesses that provide 90% of the earnings of the parent company, GE.

LIGHTING

GE Lighting introduces the 2D® compact fluorescent lamp (CFL). Its unique flat design makes the 2D CFL particularly well suited for torchiere-style floor lamps. The compact fluorescent also is cooler, lasts longer and is more energy efficient than halogen lamps.

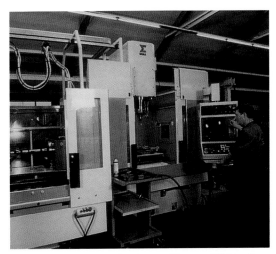

GE Capital's European Equipment Finance (EEF) offers unique financial solutions to industrial and commercial customers throughout Europe. MUST Co. of France, for example, financed this new plastics machining facility through a lease contract with EEF in 1998.

INDUSTRIAL SYSTEMS

GE Industrial Systems is formed by combining the former Electrical Distribution and Control business with the Industrial Control business. This $4.8 billion global business provides customers with a single, integrated source for electrical and electronic systems, services and solutions.

New torchiere-style floor lamps feature cooler, more energy efficient 2D® compact fluorescent lamps.

GE installation engineer inspects a roll of galvanized steel coil at the Nucor mill in Hickman, Arkansas, where GE Industrial Systems provided a compete production solution: drives, motors, switchgear, control centers, software and related equipment and services.

Design for Six Sigma - Extending Six Sigma Quality to Product Performance and Reliability

In its classic form, as developed by Motorola, Six Sigma is focused primarily on improving manufacturing operations. It was found that the method rapidly led to reduced scrap and rework and improved factory productivity. But, even with the best manufacturing technology and factory control, getting beyond about 4 sigma proved to be elusive. Over time, people learned that further quality improvements could only come by redesigning the products to be compatible with the improved manufacturing capability.

Very early in its own Six Sigma initiative, GE resolved to learn from the experience of other companies and attack improvements in product design in parallel with manufacturing improvements. GE also broadened the definition of six sigma design to include creating products which would be six sigma in performance and reliability as well as in manufacturability. The reason for this is that customers see a product's performance and reliability, not the ease with which it was made. In designing new products, those performance features that the customer wanted would become the critical-to-quality characteristics (CTQs) that were subjected to the rigorous statistical Design for Six Sigma (DFSS) process. Thus, this broadened definition, embodied in DFSS, would be the best way to make GE's customers participate in and realize the benefits of Six Sigma, leading to benefits in business growth and market share, as well as internal productivity.

Led by Corporate Research & Development (CRD), the Engineering, DFSS and Quality Leaders in the GE operations formed a partnership to revolutionize GE's design and product development processes. A new DFSS design process, based on careful identification of the customers' needs, systems engineering, computer simulation of product performance, and statistical design incorporating true process capability was developed and disseminated throughout GE. The goal was to design in quality from the start, rather than achieve it later through inspection and field experience.

The new DFSS process was quickly implemented in all of GE's manufacturing businesses and is proving to be a winner. The first major DFSS product, GE Medical Systems' Performix™ x-ray tube, was released in 1997. It improved the operating life of an x-ray tube from about 75,000 scans to over 300,000 scans, resulting in significant reductions in equipment downtime and cost for radiology customers. This was followed in 1998 by GE Medical Systems' LightSpeed™ CT scanner, a major breakthrough in scanning speed, image quality, patient comfort, reliability and clinical productivity. In the same year, other DFSS products were released, including GE Industrial Systems' Innovation™ Drives, GE Appliances' Spectra True Temp™ range and GE Plastics' Ultem™ 1285 material for housewares manufacturer, Tupperware. GE is now poised to release many DFSS products in 1999 and beyond.

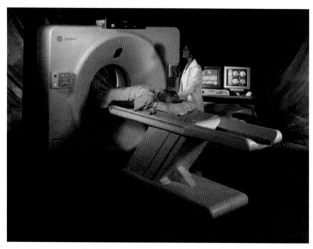

The LightSpeed™ CT scanner, one of the earliest major products of the DFSS initiative.

The Spectra True Temp™ Range, the first household consumer product of the DFSS initiative.

Product Services - A Major GE Growth Initiative

The product services initiative that was conceived in the closing years of the 1990s commits GE to a larger and bolder vision of services than it had ever known. GE has long been a service company and its growth in financial services, in particular, had been phenomenal. The 1997 Annual Report noted that more than two thirds of revenues in the coming year would come from financial, information, and product services. The new element for the late 1990s and 21st century was a broadening of the definition of product services. Beyond the traditional activities of parts replacement and overhauling high-technology equipment, such as jet engines and turbines, the new vision saw GE working with the customer to apply engineering, R&D and product knowledge to improve the performance, reliability and quality of the installed base of GE equipment. The benefit to customers, such as utilities, hospitals, railroads, factories and airlines, would be gains in their competitiveness and productivity. The benefit to GE would be a continuing growth in product services revenues from less than $8 billion in 1995 to an estimated $17 billion in the year 2000.

This initiative aimed to change not only the size but also the nature of the product services businesses — previously parts and labor businesses. The customer waited until something needed to be repaired and then called GE to supply the parts and labor required. Obviously, the more service calls that the GE service business made, the greater its revenues. That did not, however, always result in customers who were happy with the quality of the product manufactured by GE. The Six Sigma initiative was implemented at GE to reduce, if not eliminate, that problem.

The new nature of services was to align the interests of GE more closely with those of the customer through long term service agreements. The customer agreed to pay GE a continued revenue stream in exchange for GE's promise to keep the equipment running. In other words, the less things break, the greater the benefit to both the customer and GE. This put a premium on rapid response, and solving problems before they got serious and expensive.

For example, a problem with a medical diagnostic machine encountered in the middle of the night by personnel at a hospital in Japan or detected by monitoring equipment built into the machine, could be communicated electronically through Milwaukee halfway around the world to Buc, France, where it was daytime and experts were on duty to provide solutions. Similarly, GE Aircraft Engines personnel could monitor many aircraft engines in flight through the use of strategically placed sensors. If an indication of a future problem emerged, the GEAE service team could have

a part ready at the airport when the plane landed, for fast turnaround with no delays to the airline's schedule. This prevents both costly repairs and costly delays or cancellations of flights.

The essence of the service initiative is to deliver benefits that the customer can see, such as better on-time performance and improved "burn" rates in engines, higher efficiency in turbines and better resolution in CT scanners. Looking forward, service technology also can extend the GE role into such areas as information management or logistics — for example, helping run not just a locomotive, but a railroad. In specific terms, the services initiative of the late 1990s across GE included the following:

* GE Medical Systems continued to expand its InSite system, the pioneering GE effort of remotely monitoring and diagnosing the problems of high-tech equipment. InSite enabled the top GE service people at three world service centers to provide round-the-clock solutions to problems that might emerge thousands of miles away with GE Magnetic Resonance Imagers, Computed Tomogrphy machines, ultrasound scanners or other diagnostic imaging machines. Current initiatives to further improve this world-leading capability included more use of digital technology, increased use of "predictive repair," and improved product interfaces.

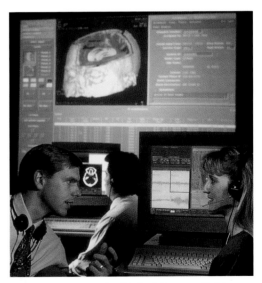

Technical experts at the Medical Systems OnLine Center are linked, via the InSite network, to more than 10,000 imaging systems worldwide. Using state-of-the-art work stations, highly skilled engineers and applications specialists can remotely analyze and actually repair equipment problems half a world away.

Product Services - A Major GE Growth Initiative

GE Transportation Systems completely rebuilt this service facility in San Luis Potosi, Mexico, to service locomotives for TFM under a 20-year contract with the privatized Mexican railroad. GE also delivered 50 new locomotives to TFM in 1998.

day, with multiple language capability, to provide continuous service to thousands of operators of GE power generation equipment around the globe. Major areas of effort included improved energy information services, distributed power, and power system management, monitoring and control.

GE engineers from Industrial Systems can access a distant customer's equipment and process systems to troubleshoot and resolve problems quickly from this new remote diagnostics center in Virginia.

* GE Transportation Systems had more than 2700 locomotives under long-term service contracts in 1998. Service facilities were acquired or built worldwide to maintain and upgrade these and other locomotives. New products and systems in the area of railway electronics were being developed to enable customers to operate not only their GE locomotives more effectively but also entire trains and ultimately entire railroad systems.

* GE Aircraft Engines experienced dramatic growth in its Engine Services business, as customers increasingly outsourced life cycle and maintenance activities. The service network and joint ventures were extended globally, from Brazil to China. Thousands of GE engines began to be monitored from GE service centers while in the air and a new joint venture, GE Harris Information Solutions, gave customers the ability to monitor and analyze data directly to and from aircraft in a real-time. By early 1999, the total value of multi-year agreements to service and maintain aircraft engines would reach $9 billion.

* GE's Industrial Systems Solutions business helped customers increase their productivity in a wide range of process industries, such as steel mills, paper mills and chemical plants.

* GE Power Systems saw an 85% increase in revenues from contractual services in 1998. A new customer service support center operated seven days a week, 24 hours a

Aircraft Engines launched its Technical Response Center in 1996 to speed up and improve engine maintenance. By monitoring engines in flight from the ground via satellite and other systems, GE engineers can diagnose potential engine problems, plan for maintenance or overhaul, and resolve problems more quickly than ever before.

Responding to Jack Welch's call for an "infusion of technology" into these services businesses, efforts in the development of advanced services technologies accelerated both in the businesses themselves, and at the Corporate-level R&D Center. The Center carried out some 300 service related projects with Company-wide impact in the 1998 -1999 timeframe. They focused on everything from rapid engine overhauls and remote monitoring and diagnostics, to hardware upgrades that improve efficiency and reduce emissions. Investment in new technology across the businesses in 1999 was measured in the billions of dollars.

Here are just a few examples of Company-wide technology initiatives backing up the services thrust on the eve of the twenty first century:

*   GE metallurgists developed a process for the crack-free welding of engine superalloys. The payoff was good-as-new refurbished parts at much lower cost than a newly made replacement. In some cases, the quality of parts could even be upgraded by new service processes such as "laser shock peening" which made airfoils more resistant to foreign object damage than ever before.

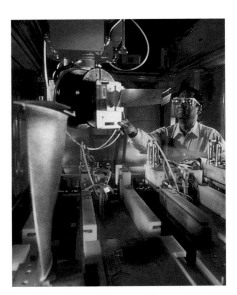

An engineer from GE Aircraft Engines readies a fan blade for laser shock peening, a new GE process aimed at increasing the durability of aircraft engine components.

*   Engineers developed new computerized methods of designing turbine blades. This enabled GE to offer upgraded blades that, because of subtle changes in their shape, reduce turbulence and other fluid flow losses. This can add perhaps a percentage point of efficiency to the turbine, which can be worth hundreds of thousands of dollars to the customer. Other designers developed a new "head end liner" that fits into the combustor of an existing gas turbine. It cut emissions sufficiently to bring back into compliance and operation turbines that had been shut down because they could not meet emission standards.

*   Technologies at the forefront of medical diagnostics provided GE with a synergy that few, if any, service companies can match. For example, phased array ultrasound became crucial for the inspection of metals. And GE's newest 1999 imaging breakthrough, all-solid-state digital x-ray imaging, was put to work in parts inspection because of the superior contrast and range of imaging it provides compared to previous techniques.

*   GE information technologists developed information processing methods that make consumer call centers work more effectively, and put Web technology to work in services. GE communications engineers helped the GE businesses and their customers improve reliability and security of communications, while taking advantage of evolving technology to reduce telecommunications costs.

The service initiative in the late 1990s became one of using services to drive customer productivity in a way that the customer will be willing to pay for. The biggest challenge became following through on long term service agreements to make them mutually beneficial for both the customer and GE.

Summing up the effort in his 1999 letter to share owners, employees and customers, Jack Welch wrote: ***"This initiative has already changed the headset of the Company from that of a provider of products augmented by ancillary services to a that of a Company that is overwhelmingly a source of customer-focused, high-value information, technology-based productivity solutions — as well as a provider of high quality products."***

The GE R&D Center: A Century of Pioneering

The GE R&D Center holds a place in history as the first industrial laboratory in the United States where fundamental scientific research was performed in a business setting. It has reinvented itself in every generation, and remains today a world leader in advanced technology innovation.

Prior to the R&D Center's founding in 1900, there had been industrial laboratories, such as Thomas Edison's "invention factory" at Menlo Park, New Jersey, in the 1870s, out of which GE sprang, and Edison's larger and better equipped West Orange Laboratory in the 1880s. There had been scientific laboratories in Europe supporting the chemical and pharmaceutical industries. But no U.S. company had created such an effort before 1900 (*see* 1900).

Major contributions during the laboratory's early years under the direction of Willis R. Whitney, included two epochal inventions by William D. Coolidge: ductile tungsten filament, the type of wire used to produce light in virtually all of today's incandescent lamps, and the modern form of X-ray tube, named the "Coolidge" tube in his honor. Irving Langmuir introduced another major improvement in the efficiency of lighting, the "gas filled" lamp, the type used today in most lamps of 100 watts or more. Albert Hull's invention of the screen grid tube resulted in tremendous improvements to radio reception. The magnetron tube that he developed is the ancestor of the tubes that today are used to generate the microwaves in essentially all the world's microwave ovens. Other major contributions of the lab's early years ranged from the modern process for making silicones to big improvements in the quality and life of Calrod heating elements used in electric stoves.

The laboratory also made great contributions to science. Irving Langmuir's discoveries in the field of surface chemistry won him the 1932 Nobel Prize for Chemistry. Chemist Katharine Blodgett discovered important new ways of producing liquid films only one molecule thick, and used her techniques to invent glareless glass, today used in many types of optical equipment. Hull independently co-discovered, along with two European scientists, Debye and Scheerer, an important way to use x-rays to analyze the composition of materials that are in the form of powders.

In 1950, the laboratory moved to its current home in the Schenectady, New York, suburb of Niskayuna. In the 1980s, its main laboratory building was expanded by over 50% to support increased effort in electronics and software. On other parts of the 550 acre laboratory site, some 20 other specialized buildings were either upgraded or constructed to support work in such areas as engineering sciences, medical equipment development, and polymer processing.

Achievements in the lab's second half century at this new site included the development of two major engineering plastics, Lexan and PPO/Noryl; development of the world's first reproducible process for making diamond; development of a translucent ceramic making possible the Lucalox lamp, today a major form of outdoor illumination; and development of the forms of computed tomography (CT) scanners and magnetic resonance imaging (MRI) systems used in hospitals around the globe.

Scientific achievements of this era included the discovery of superconductive tunneling, which won Ivar Giaever the 1973 Nobel Prize in Physics, and the invention of the solid state laser by physicist Robert N. Hall, a breakthrough which later made such products as the laser printer and the compact disk player possible.

This evolution of the GE Research Laboratory was paralleled by the growth of the GE General Engineering laboratory, also headquartered in Schenectady. Its focus was on company engineering problems and it also included world leaders in invention. Most notable among them was Ernst F.W. Alexanderson, whose more than 300 patents made him GE's most prolific inventor ever (not counting Edison). Alexanderson built the equipment used in the world's first radio broadcast in 1906, and then developed the system used to create the world's first television broadcast in 1928.

The 550 acre site of the GE Research and Development Center, overlooking the Mohawk River in Niskayuna, New York.

In 1965, the Research Laboratory and the Advanced Technology laboratories (successor to the General Engineering Laboratory) were combined to create today's GE Research and Development Center. The Center has continually evolved to achieve greater relevance and contributions to GE, at the same time as it has sought to preserve the capability for technology leadership.

At the Center in the late 1990s, some 1600 people, more than 515 of them with Ph.D. degrees, carried out work across, arguably, a broader span of science and technology activities than practiced at any other company in the world. Efforts included not only the expected areas of physics, chemistry, mechanical, electrical and chemical engineering, metallurgy and polymer science, but also such realms as economics and business processes, computer science and artificial intelligence, ceramics, and biology. The Center's forefront areas of research and development in the 1990s included:

* Development of a revolutionary new method of producing digital x-ray images that could vastly improve medical diagnostics worldwide in such areas as mammography.

* World leadership in three dimensional visualization, with impact across a half dozen GE businesses — from aiding the design of easier-to-maintain aircraft engines to assisting surgeons in performing faster, safer operations.

* New polymers that will lead to more weatherable plastics for outdoor use and perhaps widen the use of safer, lighter polycarbonate automobile windows.

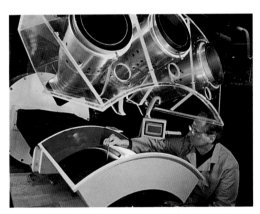

A new low-cost, high performance, heat cured silicone rubber was developed for such applications as medical tubing and automotive gaskets.

* World-class analysis and design of new combustion processes that find application in everything from turbine combustors with lower emissions to more efficient gas range burners.

* Support in helping to bring GE's NBC television network into the digital age with ways to replace videotape with computer storage of programming. This leads to faster and more efficient distribution of tailored programs to NBC's many stations across the country and to other media outlets around the world.

* Work with GE Capital on ways of applying computer science and artificial intelligence to automate credit analysis processes and reduce risk in capital transactions.

* Processes for reducing the environmental impact of manufacturing , by recycling materials or increasing the efficiency of chemical processes.

* Continuing research leadership across a wide range of areas from aerodynamics to x-ray materials.

New "H" technology gas turbines in the final stages of development at GE Power Systems will be the first to convert 60% of a fuel's energy to electricity in a combined-cycle (gas and steam turbine-generator) operation. To accomplish this, the "H" gas turbine will use new materials and processes from GE's R&D Center, along with the latest advances in compressor design and coatings employed in GE aircraft engines.

The Center's mission, like its technologies, has evolved far beyond what went on in the Schenectady barn which was the first site of the Research Laboratory in 1900 (see 1900). That mission in 1999 included not only providing major technology breakthroughs and a steady stream of key inventions, but also helping solve GE's technical problems, teaming with the businesses on product and process development, helping provide GE's next generation of technical leaders, sourcing technology worldwide, and helping lead such GE thrusts as services and quality.

1999

LIGHTING SYSTEMS

GE Lighting and EMCORE Corporation form GELcore LLC, a joint venture company that will develop and market high-brightness "white light" and colored LEDs (light-emitting diodes) on a worldwide basis. White light LEDs are seen by many as the greatest revolution in lighting since the development of the Edison light bulb. Their life can exceed 100,000 hours and they have dramatically reduced energy consumption and enhanced durability. Those attributes as well as the design flexibility which comes from their compact size and method of fabrication, make LEDs particularly suitable for automotive, traffic, flat panel display and other specialty lighting applications.

Engineer holds sample containing an array of white light LEDs. Such arrays can be assembled into a variety of lighting panel shapes.

APPLIANCES

GE Appliances introduces the revolutionary Advantium™ speed cooking oven, the first oven to deliver the cooking quality and versatility of a conventional oven with the "speed of light." It uses high intensity halogen lamps which produce lighwaves that cook the outside of the food much like conventional radiant heat but also penetrate the surface so that the inside is cooked at the same time. As a result, food cooks evenly and so fast that more of the natural moisture is retained than even with "conventional" cooking. The Advantium™ can bake a potato in ten minutes, broil an inch-thick steak in seven minutes or roast a whole four-pound chicken in 20 minutes. With the touch of a button it can convert to a fully functional microwave oven and can use regular cookware.

New Advantium™ oven uses lightwaves to bake, broil, grill and roast food four to five times faster than conventional ovens with no compromise in quality.

MEDICAL SYSTEMS

Medical Systems announces the development of a major breakthrough in imaging technology, known as functional anatomical mapping. This new technology is expected to improve the physician's ability to accurately diagnose patients by providing a clearer picture of the extent and precise location of disease. It merges the ability of nuclear medicine to show the functioning of internal organs with the anatomical images of digital X-rays. After review by the U.S. Food and Drug Administration, it is expected to be commercially available during the year 2000.

INDUSTRIAL SYSTEMS

GE Fanuc Automation, Inc., purchases Total Control Products, Inc., a producer of industrial control systems based in Melrose Park, Illinois. Total Control offers a broad range of products used to define, monitor and maintain the operation, sequencing and safety of industrial equipment.

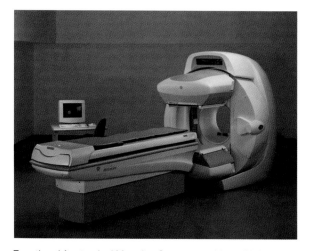

Functional Anatomical Mapping System combines the functional imaging of nuclear medicine with the anatomic imaging features of digital X-ray.

AIRCRAFT ENGINES

Boeing reaches an agreement with GE to develop a 115,000-pound-thrust engine for its long-range 777-200X and 777-300X airplanes. The GE90-115B engine, projected to enter service in 2003, will be the world's most powerful engine; and the 777-200X, which can fly 10,100 statute miles, will be the longest-range commercial airplane ever designed.

Embraer selects GE's 14,000-pound-thrust CF34-8E and 18,000-pound-thrust CF34-10E turbofan engines to power its new 70-passenger ERJ-170 and 98 to 108-passenger ERJ-190 regional airliners. Other jet aircraft manufacturers that have selected CF34-8 and -10 series engines are Fairchild Aerospace and Bombardier. In this fastest growing segment of the commercial aviation industry, almost 1,300 of these engines have been ordered by regional airlines — before their new aircraft have even entered passenger service.

CF34-8C1 engine at the crosswind test site at the GE Aircraft Engines test complex near Peebles, Ohio. Earlier versions of this engine demonstrated exceptional in-flight reliability in the course of accumulating more than 3 million flighthours in service with 18 airlines worldwide.

The new high efficiency "H" technology gas turbine is the heart of the GE STAG 109H combined-cycle system.

CAPITAL SERVICES

Capital Services (GECS) buys $7 billion in commercial equipment and auto leasing assets held by Japan Leasing Corporation and Japan Lease Auto. The transaction, one of the largest ever made by a foreign company in Japan, provides GE Capital's Japan Leasing subsidiary with access to 71,000 new corporate equipment leasing clients. It also adds more than $1 billion in assets and 130,000 vehicles under lease and service management in Japan to the business of GE Capital Car Systems. Japan is the world's largest market for commercial fleet leasing. GECS will also acquire the $4.5 billion U.S. commercial loan portfolio of Japan's Long Term Credit Bank. In Australia and New Zealand, GECS purchases the consumer and commercial financial services assets of AVCO.

POWER SYSTEMS

Power Systems and BP Amoco of the U.K receive final approval from the British Government to build a 500-megawatt power station at the Baglan Energy Park in South Wales. The plant will use GE's new "H" technology gas turbine, which is designed to reach 60% fuel efficiency in a combined-cycle operation. This compares to the 57-58% level of efficiency achieved in the most efficient combined-cycle plants in operation. Lower fuel utilization will not only reduce operating costs over the life of the plant but will significantly reduce emissions. This, combined with the burning of natural gas and the use of nozzle steam cooling to reduce nitrous oxide emissions, will enable the H system to meet or surpass the most stringent environmental regulations in place in the world.

GE strengthens its ability to meet global demand for 50Hz power generation equipment by acquiring the heavy-duty gas turbine business of Alstom France S.A. As a result, it expands its industry-leading installed base of gas turbines by 1,100 units to 7,300.

Power Systems and Plug Power create "GE Fuel Cell Systems," a joint venture company that will distribute fuel cells worldwide. The new company will market, sell, install and service Plug Power-designed and manufactured fuel cells of up to 35KW for residential and small business power applications on a worldwide basis. It expects to offer commercial units beginning in January 2001.

1999

NBC and THE INTERNET

NBC, CNET and XOOM.com, Inc. announce that NBC will merge several of its key Internet assets with XOOM.com and Snap.com to form the seventh-largest Internet site and the first publicly traded Internet company integrated with a major broadcaster. The new company, to be called NBC Internet (NBCi) will use Snap as its umbrella consumer brand, integrating broadcast, portal and e-commerce for more than 18 million unique users per month. In addition to high-quality free Web services such as search and navigation, a directory of Web sites, home page building, chat rooms, downloadable software, message boards and greeting cards, NBCi will offer innovative NBC content, including full motion video programming, sites for a number of its popular shows and localized community guides connected to local NBC stations.

GE Chairman, John F. Welch, Jr., will join five other GE and NBC executives on the 13-member board of the new company. NBC President and CEO Robert Wright will be chairman of NBC Internet.

MSNBC.com, a partnership between NBC and Microsoft, is not part of the transaction but will continue premium positioning on the merged site. MSNBC.com, the leading site for general news on the Internet, has a combined Home/Work audience of 9.5% of the Internet audience and, on July 21, 1999, it recorded a record breaking traffic of 2.4 million unique users logging on in one day.

MSNBC.com announces agreements with broadband service providers, Road Runner, Sprint High Speed DSL and Excite @Home, to provide them with streaming video with the latest content from the global operations of NBC news and clips from other popular NBC programming, such as the "Today Show," "NBC Nightly New," "Dateline NBC" and "NBC Sports." Links will be provided back to MSNBC.com.

NBC

NBC and AT&T Broadband & Internet Services announce a wide-ranging pact for AT&T's cable network to carry NBC programs in high-definition television (HDTV). Under the agreement, AT&T Broadband & Network will also carry NBC's cable services CNBC and MSNBC, and the network's Olympic programming. The companies will work to provide digital programming for new high-definition television sets as well as traditional TVs through set-top boxes that will be compatible with high-definition signals.

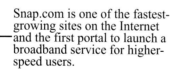

Snap.com is one of the fastest-growing sites on the Internet and the first portal to launch a broadband service for higher-speed users.

XOOM.com is the fastest-growing community-based site on the Web and a leading direct e-commerce company.

NBC.com is the online home for NBC shows and celebrities, and extends popular NBC shows to the Internet, featuring interactive episodes, characters and plot twists.

NBC Interactive Neighborhood (IN) is the first network of customized community guide services for local communities and local TV stations.

Videoseeker.com is an on-demand Internet video service, featuring professionally developed content.

CNBC is one of the fastest growing cable networks and will launch a comprehensive financial Internet service in the summer of 1999.

e-Business- A Growth Initiative for the New Millennium

Developments in digital technology and the emergence of the Internet paved the way for a revolution in communications, information transfer and ways of doing business in the late 1990s. Asked by a reporter from BusinessWeek *ONLINE* how high the Internet (e-Business) was on his agenda, Jack Welch replied, ***"I don't think that there's been anything more important or more widespread in all my years at GE. Where does the Internet rank in priority? We've been talking about the boundaryless corporation, and this moves us closer to being that boundaryless corporation."***

At the beginning of 1999, e-Business became a major GE company wide initiative. A number of GE's units, particularly Capital Services and Information Services, had already been heavily involved in various aspects of Web-based business. Their experience, as well as the information technology experience and other resources of GE's R&D Center, are key assets in realizing the potential of this new initiative.

The Internet and e-Business

By establishing a Web site, a business can create a 24 hour a day, 7 day a week presence in the global marketplace. If it has the appropriate resources and infrastructure, it can use the Internet as an efficient, low cost enabler to expand its markets for goods and services; attract potential suppliers and business partners; recruit prospective employees; execute a broad range of transactions; broaden and simplify its communications with its employees; exchange engineering information; and even monitor and service equipment installed thousands of miles away. The possibilities for innovative approaches to growth, information transfer and cost reduction are limited only by the imagination and capabilities of those participating in the e-business of the enterprise.

On the other hand, any information made available publicly online is as accessible to the competition as it is to prospective customers. The effect is to make the global marketplace even more competitive. In that sense, the Internet creates an even greater challenge for businesses to differentiate themselves from their competitors. For example, it is not enough for them to find more creative ways to attract and educate potential customers and suppliers. They must also have the business culture and the infrastructure to ensure that those who access their Web sites are consistently satisfied with the quality of the information supplied, the quality of the transaction and the quality and value of the product or service received. If they are not satisfied with any of these factors or even the format of the Web site,

they need only to exercise their prerogative to remove it from their list of bookmarks.

To build credibility and customer loyalty, one goal is to use the virtually automated medium of the Web to establish user-friendly, interactive relationships with the customers, and to be highly responsive to their needs. Another goal is to take full advantage of the efficiencies and productivity gains offered by the use of information technology and the Internet in order to reduce costs and increase value for the customer.

Expanding e-Business at GE

From the outset of the e-Business initiative, the now familiar tools of Work-Out and the Change Acceleration Process, as well as many of the Six Sigma and Design for Six Sigma methodologies, were applied in the activities of cross-functional e-business teams. These teams were organized at each major business and at the corporate level, and consisted of seasoned experts as well as newcomers. Their job was to analyze how various alternative Web-based models for e-business might alter the nature of their own business. If the potential threat presented by one of these models was deemed to be significant, the team would have to determine whether that model should be adopted in place of one that might already be in use.

Other teams were committed to accelerating the transition of their organization to e-Business and finding new business opportunities in the form of acquisitions, joint ventures or strategic alliances that they could forge with other companies. In e-Business, alliances typically take the form of sharing specialized information content, infrastructure and other resources, and they frequently lead to arrangements for linked Web sites. Such links are key to increased accessibility and exposure, as well as greater convenience for the users.

Key GE Initiatives to Drive
Business Growth

e-Business- A Growth Initiative for the New Millennium

Examples of e-Business Activities by GE Businesses (as of August 1999)

At the corporate level, **GE.com** serves as an information portal for consumers and businesses interested in GE's products and services. It offers well integrated and comprehensively linked access to virtually all of its businesses and support organizations, as well as to investor relations, employee relations and other functions including GE's community volunteer organization, and the GE Fund, its philanthropic organization.

Most of GE's businesses provide detailed descriptions of their products and services through the World Wide Web. Listed below, are examples of some of their innovative approaches to e-Business.

- **Information Services** established the GE Trading Process Network (TPN) as an Internet-based trading network that enables buyers and sellers to conduct business-to-business electronic commerce, including transactions. Conceived in 1995 as an internal GE Corporate initiative, TPN has evolved into a commercial offering.

With Thomas Publishing, Information Services formed a joint venture, TPN Register, for Internet-based procurement of goods and services used for maintenance, repair and operations.

- **Appliances** entered into an innovative distribution agreement with BuildNet, Inc., to sell home appliances online to the homebuilder market through an integrated e-commerce platform provided by that company. The BuildNet platform will be the largest business-to-business Internet-based purchasing system serving the homebuilder industry. It will manage e-commerce volume for all materials and appliances for nearly 350,000 homes annually. Almost one in every three homes constructed in the U.S. BuildNet's family of project management software packages will link the builder's purchasing and accounting systems to the suppliers' inventory control systems, making it easier for the builder to place orders for building materials and appliances and to track all shipments online. GE Appliances and GE Capital joined a number of other companies in making an equity investment in BuildNet.

- **Plastics'** ColorXpress Web site offers an online palette for customers to match a color of plastic that they need. With the color selected, a sample chip of plastic is sent to the customer for evaluation prior to their placement of a larger order. Considerable time and cost is saved in servicing the customer's needs compared to methods previously used.

Polymerland, GE's plastics distribution business, provides total transaction capability and personalized customer web pages. The site provides access to industry information and bulletin boards on which customers can exchange technical tips. By the middle of 1999, 15% of its business was conducted over the Internet and sales had increased 300% over the previous year.

GE Plastics also increased its business volume when it commercialized online monitoring of customer storage silos by installing sensors in them to allow automatic replenishment of inventories.

- **Capital Services'** GE Commercial Shopping Network (CSN™) offers X-Change, a location where businesses can store their capital equipment listings and have them available, password protected, for reference by other segments of their business or for sale to other businesses that are seeking such equipment. Each piece of equipment can be displayed in photos or on video with a list of specifications and price. There are also well integrated links to Commercial Services, which can arrange for equipment financing and insurance, and Asset Management Services, which can help customers to optimize equipment usage and productivity by simplifying the tracking and management of surplus and idle equipment across any number of business locations.

Additional examples can be taken from virtually all of Capital Services 28 businesses. In 1999, Capital Services strengthened its Internet position with a number of investments, including an additional $50 million investment in Consumer Financial Network.

- **Medical Systems** entered into alliances with HealthStream and HealthGate Data Corp., two Internet leaders in content development and distribution technology for the health care industry. Medical Systems will integrate its existing online health care content into HealthGate's CHOICE™ Web site.

It will expand its education offerings by giving customers access to HealthStream's online Continuing Education course library and by using HealthStream's infrastructure to offer its own courses and to develop other services. This will complement Medical Systems' Training in Partnership TiP-TV Satellite Broadcast Training network, which provides medical, in-service and leadership education to health care providers in more than 2,600 hospitals in the United States.

More than 10,000 imaging systems worldwide are monitored at the Medical Systems OnLine Center via its InSite network.

In 1998, the Web Marketing Association honored GE Medical Systems with the *Web Award* for ***Best Employment-Related Internet site for 1998*** among 500 sites in a range of other categories.

- GE Supply developed a customized version of its Internet-based procurement system, GE Supply Net™ to meet the needs of individual customers. It gives technicians throughout a customer's plant real-time access to GE Supply's national network of 150 branches, allowing them to locate inventory, read product specifications, find substitutes, determine pricing and availability and place and track orders. In effect, it enables a customer to run its storerooms like a GE Supply warehouse.

-Lighting offers *info*light,* a service that allows customers to check order and stock status online. Customers can also track domestic U.S. truck shipments to their destinations from GE Lighting's distribution sites. Reservations can also be made for courses given by The Lighting Institute, an educational facility devoted solely to the lighting industry. It offers courses on topics such as the efficient use of lighting and the marketing of lamps and other lighting supplies.

-Transportation Systems provides online customer reports on order status and invoice history for parts and services and it reports reliability data.

-NBC is the leader among traditional media companies in Internet and new media businesses, and it has made dozens of strategic investments in that space. In 1998, NBC partnered with CNET to operate Snap.com, the fastest growing Internet portal service. In 1999, NBC announced that it would combine its Web assets with Snap.com and Xoom.com – a pioneer in direct e-commerce that targets its 9.5 million members with product and service offers – to form NBC Internet (NBCi) which will be supported by transaction and advertising revenues. NBC.com was the first full-scale Internet offering from a major television network, featuring original episodic programming and online extensions of popular NBC programming like "The Tonight Show with Jay Leno" and "Late Night with Conan O'Brien."

NBC's cable businesses, CNBC and MSNBC, also closely integrate their online programming with the Web. MSNBC.com is the number one news site on the Internet, while CNBC.com features the best of CNBC on the Internet.

This newly-launched personal finance portal is designed to help investors profit from today's lightning-paced financial activity with company information, stock quotes, data and analyses. Also, together with Microsoft and Dow Jones, NBC operates CNBC-Dow Jones Business Video, offering video and audio-based financial information to financial professionals and institutions.

The Future of e-Business at GE

While launching its e-Business initiative on a company-wide scale, GE took advantage of opportunities to learn from the experience of its own businesses as well as those of others, just as it had learned from Motorola, Texas Instruments and AlliedSignal when it opened its Six Sigma initiative in 1999. In this case, however, a good deal of the expertise came from among the legions of relatively new companies that were born of the information technology revolution and the emergence of the Internet.

In 1999, e-Business offered the potential for even greater growth for GE – by expanding the scope of its existing initiatives and by becoming an enabler for them.

Globalization now meant access to all of cyberspace and to a vastly larger audience than can be reached by marketing groups, sourcing personnel, recruiters, business investment groups, etc.

Service, whether providing insurance, monitoring equipment, or providing news and entertainment, was provided virtually instantaneously through interactive communications and information transfer with customers, machines or with entire systems.

Six Sigma and Design for Six Sigma, the customer focussed methodologies aimed at virtually removing all defects from products and services, were enhanced by the ability to simplify and automate many of the activities that might produce flaws – and by the ability to encourage and speed the process of getting feedback from the customers, who are key to the process of defining quality.

e-Business is, in fact, a vehicle for producing that "*boundaryless corporation*" that Jack Welch referred to in his BusinessWeek ONLINE interview. Advances in information technology and the ways in which information was transmitted would provide virtually unlimited opportunities for GE and other enterprises to expand the scope of their e-business – and their ability to do so in the 21st Century could determine their success.

GE Volunteers in the Community

"The spirit of boundarylessness is nowhere more evident than in the renaissance of volunteerism that is bringing GE talent and enthusiasm to bear on the problems and potential of the communities that the Company's hundreds of plants and installations call home." from GE 1991 Annual Report

Since 1991, every issue of the GE Annual Report has included a section describing representative examples of community service activities performed by GE volunteers. This is not a recognition of a newly established philosophy of volunteerism and philanthropy but a confirmation of the fact that the vision of a boundaryless Company has implications well beyond the confines of the businesses and their dealings with customers. More than ever, encouragement and support are provided to those who would break down the barriers between the GE work life and community life by contributing their time, talents and other resources for the benefit of the community.

The Elfun Society

Spearheading these efforts along with other GE volunteers are the members of the Elfun Society, an organization of GE employees and retirees founded in 1928 at the suggestion of Gerard Swope, president of General Electric. The original purpose of Elfun (a contraction of the words "Electrical Fund") was to make available to the leaders of GE a vehicle for financial investments, fraternal activities and open discussions of business-related issues. As the Elfun Society evolved, its activities expanded to include a number of community service projects.

Early in the 1980s, GE Chairman Jack Welch challenged the leaders of the Elfun Society to make a searching and fundamental evaluation of what its role should be, given the strategic thrusts and operating philosophies projected for the Company in the coming decades. Responding to that challenge, the Society stated its intent to make Elfun an organization built around volunteerism, community service and communications. The constitution was revised to reflect these intentions and the new bylaws broadened membership eligibility criteria to include employees of GE who "have demonstrated sustained contributions to the Elfun spirit of volunteerism." This presented these volunteers with opportunities to leverage the resources of Elfun to help support their favorite community service projects as well as to participate in the implementation of new project ideas.

By the late 1990s, the Elfun Society had grown to over 40,000 members, grouped geographically into 90 chapters located in the United States and 12 other countries.

The GE Fund

A wide variety of education and community service projects are supported by GE and by the GE Fund, a philanthropic organization whose roots go back to the early 1950s. In 1953, the GE Foundation, the predecessor of the GE Fund, established the **Corporate Alumni Program,** the first corporate matching gift program of its kind. Since then, more than 1,000 other companies have followed the GE Fund's lead.

Another pioneering program, **More Gifts ... More Givers**, helps leverage the generosity of GE employees and retirees by matching their donations to eligible social service agencies, arts groups, and other community-based organizations as well as special disaster relief programs.

In addition to these matching fund donations, the GE Fund has provided support for a wide variety of special educational and enrichment projects in such areas as: Science and Engineering, Management, Pre-College (pre-kindergarten through High School), Arts and Culture and Public Policy. In many cases, these initiatives represented partnerships between the grantees, other organizations, the GE Fund and volunteers from the Elfun Society.

In the Creative Connections Program, funded by a grant from the GE Fund, Elfun Society volunteers from GE businesses in Upstate New York work with seventh- graders on a mural depicting Native American History.

In the global community, where the needs are frequently more basic than in more developed countries, the GE Fund supports programs such as those that provide health care for children, train future managers and engineers and strengthen community self-help projects. In 1997, total grants by the GE Fund were over $30 million.

Helping Communities

A small sampling of the thousands of community service projects that Elfun and other GE volunteers have successfully undertaken, with substantial support from GE and the GE Fund includes:

- Literacy programs
- Computer rehabilitation for redistribution to schools
- Repair of tape players for the blind
- Parks and playground construction
- Habitat for Humanity projects
- Drug awareness programs
- Food and clothing drives
- Environmental cleanups
- Help for the disabled and disadvantaged
- Special Olympics

Many of these and other community projects also are financially supported by the Elfun Society's *Sharing the Gold Program* which returns a royalty of 1% to the organization for purchases made by Elfun credit card holders. The proceeds are then allocated for community service projects suggested and implemented by Elfun volunteers. In the program's first few years of existence, over $3 million has been returned for use on more than 1300 projects in GE communities.

Elfuns repair tape players for the visually impaired.

Helping Students

Support for the education of our youth is the cornerstone of involvement by GE volunteers in the community. They serve as mentors and friends to school children in scores of GE communities, particularly those with inner city and rural schools. Although hundreds of individual educational activities take place throughout the course of any single year, ongoing emphasis is concentrated around three creative programs:

Challenge Grants to enrich the educational activities of students, teachers and parents, the *College Bound Program,* a 10 - year, $20 million commitment to double the college entrance rates of students from selected inner-city and rural schools, and the *Early Years Initiative* to help elementary students improve their reading. In the first three years of the Early Years Initiative, Elfuns volunteered in more than 200 schools and the GE Fund contributed more than half a million dollars.

Volunteers from GE Capital Mortgage and GE Electrical Distribution and Control research colleges with students at a Durham, North Carolina, High School as part of the College Bound Program.

Coming together for a business meeting in Cartagena, Spain, a team of GE Plastics employees from all over Europe held a special work day at an old farmhouse that serves as a weekend retreat for underprivileged children. In one day the team totally upgraded the facility so that it can accommodate four times as many children on weekends. During the week, Caritas, the nonprofit organization that runs the refurbished facility, uses it for a variety of social service activities.

GE Volunteers in the Community

GE Capital donated several modular space buildings to churches that were destroyed by arson in 1996. Shown here with young members of his congregation, the Reverend Ted Myers of South Richland Bible Way in Gadsden, South Carolina, is using one of those buildings for office space while funds are raised to rebuild his church.

Students and teachers from nine high schools in the GE College Bound Program spent a week during the summer of 1997 at the Northeastern University Marine Biology Lab in Massachusetts, where they collected scientific data and specimens from the local marine environment for review with students at home.

Instead of dining out, Meredith Klein and more than 70 other NBC employees in New York City take an hour of their time once a week to share food and instill a love for reading in students at nearby P.S. 111. The program is coordinated with Everbody Wins, a nonprofit organization that runs similar programs at 20 other schools.

Students at the Ernest C. Drury School for the Deaf in Toronto, Canada, learn computer design as well as printing and video production in a new desktop publishing lab created through the efforts of GE volunteers and a GE Fund grant.

Volunteers from the GE Plastics plant in Burkville, Alabama, work at a 6,300 - acre wildlife habitat created in 1988, a year after the plant opened.

Honors

One of the most prestigious Company-wide awards to employees is the Gerald L. Phillippe Award for Leadership in Community Service. Since 1970, the awards program has honored GE employees who set the highest standards for commitment, creativity and achievement in volunteer service and heroism. Named for a former GE Chairman with a long record of public service, the awards enable each recipient to select a charitable cause that will benefit from GE's contribution. In 1998, 14 of the 26 recipients of Phillippe awards were Elfuns.

The Elfun Society maintains a similar tradition of "International Elfun of the Year" awards, accompanied by charitable donations in honor of members who have made outstanding contributions in the area of community service.

In 1989, Elfun received the Presidential C-Flag Honor ("We Can - We Care") from the White House. It was awarded to both Elfun and the GE Fund for outstanding contributions to the American spirit of volunteerism and community action. In 1990, President Bush sent a letter directed to Elfun with thanks for their work to, "…improve educational opportunities of disadvantaged youth." In 1994, President Clinton named Elfun to receive the "President's Volunteer Action Award" for engagement in community service. GE was one of only two companies receiving the honor.

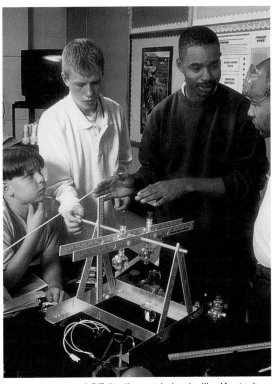

Bob Baughman of GE Appliances in Louisville, Kentucky, was selected as 1998 Outstanding New Elfun of the Year and was one of 14 winners of the Gerald L. Phillippe Award for his work in enhancing students' interest in science and engineering.

The GE Promise for the New Millennium

In April, 1997, at the President's Summit for America's Future, a pledge was made committing the GE family to one million volunteer hours annually in service to children by the year 2000. Elfuns and other GE volunteers mobilized to honor that promise and, in April 1999, it was announced that 1.3 million hours had been logged, a year ahead of the commitment.

Epilogue - Toward the 21st Century

As we approach the 21st century and look back to the beginnings of the General Electric Company in the late 19th century, it is tempting to reflect on the changes that have taken place in society since the era of Thomas Alva Edison. This selection of milestones in the history of the company summarizes some of the key technological and business innovations and accomplishments that influenced these changes. Just as technology has changed the way that people live throughout the world, transformations in the global economy, particularly in the last half of the 20th century, have changed the way that companies create, market and provide their products and services in order to survive and grow.

Improved global transportation, advances in information technology and the revolution in communications brought about by the Internet have opened up new markets, new sources of materials and new sources of labor. But, these opportunities have increased competitive forces to the extent that businesses have to compete vigorously on several fronts: the quality of their goods and services; prices; productivity; the innovation of new products and services; and the ability to respond rapidly to political and social change as well as to market change.

When Jack Welch became Chief Executive Officer and Chairman of the Board of General Electric in 1981, he established a set of standards by which the status of each of GE's businesses would be measured. He then proceeded to make the organizational, operational and cultural changes, as well as the investments, that would set the company on a path to continuing growth in the global economy. In the 1990s four major initiatives for growth were launched :

Services were expanded (*in the words of Chairman Welch in the 1998 GE Annual Report*) "*from the traditional activities of parts replacement, overhauling and reconditioning high-value machines like jet engines, turbines, medical equipment and locomotives, to a larger and bolder vision. We have the engineering, the R&D, the product knowledge, the resources and the management commitment to make the series of hundred-million-dollar investments that will allow us to truly change the performance of our installed base, and by doing so upgrade the competitiveness and profitability of our customers: utilities, hospitals, railroads, factories and airlines.*" Mr. Welch said at the 1999 Annual Meeting, " *We service airlines rather than just engines, railroads rather than locomotives, hospitals rather than CT scanners. We sell solutions and answers rather than just products.*" Taking into account the results of this initiative and the outstanding growth and contribution of GE Capital, he projected that,

by the year 2000, 75% of GE's revenues would be derived from high margin, higher growth, services. In 1998, GE Capital businesses accounted for 11 of the 20 leading businesses that provided 90% of GE's earnings. Employer's Reinsurance, Commercial Equipment Finance and Global Consumer Finance were among the top 10.

Six Sigma, a rigorous defect reduction methodology aimed at improving the quality of all of the Company's products, processes and services, was introduced in what was perhaps one of the most extensive training programs in the history of American industry. Within a few years the investment had paid for itself many times over in higher total productivity and in increased sales to satisfied customers. A growing stream of innovative new offerings, designed using the customer-focussed Design for Six Sigma process, is receiving enthusiastic reception in world markets and, in the words of Jack Welch, " **.....** will truly take us to a new definition of *World Class.*" Reviewing the effect of Six Sigma on the workplace at GE and its future, Jack Welch said, "Six Sigma has changed the DNA of GE — it is now the *way we work* — in everything we do and in every product that we design."

Globalization, driven by the internal expansion of GE's businesses, joint ventures, partnerships and acquisitions, resulted in a rate of revenue growth outside of the United States which was double that of GE's U.S. growth during the decade ending in 1998. For the future, it promises to be even larger as GE Capital and other parts of the Company work to reap rewards from their very large investments made during the late 1990s. An added dimension of this initiative has been the increased procurement of products, components, technology and intellectual capital on a global basis. Talented personnel from countries outside of the United States are being recruited to a greater extent than ever to meet the needs of a global organization. The GE of the future will have no geographic boundaries in how it conducts the operations of its businesses.

e-Business became a company-wide initiative early in 1999. Its goal was to take advantage of the significant opportunities for market growth and cost reduction presented by the rapidly accelerating growth of digital technology and the use of the Internet. This meant finding ways to use the Web to establish competitive advantage everywhere in the enterprise from the buy side (interacting with present and potential suppliers) — to internal processes (engineering, internal communications, recruiting personnel, etc.) — to the sell side (offering products and service – business to business and business to consumer).

Using the methodologies of Work-Out and Six Sigma, GE's businesses moved rapidly to build on experience already gained in a significant range of Internet - based activities and to invest in acquiring the best resources needed to make this new initiative a success. e-Business had become a major driving force globally and, with its tremendous potential as a vehicle for growth, it would become just as ingrained in the operations of GE as its other initiatives.

There will no doubt be new and dynamic initiatives that grow out of the identification of important company wide opportunities for technological and business growth. The realization of these initiatives will require men and women who share a success-oriented, horizontal learning culture such as that created and fostered by Jack Welch. The set

of values that epitomizes this culture and incorporates such terms as **Work-Out, speed, simplicity and boundaryless**, has progressed from a vision to a proven, efficient method for people of diverse interests and backgrounds to work together as a team to reach a common goal. It has helped make possible the growing success of GE's business initiatives in the 1990s and it has laid the groundwork for even greater technological and business success in the next millennium.

Looking toward that milestone, Jack Welch told the attendees at the 1999 Annual Meeting, "***The next time we gather again, on this occasion in April of 2000, as GE begins operations in its third century, you can be certain that your Company will never have been newer, fresher, or more energized.***"

Chairman and Chief Executive Officer John F. Welch, Jr. (center) and Vice Chairmen and Executive Officers Dennis D. Dammerman (left), Eugene F. Murphy (back) and John D. Opie (right) form GE's Corporate Executive Office. (April,1999)

BIBLIOGRAPHY

A Chronological History of Electrical Development, National Electric Lamp Manufacturers Association, New York, 1946

Alger, Philip L.; *The Human Side of Engineering*, Schenectady, New York, Mohawk Development Service, Inc., 1972

Alger, Philip L. and Caldecott, Ernest; *Steinmetz-The Philosopher*, Schenectady, New York, Mohawk Development Service, Inc., 1965

Birr, Kendall; *Pioneering in Industrial Research; The Story of the General Electric Research Laboratory,* Washington, Public Affairs Press, 1957

Broderick, John T.; *Forty Years with General Electric*, Albany, New York, Fort Orange Press, 1929

Emmet, William LeRoy; *The Autobiography of an Engineer,* Albany, New York, Fort Orange Press, 1931

Hammond, John W.; *Men and Volts, The Story of General Electric*, New York, Lippincott Company, 1941

Jones, Payson; *A Power History of the Consolidated Edison System, 1878-1900*, New York, Consolidated Edison Co. of New York, 1940.

Josephson, Matthew; *Edison, A Biography*, New York, McGraw-Hill Book Company, Inc., 1959.

Keating, Paul W.; *Lamps for a Brighter America*, New York, McGraw-Hill Book Co., Inc., 1954

Liebhafsky, Herman A.; *William David Coolidge, A Centenarian and His Work,* New York, John Wiley & Sons, 1974

Miller, John A.; *Workshop of Engineers; The Story of the General Engineering Laboratory of the General Electric Company*, Schenectady, NY, General Electric Company, 1953

Passer, Harold C.; *The Electrical Manufacturers*, Boston., Harvard Press, 1953

Slater, Robert; *The New GE - How Jack Welch Revived an American Institution*, Homewood, IL, Richard D. Irwin, Inc., 1993

Woodbury, David O.; *Beloved Scientist, Elihu Thomson*, New York, McGraw-Hill Co., Inc., 1944

The *General Electric Review*, Schenectady, NY, General Electric Company, 1924-1952

The *Investor*, Fairfield, CT., General Electric Company, 1970-1979

General Electric Company Annual Report, 1979-1998

The *Monogram*, Schenectady, NY and Fairfield, CT., General Electric Company, 1924-1985

GE Internet Web Site, **www.ge.com**

*COMPANY NAME INDEX

AEG, 353
Agrabanka, 363
Akzo Chemical Co.,316
Alsthom, 337, 371
American Electric Co., 22, 31
American Locomotive, 133
Auto Financial Services, 361
Bayer AG, 362
Bentley-Knight Electric Railway Co., 9
    31-32, 43
Bergmann and Co., 22
BG Automotive Motors, 337
Black and Decker Mfg. Co., 323
BMW, 333
Borg Warner, 335
BP Amoco, 371
Brady Manufacturing Co, 21
Broken Hill Proprietary Co.,323
Brush Electric Co., 22-3, 34
Burton Group, 341
California Electric Light Company, 15
CALMA Corp., 317
Canadian GE Co.,Ltd., 284
Canal de Noticias NBC, 348
Cleveland Telegraph and Supply Co.,
    12, 17, 23
COGEMEC, 337
Consumer News and Business Channel
    (CNBC), 336, 342, 361
CMI International, 325
COGEMEC, 337
Compagnie Generale de Radiologie (CGR),
    332, 337
DAKO S.A., 356
Dow Jones, 357
Echostar Satellite Corp.,346
Edison Companies, 9 -11, 18, 27, 28 ,31,
    36, 43, 50-1, 80, 89, 120
EG&G, 360
Eickemeyer and Osterheld, 43, 47-8, 63
Electric Bond & Share, 88
ELGEMS, 362
Elscint, Ltd., (Israel), 362
EMCORE Corp., 370
Employers Reinsurance Co., 322
Ericsson, 337, 347
Exatec, 362
Fanuc Ltd (Japan), 329
Fiat-Avio, 340
Financial Guaranty Insurance Co., 335
Financial News Network (FNN), 342
First Colony and Life of Virgina, 357
Focus S.A., 350
Fort Wayne Electric Co., 27, 74 -5, 127
GE Apar Lighting Private Ltd.347
GE Bayer Silicones Europe, 362
GEC, 337
GE Capital, 335, 341, 347, 357
    361, 363, 371
GE Capital Fleet Services, 341
GE Credit Corp., 199, 296-7, 312, 316,
    322
GE Edison Life, 363
GE Employees Security Corp., 121
GE Espanola, 276
GE Fanuc Automation Corp,
    329, 332, 370
GE Financial Assurance, 363
GE Harris Energy Control Systems, 361

GE Harris Railway Electronics, 352
GE Information Systems, 335
GE Jiabao Lighting Co. Ltd., 349
GELcore LLC, 370
GE-Thorn Lamp Ltd., 341
GE Power Controls, 350
GE Vapor Lamp Co.,180
GE Cablevision Corp., 265
GE Capital Aviation Services, 335
GE Communications (Americom), 334
General Electric Co., 48
General Electric Contracts Corp., 163
GE Financial Services, 322
General Electric plc,(GEC), 337
GE Information Services Co., 304
General Electric Supply Co., 146, 230
General Electric Trading Corp., 319
General Electric X-ray Corp., 152
Genstar Container Corp., 335
Gold and Stock Telegraph, 10
Greenwich Air Services Inc., 360
Hamamatsu Photonic (Japan), 337
Harris Corp., 317
Hitachi GE Lighting, 347, 399
Hotpoint, 334
Honeywell, 309
IHI (Japan), 340
International GE Co., 116, 144, 283
International Wagon Services, 363
Japan Lease Auto, 371
Japan Leasing Corp., 371
Kidder Peabody & Co., 329
Koei Credit, 363
Kojima Inc., 352
Ladd Petroleum, 341
Lake Corporataion, 363
Lindner Licht, 350
MABE (Mexico), 341
Marconi Wireless Telegraph
    Company of America, 116
Marquette Medical Systems, 362
Martin Marietta, 346, 349
McCullogh Leasing, 341
Multilin of Canada, 353
Montgomery Ward Credit Corp., 335
MSNBC, 356, 361
National Electric Lamp Assn.,
    100 , 111, 127
National Electric Lamp Co., 80, 100
NBC, 331, 342, 348, 361, 372
NBC Internet, 372
NBC Super Channel, 348
NBC-TV, 336
NC Card Senrai, 363
Nuovo Pignone, 351
Paine Webber, 329
Penske Corp., 335
Philips Co., 47
Plug Power, 371
Polish American Mortgage Bank, 363
Polaris Aircraft Leasing, 335
Pratt & Whitney, 340, 356
Prime Computer Corp., 317
PT GE Angaska, 350
Radio Corporation of America
    (RCA), 116, 152-3, 327
Railcar Services, 361
Robert Bosch, 337
Roper Corp., 334

Scanditronix AB, 337
Schuyler Electric Light Co., 28, 39
Sivi Illuminazione, 350
SNECMA (France), 325, 340
Sprague Electric Co., 74
Sprague Electric Elevator Company, 30
Sprague Electric Railway Motor Co.,
    30, 32
Stanley Electric Manufacturing Co.,
    44, 86, 93
Stewart & Stevenson Energy Products,
    362
Swan Incandescent Electric Light Co., 32
The Burton Group, 341
Thomson-Houston Companies,
    9, 21, 22, 25, 31, 35, 39, 48
Thomson SA (France), 332
Thomson -Van Depoele Electric Mining
    Co., 35
Thorn EMI, 341
Toho Medical Life, 363
Toshiba, 337
Total Control Products, Inc., 370
Travelers, 341
Tungsram, 341
UNC, Inc., 360
Unelec (France), 337
Utah International,283, 287, 302, 323, 341
Utah-Marcona Corp., 323
Van Depoele Electric Light Co, 35, 38
Victor X-Ray Corp., 151
Vynckier NV (Belgium), 337
Warren Telechron Co., 150
Western Union, 12
Westinghouse Electric & Manufacturing
    Co., 32, 47
Weston Electrical Instrument Co., 40
Woodchester (Ireland), 361
Yokogawa Medical Systems, 328, 332

LABORATORY INDEX

Advanced Technology Lab., 261
Consulting Engineering Dept., 153
Consulting Engineering Lab., 116, 152 -3
GE Researh Lab.,
    78, 79 , 99, 142-3, 154, 163, 201
GE Research and Development Center,
    261,319, 328, 368-9
General Engineering Lab., 116, 153-4, 196
High Voltage Engineering Lab.
    (Pittsfield), 133, 147, 150
Illuminating Engineering, Lab., 82
Knolls Atomic Power Lab., 205, 213, 241
Lamp Development Lab. (Nela Park), 162
Menlo Park, 18, 22-27
Plastics Technology Center (Pittsfield),
    323
Radio Engineering Dept., 152
Schenectady Works Lab., 198
Standardizing Laboratory, 68, 116
Thomson Laboratory (Lynn) 132

*In the above Index, GE is sometimes
substituted for General Electric due to
column space considerations only.*

383

INDEX OF NAMES OF INDIVIDUALS

Ackerman, J. 336
Ackerman, S. 240
Agens, M. 187, 198
Alexanderson, E.F.W. 59, 84, 90, 104, 110, 112, 113, 118, 119,139, 143, 151-153, 166, 291, 368
Aldrin, E. 274
Alger, P. 83, 158, 173
Ames, F.L. 51
Amra, L. 246
Armstrong, E.H. 183
Auchmoody, L.H. 294
Audiffren, M. 140, 141
Bachman, C.H. 191
Baker, W.R.G. 183
Barr, W. 339
Barton, S. 6
Baughman, R. 379
Beams, J. 204
Bedford, B.D. 291
Bell, AG. 12
Benander, G.B. 291
Benbow, B.L. 174, 203
Bentley, E. 27-29, 39
Benz, M.G. 254
Berg, G.R. 202
Bergmann, S. 9, 18
Betts, E. 276
Blodgett, K.B. 181, 198, 368
Blowney, W.E. 149
Bochan, J. 227, 291
Borch, F.J. 254, 269, 286
Bossidy, L.A. 338
Bovenkerk, H.P. 227
Bradley, C.S. 65
Brady, J. 21
Brinn, W. 236
Brokaw, T. 331
Brown, B.P. 220
Bruch, A.A. 254
Brush, C.F. 7-9, 12, 15-18, 145, 290
Buck, H.W. 92
Bueche, A.M. 2, 186, 224, 262, 286, 290
Bundy, F.P. 227
Burger, E.E. 139
Burgess, N. 245
Burke, H.K. 288
Burke, J. 240, 263
Burlingame, J.F. 310
Bush, G. 379
Butch, R. 292
Carolan, S.D. 73
Carrel, A. 161
Cermak, W. 65
Chambers. D. 183
Charlton, F.F. 155, 198, 199
Chausse, P. 260
Chesney, C.C. 86, 93, 137
Clark, F.M. 161, 291
Clarke, E. 250
Clinton, W. 379
Coble, B.C. 249, 263
Coffin, C.A. 44, 51, 60, 61, 103, 166, 167
Compton, A. 161, 203, 204
Concordia, C. 250

Coolidge, W.D. 59, 88, 90, 96,97, 99, 100, 103, 104, 118, 122, 151, 155, 162, 185, 201, 204, 212, 368
Cordiner, R.J. 203, 219, 229, 234, 254, 286,358
Coster, C.H. 51
Cowles, A 32
Cox,G.B. 306
Crary, S.B. 250
Crouse, J.B. 80
Cunningham, J.F. 193
Curtis, C. G. 72, 81, 84, 89, 98
Cushing, D.S. 265
Dammerman, D. D. 381
Dance, W.D. 286
Dantsizen, C. 104
Davey, W.P. 107
Davis, A. 78
Davis, L.B. 222
Dawes, C.G. 157, 161
DeBell, J. 135
DeLiberato. V. 265
Dempster, J.T.H 78
Denny, W.M. 269
DePaolo, P. 135
Devers, J.L. 193
Disney. W. 175
Dobbins, P.W. 306
Duesenberg, A. 135
Dushman, S. 104
Edison, T.A. Most pages of Chapter 1 77, 87, 123, 136, 145, 290, 368
Eickemeyer, R. 63
Einstein, A. 95
Eisenhower, D.E. 242
Elston, C.W. 243
Ely, W.G. 259
Emmet, W.L. 80, 81, 89, 98, 103, 124, 148
Emmons, G.E. 73
Esaki, L. 289
Evans, J.S. 196
Eveleth, C.E. 147
Faccioli, G. 122, 137
Farrell, J.J. 220
Fessenden, R.A. 85
Fink, C.G. 103
Fink, D.G. 183
Fleisher, R.L. 256
Fleming, A. 87
Flynn, E.J. 179, 198
Fonda, G.R. 112
Foote, A. 240
Ford, H. 145
Foust, C.M. 199
Fox, D.W. 222
Frisch, O.R. 204
Fritz, J. 149
Fujimori, Y. 339
Fuller, T.S. 163
Gearheart, R. 307
Giaever, I. 289
Gilliam, W.F. 185, 187
Gilson, G.E., 143
Glover, G.H. 328
Grasso, R. 357

Graves, D.E. 264
Green, H. 236
Griffin, E. 51
Grubb, W.T. 262
Gustav, C. King 289
Hall, H.T. 227
Hall, R.N. 220
Haller, C.L. 261
Halvorson, C.A.B. 84, 116, 166
Hannan, H. 244
Hanson, L 348
Hardy, A.C. 175
Hay, A.S. 238, 34
Hayden, J.L. 122
Hewitt, P.C. 80, 82
Hewlett, E.M. 66, 92
Hildebrand, L.E. 173
Hill, W.B. 190
Hoffer, E. 308
Hogue, M.P. 255
Holub, F. 276, 291, 294
Hood, E.E., Jr. 313, 338, 43
Houston, E.T. 6, 17, 46, 47, 51
Houston, F.D.E. 291
Hoyt, S. 142, 143, 203
Howard, A. 149, 202, 206
Howell, J.W. 64, 68
Hoxie, C.A. 137
Hughes, G.A. 100
Hughes, H. 176
Hughes, P. 227
Hull, A.W. 120, 368
Humphrey, H.H. 265
Hurd, D.T. 246
Hurwitz, H. 205
Inman, G. 168, 188
Insull, S. 148
Jeffries, Z. 203, 75
Jehl, F. 19, 20, 145
Jenkins, T.E. 265
Jeram, E. 353
Johnson, F.V. 233
Jones, R.D. 240
Jones, R.H. 283, 286, 287, 308, 344
Josephson, B. 289
Junggren, O. 103, 148
Kaiser, C. 236
Kann, P. 357
Kearsley, W.K. 174
Kellogg. E.W. 137
Kellogg, F.B. 161
Kelly, F. 143
Kelvin, Lord 73
Kemp, J. 135
Kerst, D.W. 199
Kesselring, K.A. 226
Kienle, R.H. 135
Kingdon, K.H. 185, 204
Kinnard, I. 213
Klein, M. 378
Knight, W. 31, 32, 33, 43, 83
Knox, F. 192, 193
Koch, C.J. 172
Konig, H.F. 298
Konrad, C.E. 324
Kruesi, J. 36

Landsteiner, K. 161
Lang, C.H. 193
Langmuir, I. 99, 103-105, 107, 114, 123, 124, 134, 152, 154, 161, 181, 182, 198, 204
Lawrence, E. 204
Lawton, E.J. 224
Lee, E.S. 154
Lemp, H. 72, 290
Littlefield, E.W. 303
Louden, W. 263
Lovejoy, J.R. 51, 121
Lowrey, C.T. 18, 19
Marconi, G. 76, 112, 152
Marsden, J. 198
Marshall, A.L. 174, 179, 185-187, 198
Marshall, J.T. 98
Martin. D.L. 254
Marvin, H.B. 132
Maxwell, H. 110, 118, 172
McDonald R.T. 25, 75
McEachron, K.B. 150
McInerney, E. 292
Meikle, G.S. 110
Mercer, R.W. 135
Merrill, W.L. 141, 170
Michelson, A.A. 161
Michon, G.J. 288
Miller, J.A. 192
Millikan, R.A. 161
Mittag, A.H. 153
Moody, W.S. 137
Moore, C. 146
Moore, C.N. 104
Moore, R. 163
Morgan, J.P. 1-14
Morton, M. 265
Mosby, F. 240
Mosher, G.F. 199
Moss, S.A. 31, 58, 135, 189
Mulvey, P. 152
Murphy, E. F. 381
Myers, A. 141
Myers, T 378
Navias, L. 154, 163, 166, 174, 185
Nerad, A.J. 227
Neumann, G. 245
Nichols,T. 307
Niedrach. L.W. 262
Nobel, A.B. 289
Noble, P.O. 173
Nordlander, B.W. 138
Noyes, A.A. 99
Opie, J. D. 381
Ord, J. P 48, 74
Pacz, A. 112
Paige, H.V. 265
Parker, J.S. 286
Patnode, W.I. 179, 185, 187
Patterson, C.E. 146, 230
Pauly, K.A. 173
Payne, J.H. 116, 122, 174
Peabody, G.F. 73
Peek, F.W. Jr. 122, 133
Perkins, F. 158
Phillippe, G.L. 249, 254, 378

Pierce, L. 307
Piper, W.W. 301
Pipkin, M. 134, 214
Pollock, H.G. 185, 204
Porter, R.W. 206
Potter, W.B. 83
Potts, H.N. 182
Powar, P. 353
Powell, C 345
Price, P.R. 256
Prideauz, G. 162
Prince, D.C. 291
Pritchard, P.J. 178
Prochazka, S. 293
Pugh, J. 246
Rader, L.T. 210, 235, 267
Rabatin, J.G. 268
Ramo, S. 191
Rasmussen, T.J. 198
Redington, R.W. 328
Reed, C.E. 185, 187, 191, 201
Reed, P.D. 159, 180, 190, 193, 217
Reiling, G. 263
Reinker, G.E. 240
Reist, H.G. 84, 110, 172
Rice, C.W. 137, 142
Rice, E.W. 51, 66, 99, 106, 121, 135, 258
Rich, T.A. 291
Richards, T.W. 161
Ridgley, C.H. 257
Riggert, M.C. 224, 263
Robb, W. L. 256, 328
Robinson, L.T. 68, 116
Rochow, E.G. 185
Rohrer, A.L. 80
Roper. V.J. 224
Rosner, C.H. 254
Rowe, B. 311
Ryan, W.D. 74, 82, 92
Safford, M.M. 174
Sauer, R.B. 187
Saupe, W.E. 193
Schaefer, V.J. 198, 206
Schlough, Nabuko 339
Schmidt, K. 263
Schmitt, R.W. 290, 306
Schottky. W. 134
Schreiber, W.J. 187
Scott, F.T. 252
Scott, M. 350
Seitz, F. 204
Sharansky, A. 331
Shreve, E.O. 164
Singrun.A. 141
Slattery, M.M.M. 41
Smith, W. 288
Snell, J.K. 267
Speicher. W. 254
Sperry, E. 145
Sprague, F.J. 7-9, 28, 30, 32, 43, 48 72, 84, 96, 145, 290
Sprung, M. 187
Stanley, W. 30, 31, 38, 45, 86, 93, 290
Steenstrup, C. 140, 141
Steinmetz, C.P. Most pages Chapter 2 43, 47, 48, 51

Stevenson, A. 141
Streid, D.D. 202
Strong, H.M. 227, 70
Suits, C.G. 219, 261
Swope, G. 64, 116, 128, 216, 230, 282, 376
Taylor, D.W. 149
Terry, F.S. 80, 111
Thayer, R. 168
Thomson. E. Most pages of Vol. I 145, 179, 189, 290
Stask, S. 73
Tremaine, B.G. 80, 111
Upton, F.R. 51
Van Depoele. C.J. 7, 9, 35, 38, 80, 290
Vakil, Shereyar 339
Vance, J. 292
Villard, H. 44
Walker, R.M. 256
Walker, C. 206
Wallace, T.M. 263
Wargo, P. 244
Warren, G.B. 149, 206
Warren, H.E. 150
Webster, H.F. 294
Weintraub, E. 82
Weiser, E.F. 252
Welch, J.F. Jr. 311, 312, 315, 323, 338, 343-345, 357, 367, 372, 375, 376, 381
Wells, M.H. 172
Wentorf, R.H. 227, 236, 276
Westendorp, W.F. 199
Westinghouse, G. 32, 47
Weston, E. 35
White, T.D. 242
White, W.C. 110, 112, 171, 191
Whitney, W.R. 54, 78, 99, 142, 151, 163, 186, 204
Wilson, C.E. 159, 180, 190, 192, 193, 199, 203, 208, 216, 219, 230,
Wilson, C.T.R. 161
Wilson, F.P. 259
Winn, O.H. 256
Winne, H.A. 193, 205
Wirt, H.L. 149
Wood, J.J. 7, 8, 21, 74, 75, 82, 140, 141, 290
Woodall, E.L. 240
Wright, D.K. 162
Wright, J.G.E. 135, 174
Wright, R. 372
Young, C. 196
Young, O.D. 103, 122, 129, 156-159, 180, 190
Zubler, E. 240

Aerospace and Defense
206, 214, 219, 220, 227, 233, 239-242, 247, 265, 266,
274, 275, 294, 317, 322, 326, 327, 333, 346, 349

Aircraft Engines
114-116, 120, 178, 181, 188-190, 200, 202, 206, 215,
221, 225, 233, 239, 245, 261, 262, 277, 280, 311, 322,
325, 334, 340, 342, 346, 347, 351, 353, 356, 360, 362,
366, 367, 369, 371

Apparatus Service Business Division
258, 259

Appliances
82, 87, 88, 93, 98, 100, 101, 104, 112, 131, 135, 138,
140, 141, 146, 150, 154, 162, 164, 165, 168, 170, 174,
176, 184, 206, 207, 211, 225, 227, 228, 233, 236, 239,
246, 253, 255, 260, 265, 272, 280, 281, 285, 292, 294,
298, 300, 301, 305, 309, 312, 318, 323, 330, 334, 337,
341, 350, 352, 360, 362, 364, 370, 374

Automation Systems
219, 226, 233

Canadian General Electric Ltd.
262, 284, 285

Capital Services (See also Credit Corp.)
312, 313, 322, 329, 335, 341, 347, 355 - 357, 361,
363, 365, 369, 371, 374, 380

Communications and Electronics
10, 12, 14, 17, 38, 39, 47, 59, 84, 85, 87, 90, 98, 99,
103, 104, 107, 108, 110, 112, 114, 115, 117-120,
122-124,132, 134, 137, 139, 143, 146, 151-154, 168,
171, 175, 176, 179, 180, 182-184, 190, 194, 200, 206,
207, 210, 220, 222, 226, 228, 241,.244, 248, 252, 255,
260, 265 - 267, 271, 283-285, 288, 289, 292, 295, 299 -
301, 305 309, 311, 312, 315, 318, 320, 321, 325, 327, 334

Community Service
376-379

Credit Corporation
296, 297, 316, 322, 344

Crotonville Leadership Development Center
234, 358, 359

e-Business (e-Commerce)
345, 372-375, 380, 381

Dow Jones Industrial Average
357

**Electrical Distribution and Control (see also Industrial
Electronics)**
324, 340, 353

Electric Power Generation

  Cogeneration
316, 322

  Dynamos
8, 10, 12, 15-18, 21, 22, 26 - 28, 32, 35

  Fuel Cells
262, 371

  Gas Turbines
200, 202, 206, 215, 245, 247, 254, 259, 263, 267, 277,
295, 326, 331, 362

  Hydroelectric
65-68, 70, 89, 105, 112, 114, 117, 124, 166, 169, 311

  Nuclear
132 - 134, 206, 213, 223, 226, 237, 241, 243, 252, 257,
270, 273, 280, 293, 307, 317

  Steam
72, 80, 81, 84, 85, 87, 89, 96, 98, 103, 107, 108, 147,
149, 155, 212, 218, 254, 264, 267, 270, 273, 299, 316,
319, 326

  Electric Power Transmission
26, 36, 43, 47, 65, 66, 68, 86, 89, 92, 133, 136, 140,
149, 171, 228, 247, 250, 251, 262, 264, 276, 280, 300

Electric Utilities System Engeering Department
250, 251

Elfun Society
376 - 379

Factory Automation
  (see Industrial Electronics)

GE Fund (formerly GE Foundation)
376-379

General Electric International
283, 284

Industrial Electronics
317, 318, 321, 324, 329, 332

Industrial Power Systems
217, 227

Information Services
271, 301, 304, 324, 335, 356

Initiatives
313, 354, 355, 358, 359, 364 -367, 373 - 375

Insulators
41, 45, 65, 95, 163, 174, 177, 179, 214, 232, 238, 240, 256, 276, 298

Leadership Development Center
(see Crotonville)

Lighting

Arc
15-18, 21-23, 25, 26, 29, 32 -35, 38, 46, 64, 67, 72, 75, 78, 80, 82, 84, 87, 92, 95, 99, 105, 118

Automobile
132, 180, 224, 278, 301, 304

Compact Fluorescent
341, 350, 352, 363

Fluorescent
168, 170, 178, 188, 200, 212, 232, 301, 320, 337

Incandescent
17, 20-22, 24, 27, 40, 43, 47, 48, 64, 66, 66, 68, 78, 87, 90, 92, 93, 96-99, 101, 103, 105, 111, 116-118, 134, 136, 145, 161, 162, 166, 168, 174, 180, 214, 224, 283, 304, 320, 336, 350

Light Emitting Diodes (LEDs)
370

Outdoor (see also Arc Lighting)
108, 109, 114, 115, 124, 142, 144, 154, 166, 174, 178, 240, 242, 253, 263

Photographic
50, 162, 239, 278, 294

Specialty and Misc.
146, 168, 178, 188, 224, 330

Management Development Institute (see Crotonville)

Matenals
(see also Insulators, Polymers)
100, 135, 143, 150, 154, 171, 174, 177, 181, 185, 186 -188, 190, 198, 201, 203, 206, 210, 214, 219, 221-223, 224, 225, 227, 232, 233, 236, 238, 240, 244, 246, 252, 256, 265, 268, 271, 276, 278, 293, 295, 298, 301-303, 306, 311

Medical Equipment/Systems
70, 99, 104, 105, 107, 118, 122, 132,151, 155, 168, 212, 257, 260, 264, 268, 299, 300, 306, 312, 318, 321, 323, 331, 332, 340, 349, 355, 360, 362, 364, 365, 368, 370, 374

Motors
30, 39, 40, 65, 68, 70, 72, 74, 80, 82-84, 89, 96, 116, 118, 124, 210, 212, 213, 220, 222, 228, 232, 238, 240, 321, 322, 337, 347

NBC
327, 331, 336, 342, 348, 351, 356, 361, 369, 372, 375, 378

Organization/Culture/Values
312, 315, 317, 326, 338, 339, 343

Polymers/Plastics
135, 150, 185, 187, 188, 190, 198, 201, 210, 221-224, 232, 238, 268, 271, 278, 304, 306, 312, 316, 319, 320, 323, 324,329, 333, 335, 336, 340, 344, 353, 354, 356, 362, 368, 369, 374

Quartz
132, 316

RCA
327

Research and Development Center
265, 319, 368, 369

Ships
92, 103, 108, 118, 120, 133, 134, 139,146, 151, 163, 188, 194, 228, 273

Silicones
185, 187, 198, 201, 252

Six Sigma
354, 355, 375, 380

Trading Company
319

Transformers
18, 35-37, 39, 40, 70-72, 105, 112, 120, 124, 136, 137, 169, 176, 214, 223, 224, 238, 261, 264, 279, 293, 307

Transportation Systems

Motorized wheels
254

Railways/Locomotives
22, 28, 30-33, 38, 40, 43, 47.48, 49, 64, 65, 66, 68-70, 72, 78, 79, 83, 84, 88, 90, 91, 96-98, 100, 104, 107-109, 114, 133, 135, 136, 143, 144, 154, 166, 169, 174, 176, 177, 181, 212, 221, 225, 237, 252, 268, 272, 282, 288, 296, 302, 305, 318, 325, 348, 350, 352, 366, 375

Utah International
323, 341

Volunteer Service in Community
376-379

Yokogawa Medical Systems
318

The Hall of Electrical History and the Schenectady Museum

Creating a Collection of Global Importance:
The Archives of Electrical History at The Schenectady Museum

This publication is the latest in a series of efforts to preserve and make accessible the story of one of the world's most successful corporations. Based largely upon a collection of valuable historical materials gathered together over the last twenty-five years, this edition of *The General Electric Story* represents the commitment of the Schenectady Museum to furthering the groundbreaking work begun by the founders of the Hall of Electrical History.

At the December 1974 meeting of the Schenectady Chapter of the Elfun Society, Dr. Arthur M. Bueche, GE vice president for research and development, called attention to the importance of salvaging and preserving the historical records, images and artifacts documenting the origins and growth of the General Electric Company. A group of Elfuns, recognizing the educational potential of the project, responded by resolving to establish a home for the more than one million photographs, ten thousand documents, rare journals, early films and hundreds of objects that would be made donated to them by General Electric. Thus, the Hall of History, an unprecedented collection representing an important part of the world's industrial heritage, came into being.

To support the continuing costs of caring for this one-of-a-kind collection, members of the Hall of History published a series of "photo histories" utilizing a representative selection of the available photos. A portion of this collection dates back to the 1870s — before the companies formed by Thomas Edison and Elihu Thomson merged to become the General Electric Company. *The Edison Era,* published in 1976, was the first in a series of volumes that have culminated in this most recent edition of *The General Electric Story*.

The distribution of these popular books promoted awareness of the collection to historians, researchers, educators and business leaders around the globe. As news of this historical treasure spread, contributions from private individuals as well as from a number of GE locations added to the collection and Elfun volunteers were joined by others who came forward to collect, preserve, catalog and provide access to this burgeoning resource. In 1979, reacting to overwhelming interest and the need to develop resources to support these preservation efforts, the Hall of History was incorporated as a not-for-profit foundation eligible to solicit memberships and donations, apply for grants and charge fees for services.

In 1995, the Hall of History was renamed the Hall of Electrical History to more accurately portray its mission. A year later, the organization merged with the Schenectady Museum combining its holdings with those of the Museum's already extensive electrical history archives and object collections. The Museum provides improved access to the collection, room for its growth and assistance in its use for a variety of purposes. Through its exhibitions, public educational programs, outreach to schools, publications and other services, the Schenectady Museum continues to broaden the scope and use of this valuable collection and to make it better available to those interested in the history of science and technology.

We invite you to make use of these resources and to help them grow.

Bart A. Roselli - Executive Director
Bernard Gorowitz - Editor; Chairman - Publications Committee

Schenectady Museum
Nott Terrace Heights
Schenectady, New York 12308
Telephone: (518) 382-7890
Fax: (518) 385-3575
E-mail: hoehsma@aol.com